1

KATHERINE H. BROWN

Savory,
Sweet,
&
Scandalous

SECRETS EXPOSED

Ooey Gooey
Bakery Mystery
Book Four

4

Savory, Sweet, and Scandalous

Written By: Katherine Brown

Cover Design By: Breezy Reads

Acknowledgments

It's hard to believe this is book four. I wouldn't have been able to keep up the motivation and commitment to writing book after book without so many encouragers in my life. To try and name them individually would inevitably leave someone out but each voice that says "good job" or "I'm proud of you" or "it's incredible that you are following your dreams" is precious and I am grateful to you.

Thank you to each person who picked up book one and has continued with me and Piper and Sam to book four; thanks for taking a chance and I can't tell you how glad I am that you are here!

Other Books by Katherine Brown

Ooey Gooey Bakery Mystery Series:

Rest, Relax, Run for Your Life

Pastries, Pies, & Poison

Bake, Eat, & Be Buried

Couches & Catastrophes (short story)

School is Scary Series (Children)

Kindergarten Teachers are Witches

Fingernails of First Grade

Second Grade Stinks

Third Grade's Terrible Trip

Fourth Grade's Fossil Find

Fairy Tale Retellings

Marigold and the Bear Necessities

Cloaked

Other Children's Books

Princess Bethani's First Garden Party

CHAPTER 1

"Where's Gladys?" I asked Sam as I entered the Ooey Gooey Goodness bakery café through the swinging kitchen door.

"Two guesses."

I thought about it a moment; today was Friday. "I don't know. Cooking class?" I lifted my arms, palms face up, in a *who knows* gesture.

Sam gave me a thumbs up. "Ding, ding, ding. We have a winner."

"I don't know what to think about the fact that she never brings Chef Fabio here."

"Frédéric," Sam corrected me automatically. Fabio, we had learned from Gladys, was part of his cooking persona title but not his actual name.

"Right. Hey, weren't cooking classes supposed to be over last week?"

"What are you saying?"

I waggled my eyebrows at Sam suggestively. "I'm saying, I think we've moved from assisting in cooking classes to actual date nights and someone is embarrassed to tell us."

"Maybe so." Sam chewed on her bottom lip, a habit I was shocked had survived her childhood with Sam's mother, Deidra, pushing her in and out of etiquette classes, ladylike behaviors, and so on. "Well? Are we going to snoop?" Sam rubbed the palms of her hands together.

"We can't snoop with your hair like that; it's a beacon to everyone around. If Gladys didn't spot us herself, everyone else talking about the woman with red, white, and blue hair would tip her off that we were following her." I shook my head. Sam had outdone herself with her promise to dye her hair *patriotic* as an incentive to boost sales at Flo's Flowers and the Ooey Gooey Goodness Bakery a few weeks ago, right before the Independence Day Parade.

"Are you saying you think it's time to change it?" she fingered the white and blue strands on one side of her head.

"I'm only pointing out that it isn't exactly clandestine snooping material."

"Good point. I guess it might be time to change it. It has been worth it to see the pained expression on Mother's face whenever I'm around though."

I laughed. Deidra Lowe had nearly fainted on the spot when Sam appeared on the courthouse lawn beside them on July Fourth. Deidra's pallor had first gone ashy-white and then flushed a deep crimson. Sam's father hadn't even had time to say hello before Deidra shooed us out of the spotlight. So determined was she to send Sam away before the press arrived, that she nearly broke an ankle in a gopher hole rushing us away from the courthouse steps. I pity the poor gophers who called that lawn their home; Deidra had been on a crusade to capture and kill every gopher in a five-mile radius ever since.

"Earth to Piper!" Sam spoke, breaking through my thoughts.

"Hmm?"

"Are you going to come with me to the salon? You could get your hair touched up."

I considered it, holding the ends of my hair up right in front of my nose. Tipped in turquoise and silver, the ends of my hair were definitely sporting some major split ends. She was right; it was time to trim and re-color the ends. Before I could answer, the bell over the door jingled, signaling a customer entering.

The Ooey Gooey Goodness Bakery, owned and operated by myself and Sam, had become more and more popular over the last few weeks, thanks in part to a publicized fundraising campaign to raise awareness of human trafficking, and then, more recently, to a promotional strategy where we joined forces with Flo's Flowers next door to increase Fourth of July flower and cookie orders. Still, the last hour had been dead; we had been about to close up. I looked over, quite surprised, to see who might be coming in for a cookie this late.

My jaw dropped. Speak of the devil.

"Mother?" Sam asked, eyebrows raised in disbelief.

As long as we had owned the Ooey Gooey, Deidra had not set foot inside. Until today. One time, only one, she had sent an assistant over to place a cookie order but it had been more about PR for her than support of us. This didn't bode well.

"Good evening, Mrs. Lowe," the greeting felt thick and awkward even as it slid over my tongue. "Can we get you something?"

Deidra glowered. Her fist clenched tighter around a folded newspaper in her hand. "How dare you?"

I swiveled my head to Sam. She looked at me in confusion then back to her mother.

"How dare who, what?" Sam blew out a breath. Deidra's penchant for drama wasn't new in her life.

"This, this…." Deidra stalked forward. She waved her free hand in a circle, motioning to Sam's head, or rather her hair. "This atrocity is more than enough to bring embarrassment to your father and I. But you couldn't stop there, could you?"

"Mrs. Lowe," I stepped up beside Sam, wrapping an arm around her shoulders. "I don't think anyone is judging you for Sam's hair color. Really."

"You. You stay out of this. You've done enough to drag my children down into some mediocre, ambitionless life. This doesn't concern you." Her eyes flashed daggers at me. I felt Sam stiffen at my side.

"Get out."

"Excuse me?" Deidra's voice grew cold.

I whipped my head to face Sam, concerned as I felt her begin to shake.

"Get out and don't come back. I don't know what it is you think I've done, but you will not come in our bakery and be disrespectful to me or my best friend. Don't let the door hit you on the way out." Sam crossed her arms, matching her mother stare for stare.

"Well. Don't think we are finished, young lady. This is far from over." Deidra shoved the paper into Sam's folded arms and stormed out, high-heel pumps tapping out the drum beats of impending war on her way.

I hugged Sam into my side. Rage marred her normally joyful face, her smile deep in hiding. Thank God my parents were nothing like her terrible mother. That woman didn't care a bit for anyone but herself. "What in the world was that all about?" I mused, watching the sidewalk to make sure Deidra didn't return for round two. So much for Mina, our mini-guard palm, I thought, looking at the tiny potted palm tree sitting sedately by the door. A gift from Gladys, the little palm's leaves still fluttered frantically from Deidra's recent exit.

"That," Sam interrupted my musings over Mina, "was evidently about today's biggest headline. And somehow in that paranoid, twisted mind of hers, she thinks that I helped put it in motion."

I let go of Sam and took the newspaper that she held out to me, scanning. Front page news. Didn't get much worse than that. The article itself actually contained nothing bad, unless of course you were the wife of the current mayor, obsessed with public opinion, and held a reputation for being a strait-laced, upper class socialite. For Deidra, I had no doubt the article qualified as the worst thing to happen to her in years. Possibly worse than her assistant being a psychopath who tried to kill me; although, in Deidra's opinion, that probably made the nutty assistant a hero, but that is water under the bridge.

LIKE MOTHER, LIKE DAUGHTER the title claimed in big, bold letters. Again, no big deal. The photos though, those were a different story. Or, the whole story, in this case. On the right, a photo of Sam at the Independence Day Parade with red, white, and blue hair. On the left, a snapshot of a teenage Deidra, sporting an orange mohawk. I had to look twice. Yep. Definitely Deidra. The young woman in the photo looked so…relaxed; nothing like the Deidra of today.

Sam stood silent. Shell-shocked, if her wide-eyed and open-mouthed stare were any indication.

"Deidra had a mohawk?" I broke the silence, walking over to lock up the front door before any other bombs dropped.

"It's news to me," Sam sank to a chair at the nearest table. "And I also don't understand why she thought I had anything to do with the article. I mean, how could I?"

"She probably thinks it is a publicity stunt for the bakery," I suggested as I sat down next to her, placing the paper on the table. "Deidra would pull a number of things for publicity; it makes sense that she would assume everyone operates that way."

Sam continued to stare at the photo.

I felt a grin creeping over my face. I bit my lip, tried to stop myself. I failed. "I guess now we know you're a chip off the old block."

That got her attention. She cut her eyes at me. "Don't you dare. I'm nothing like that woman."

"Exactly." I nodded. "I know that and you know that. You're nothing like her. This one photo changes nothing. Now, throw that paper in the trash where it belongs and let's forget all about it."

"Urgh." Sam groaned and wadded up the newspaper, crumpling it smaller and smaller. "You're right." She stood. "I'm going next door to see if BeeBee is ready to go or if Flo needs her longer." She dunked the paper ball in the garbage can and pushed through the swinging door to the kitchen, heading out the back way.

Flo's Flowers stood next door to the Ooey Gooey Goodness Bakery. There had been a little tension between us and Flo when Sam and I won the fundraising competition but no more. I enjoyed our good friendship, and we even created a beneficial working relationship, recommending each other's business for special occasions. Flo had struggled with sales for some time and it made me happy that she stayed busy these days. So busy, in fact, that she hired BeeBee to help full time.

I finished wiping down the counter and cleared out the last of the cookies from the display case, flipping the overhead lights off as I headed into the kitchen. Victoria had already left for the day; she and Millie, our two teenage part-timers, went to the local college to check out the Fall registration schedule and class offerings.

After unloading the industrial-sized dishwasher and putting everything away for tomorrow, I removed my apron and hung it on the pegs by the back door. My insides warmed with pride as I surveyed the sparkling kitchen; I was blessed to work my dream job every day in this place, and with amazing friends surrounding me as coworkers.

Flipping the lights, I opened the door to leave for the night with a satisfied smile stretched across my face.

"Hey."

I all but jumped out of my skin, finding a tall, muscular man just outside the door, fist poised to knock.

CHAPTER 2

"Sorry, didn't mean to scare you."

"Don't sneak up on a person like that," I swatted Griff as he moved aside for me to turn around and lock the door. "I could have pepper-sprayed you or something."

"Nah, I'm safe. You aren't wearing your glamorous bag of supplies," he joked.

Glamorous. Ha. "Don't you tell Gladys that I'm not wearing the fanny pack." I waved my finger at him. "You know how she is. Three straight weeks of peace and quiet around here and she is still waiting for the boogey man to jump out and get me at every turn."

"You really can't blame her for worrying." He pulled me closer. "I still worry. Every day," he whispered against my hair.

I tensed. A reminder of the times I had been kidnapped or attacked wasn't what I wanted.

"Hey you two, no PDA." Sam appeared from the back door of Flo's Flowers, followed closely by BeeBee and Flo herself.

I stuck my tongue out at my best friend.

BeeBee laughed out loud. "I swear, you act just like my sister." Her mouth clamped shut. "I mean, like you were sisters," she spoke quickly, then veered around Sam and headed to the yellow Juke in the center of the parking lot.

I looked around our little group. "Did I hear that right?" I asked. "Did BeeBee say she had a sister?"

Sam nodded, looking back to Flo. Flo raised her shoulders in a shrug.

"Maybe she spoke wrong." Griff lacked conviction in his voice; still, he tried to give BeeBee an out, knowing that Sam and I would pursue the details otherwise.

"There's only one way to find out," Sam gave me a look. "Piper, why don't you ride over with Griff and we'll make supper."

"Don't you mean *we'll* make supper?" I twirled my finger in a circular motion between Griff and myself. Sam could bake. She could not cook any actual meals of substance, however.

"Same thing," she shrugged. "Flo, you're welcome to join us."

"Thank you, but no. I'm going to take these tired feet home and hit the couch." Flo hugged Sam, waved to Griff and me, and left.

"Okay. We will see you in a few minutes, Sis." He took my hand. "Piper and I will stop at the store and pick up something to cook for supper. Any requests?"

"Tortellini."

"Done!" I loved pasta, something else Sam and I had in common. "Don't you start prying info from BeeBee without me."

With a flip of hair over her shoulder, Sam tilted her head high. "I do not pry." She marched off, pretending to be offended. I laughed as she shot me a tiny wink over her shoulder.

"Tortellini, huh?" Griff and I walked slowly to his truck. He opened the door for me; a southern gentleman through and through.

"You could grill some chicken breasts to slice up and add to it," I buckled my seatbelt as he got in on his side of the truck. "Or shrimp and scallops if you'd prefer seafood?"

"Shrimp are tiny," he shook his head. "Chicken it is."

"Okay."

"What are you doing?" he asked.

"Making a list."

"Why? We know what we need."

"And what we need is a list, obviously." While Sam was all too familiar with my list-making obsession, Griff obviously hadn't caught on yet. I ignored his scoff and kept writing. He would learn, eventually.

"Why don't we split up?" I suggested to Griff as we entered the grocery store.

"I'll get the chicken, you get the tortellini," he agreed, taking off toward the fresh meat section.

Grabbing a shopping basket from the stack near the door, I pulled out my list and got started. About six minutes later, my phone rang.

"Hello?"

"Where are you?"

I rolled my eyes. "Shopping."

"I've already got the chicken. Are you having trouble finding tortellini?" Griff asked.

Laughing, I juggled the phone and the basket around until the basket hung from the crook of my arm and I had a free hand. Opening up the fridge door, and holding it ajar with my hip, I picked up the heavy cream, adding it to my basket. "Weren't you listening when I told you I was making a list?" Silence answered me. I sighed.

"There is more to a good pasta dish than picking up some premade pasta. Don't worry, I'm almost done." Hanging up, I slipped the phone into a pocket of my cargo pants and checked cream off of my list.

"She did more than that, I hear." Voices carried from the next aisle; snippets of the conversation carried my way. "...isn't fit to be mayor...wife like that." At the word mayor, I stilled and listened more closely. "...talk to city council...removed." The voices trailed further away and I couldn't get the gist of the discussion. I peeked around the end of the aisle, but I saw only the back of a man's leg and leather sandal as the speaker or speakers disappeared around the corner at the opposite end.

CHAPTER 3

"Piper."

I jumped and spun around, guilt washing over me at the thought of being caught eavesdropping. "Grandpa Rex!"

"Sorry," the old man, one of our most frequent customers, smiled. "Didn't mean to scare you."

"No, that's fine. I thought I heard a friend on this aisle. Oh well." I shrugged. "Looks like I missed them. How are Tommy and Timmy?" We chatted about his twin grandsons for several minutes. They would be spending another week staying with Rex before going back home to their parents.

"I'll let you get back to your shopping," Grandpa Rex pointed to my basket. "Though I've gotta say, those don't look much like cookie ingredients."

"No. No cookies tonight." I glanced at the cream, parmesan, and nutmeg. Still hadn't made it to the tortellini. *Better pick up the pace,* I chided myself before returning my attention to Grandpa Rex. "These are for tortellini and grilled-chicken alfredo." I wished Grandpa Rex a good evening, then retreated back to the dairy aisle. I had an idea, thanks to Grandpa Rex, and there would be no better time to try it out than tonight.

"There you are!" Griff stood next to the self-checkout line, a gray grocery sack swinging from his wrist. I gathered he had given up on me and paid for the grilled chicken already.

"Sorry! I got caught up talking to Grandpa Rex." I didn't mention the overheard conversation. I believed the person or persons had been talking about Griff's parents, but I had no concrete proof nor did I even understand what I heard; I would try to forget about it, even if it had seemed particularly negative.

"No problem. What is all this stuff?" He leaned over to look in my basket. We inched forward in line.

"Mostly ingredients to make a homemade alfredo sauce. I didn't think you or Sam would have nutmeg or cream. Plus, you can never have too much parmesan." I grinned, but didn't tell Griff about my secret plan for treats to go with tonight's meal.

The line chugged slowly along. After we checked out with the rest of our purchase, we walked out to Griff's truck. I found myself trotting to keep up with his long legs. "Someone's hungry."

"What?" Griff turned and saw me struggling to keep up. "Come on slow poke, you bet I'm hungry. Someone made me wait for twenty extra minutes in the grocery store." His winked and reached back to grab my hand, tugging me up close beside him. He slowed his steps.

~

Sam and BeeBee were right where I expected to find them when we arrived at the duplex that Griff and Sam shared, he in one half and she in the other. "Food's here," I called as I walked out on the back deck. They each sat up from their respective lounge chairs. "But now we have to cook it." I laughed as they groaned, bubbles burst, and leaned back in the chairs again.

Griff set about lighting the grill. Sam stood and joined him to inspect the bag he carried. "Oh good! I love chicken with my pasta!"

"Grab the chicken and bring it inside to season, please," I directed Sam. "Come on, BeeBee. I'll teach you to make alfredo sauce. No sense in both of you living here and nobody knowing how to cook."

BeeBee followed Sam and me back inside, bringing their sweaty glasses of tea with her.

Sam opened the spice cabinet and rummaged around. "What exactly am I putting on the chicken?" she asked as she moved containers around, reading labels.

"Herbs," I answered. Then clarified, as she shot me a dirty look. "Find one that says Italian Seasoning. I'm sure I brought some over the last time I cooked stuffed chicken over here."

BeeBee refilled the glasses with ice and poured a third for me.

"Thank you," I accepted the cold, refreshing drink. "Okay," I wiped my mouth off and set the glass down. "Are you ready?"

She nodded. "I've never cooked anything before."

"Really?" I asked.

Sam shook little green flakes of Italian seasoning on the chicken breasts. "Your parents never showed you?" she kept her gaze on the chicken, as if the answer weren't at all important.

I busied myself pulling out spoons and a saucepan. From the corner of my eye, I watched BeeBee. She stared in a daze for several seconds before answering.

"No. I didn't have parents."

Sam stopped thumping the chicken breasts with the meat tenderizer.

I turned the knob on the stove to heat up the pan. Turning to BeeBee, I asked her to tell us more. "What do you mean by that? Did you have any family before you ended up in places like the Thai Massage?"

"Sometimes, it helps to talk about it." Sam moved to the sink to wash her hands. "Piper and I are here for you."

BeeBee took a long swallow of her iced tea. "Maybe after supper," she looked at us both.

Sam reached out to touch her arm. "And only what you are comfortable sharing," she added.

"Well, let's get this alfredo sauce going while Sam gets the chicken to Griff." I pulled the butter, diced garlic, and cream from the fridge. "Sam," I called to my friend as she carried the platter of chicken breasts toward the sliding glass doors. "I have a special project for you when you come back."

"Oh boy," she tossed her head back to look at the ceiling.

"It won't hurt, I promise." I laughed at her woe is me expression then focused my attention on BeeBee and the sauce.

Once the butter and garlic were sautéing in the pan, I like garlic in my alfredo though not every recipe uses it, I hunted down some measuring cups. "That woman re-organizes and moves things around more than is good for anyone's sanity," I muttered aloud.

BeeBee smothered a chuckle behind her hand.

"Gotcha!" I snatched the liquid measuring cup from a top shelf and handed it to BeeBee. Measure two-thirds of a cup of cream in this. Add it to the pan after the butter is fully melted and starting to bubble. I pointed to the marks delineating each of the measurements on the glass measuring cup and left her to it when I was certain she understood.

Sam returned and I explained my idea.

"These will be either really good, or really terrible," she mused.

"Since you're the one baking them, we get to blame you either way," I reminded her.

She pursed her lips. "Well. I guess I will have to see to it that they are delicious."

Moving back to the stove, I looked into the saucepan. "Great, stir in a little shake of nutmeg now. Then," I turned the heat up a fraction, "when the cream all starts to get tiny bubbles on top that means it is simmering. We don't want it to boil, which would be where it gets rolling, big bubbles."

"Okay," BeeBee nodded. "What do I do when I see the little bubbles then?"

"Turn this burner off with this knob," I pointed. "And slide the pan off the heat. From there, just stir in the parmesan and whisk it all together until melted and creamy." I started grating the fresh triangular block of parmesan into a bowl. "Oh! You can add a tad bit of salt and pepper, too. For just a bit more flavor."

BeeBee collected the salt and pepper shakers from the small table and shook a little of each into the saucepan while I set a pot of water to boil, tossing in the tortellini. We both moved out of the way as Sam placed a baking sheet into the oven and set the timer.

"What are those?" BeeBee asked.

"I'll tell you after you taste them," I told her before Sam could spoil the surprise.

Griff stepped inside. "Sis, I need something to carry this chicken back inside with."

Sam placed foil over a tray, grabbed some oven mitts, and went out to help Griff bring in the meat. As the sliced chicken breast arrived in the kitchen, that delicious smoky aroma of the grill filled the room.

My stomach growled, demanding sustenance. I rubbed it. "Just in time."

BeeBee slid the pan over on the stove, clicking the knob to off. I handed her the bowl of parmesan and she added it a little at a time. Smart. We would make a home cook out of this girl in no time, I smiled, pleased at being able to share my passion for food.

Sam handed a stack of bowls to Griff, grabbing the silverware and napkins herself. They set the table for the four of us, refilling drinks and adding to the comfortable bustle in the kitchen. As the timer went off, I snatched one of the oven mitts from the counter and reached to pull out the savory treats.

"What have we got here?" Griff reached toward the tray and I swatted his hand away.

"Not yet." I scooted the tray onto the last open spot of the stove. "Everyone has to try them at the same time. They're new." I loved having a room full of guinea pigs for a new recipe. The feeling it gave me was similar to that of a kid on Christmas. My spirits dampened only slightly when I remembered the reason for this impromptu gathering: getting to the bottom of BeeBee's comment about a sister.

In a flurry of final activity, the four of us got the meal put together and on the table. We sat down and Griff offered to ask the blessing. We bowed in prayer as he thanked God for providing the meal and the friends to share it with, our home and safety, jobs to meet our needs, and joy to fill our hearts.

"Amen," I echoed.

"Now, tell me what these little cookies are, please!" BeeBee passed the plate around, grabbing two for herself.

"Nope. Taste it first," I insisted. I bit into my own cookie and considered the bite thoughtfully. Sandy, crumbly, loaded with parmesan and a hint of garlic from the garlic powder sprinkled on top.

"Wow!" BeeBee polished off cookie number one right away.

"What are these?" Griff asked, befuddlement clouding his face as he would his tongue around the roof of his mouth, like when you have peanut butter stuck there.

"Do you like it?" I questioned instead of answering.

"Not sure," he admitted. "I think I really hoped it was a cookie. Now I'm not sure if I'm just disappointed or if I don't like it." He sat the cookie down beside his plate and gulped his drink.

I looked to Sam, waiting for her opinion. "Told you I would make them delicious," she winked. "Not a bad idea, not a bad idea at all."

"I'm thinking of calling them Parmesan BisCookies. Instead of a garlic bread or cheese biscuit, I thought parmesan biscuit cookies would be a fun thing to try." I told them about the idea springing from my conversation with Grandpa Rex. "They probably aren't for everybody's taste," I admitted, "but I've been thinking we should add a few more savory options to the menu. It might increase the lunch crowd, or just be a pleasant treat for people who come in with friends but don't have much of a sweet tooth themselves." I watched Sam smiling and nodding; I was happy that she thought my suggestion had merit. "Now, let's eat the rest of this deliciousness." I spooned a giant serving of pasta and chicken into my bowl.

BeeBee offered to clean up. Griff, knowing what Sam and I had planned, stepped in and insisted he would manage it. "You three go out and catch the sunset. Relax a little. I'll be done in no time."

How did I get so lucky? I wondered. A man that didn't mind helping out. I lingered behind, making a show of refilling my tea glass, as Sam and BeeBee bee-lined for the reclining chairs on the deck.

As the door slid shut behind them, I raised up on my toes and gave Griff a kiss on the cheek. "Thank you," I told him.

Arms elbow-deep in dishwater, there wasn't much he could do but turn his head to me. "If that's the payment I can expect for cleaning up, you're about to find your apartment spotless and a bill of debt in your mailbox." He smirked.

I shook my head but was unable to stop my lips from curling into a wide smile. I left him, assuming that if I didn't get outside soon, I would miss all the juicy details. Sam had shown admirable patience while I grocery shopped; she wouldn't put off asking BeeBee questions much longer.

I schooled my grin as I approached. "Thank you both for your help with supper," I told them as I lowered myself into a cushioned chair.

"I can't believe the alfredo sauce turned out so good," BeeBee admitted. "I figured I'd mess it up somehow."

"You did perfectly," I assured her.

We sat in silence as minutes ticked by. Waves rolled softly in to stroke the sand on the beach below. The horizon turned a brilliant orange as the sun sank over the water and the ocean reflected the light in rippling waves of color.

"My first memory is of an orphanage," BeeBee's voice startled me. "I think I may have been six years old."

"Honestly, I don't even know what country I was born in." She sighed. "It could have been right here in the U.S. or China for all the information I have."

I remained silent, as did Sam, not wanting to interrupt the flow.

"In my first memory, someone whipped me for hitting a little boy at the orphanage. They beat me until my legs gave out, but I didn't cry. I hit the little boy because he bit my baby sister for sticking her tongue out at him. She stuck her tongue out all of the time; she found it hilarious. I loved her; she was all that mattered to me. I knew, even as I collapsed to the floor, that I would hit him or anyone else again if they touched her."

"How long were you at the orphanage?" I asked.

"Three more years. When I turned nine, a man came and said the orphanage had to be shut down. Noise traveled freely through the thin, cracked walls. I listened to every word." She stood up and walked to the railing, overlooking the beach. Sam and I followed, but gave her space.

"What happened when they shut the orphanage down?" Sam asked into the stillness.

BeeBee didn't answer right away. She closed her eyes, breathing deeply. When she spoke, I marveled at her ability to shield all emotion from her voice. "He took us. The man who shut the orphanage down. He took all of the children, promised the strict matron that she would never set eyes on us again." She shook her head, her mouth thinning into a straight line. "I allowed myself to hope the man would take us to a better place. Maybe an orphanage where someone would smile at us, and hug us. I was an idiot."

"You were a child," I whispered.

"He took us to a boat. They loaded us into cages like animals. No food, no bathrooms."

Tears stung my eyes. Sam hugged her arms around her middle, swallowing down whatever she was feeling. I ached, as BeeBee continued the tale in a single, monotone voice, as if reciting a speech. To speak of her past as if it didn't hurt told all too well the painful blows she had been dealt.

"It could have been days or weeks, I've no idea. A few of the children died. I barely stayed awake most days, but I forced myself. I told myself I had to keep watch, had to keep Eva safe."

Eva. Her baby sister. *Oh God, please don't let this poor girl have watched her sister die.* Emotion clogged my throat. I listened helplessly to a story I was afraid I didn't want to hear.

"Eva cried a lot. I tried to keep her quiet. Her belly hurt, she told me constantly, but I had nothing to feed her. She was seven and I was nine. Somehow, we lived. The ship stopped moving one day, and a new man came down into the hold. He tossed buckets of ice-cold water on us, to wash away the stench he said." A slight shiver went through her body. "They led us up on deck. It was night. A small group of men and women were there, waiting."

"Who were they?"

"Buyers." She said the word with such disgust, still she kept her gaze fixed on the ocean. "Each of us was purchased that night. One woman bought several of us older girls. They tried to take Eva from me. I bit a chunk out of one man's hand. Two more held me down, but the woman stopped them. I found out later her name was Gina. She changed her mind, told the men that Eva could go with us. I remember feeling so happy, like I won a prize for the first time in my life." BeeBee drew a deep breath. "I didn't realize that I had just sealed Eva's fate as a blackmail piece, a means to keeping me in line."

The sound of the glass door sliding open made the three of us jump. Griff stepped outside and the spell was broken.

"I'm going to turn in," BeeBee didn't wait for a response, merely nodded to Griff as she passed by him and disappeared inside.

CHAPTER 4

I had barely finished brewing a cup of tea from the Keurig Saturday morning when Sam waltzed into the kitchen. I mentally ticked off the date, pulling up a mental image of my calendar; nothing special going on that I could think of. "Dare I say, you look even more dressed-up than normal?" I tilted my head, studying her.

Sam looked down at her outfit and gave a twirl, a feat that should have been impossible at four in the morning wearing four-inch wedge heels. A wispy chiffon material, her dress was a light pink with delicate lace around the skirt and a plunging v-neckline. She looked back up at me and asked "Do you think so?"

Sam wore pantsuits and fancier clothes than anyone in their right mind would wear to work in a bakery on a daily basis; still, this outfit put them all to shame. "Definitely. Though I'm not going to lie to you – the pink kind of clashes with your patriotic hair. What's the occasion?"

"Why does there have to be an occasion?" Sam asked, her voice raising in pitch.

"There doesn't have to be. But I know there is, so spill it."

Sam bumped me out of the way with her hip and began making herself a cup of coffee. I strictly liked tea, finding coffee to have the most terrible aftertaste in the world, but Sam enjoyed both with equal enthusiasm. "I'm helping Landon hunt for a place to live."

"In Seashell Bay?"

"Yeah. He's thinking of moving here as soon as his lease is up at the apartment he lives in now. I offered to show him some of the places around here." Sam closed her eyes and inhaled the steam rising from her coffee mug.

"I see." I took a sip of tea. "I guess I missed the memo that you're suddenly a realtor." My voice dripped with sarcasm.

"Shut up, I thought you would be glad that I offered to help. He's your friend after all."

I laughed. "Oh, I'm glad. I just hope you don't break an ankle wandering up and down apartment complex stairs today in those shoes."

"Morning."

We both turned as BeeBee approached from the hall.

"I'm sorry, did we wake you up?" I asked her. BeeBee didn't have to be at the flower shop with Flo nearly as early as Sam and I had to get to the bakery. Griff had been driving her into town most days.

"No. Didn't sleep much, to be honest."

Sam pulled a jug of orange juice out of the fridge and poured a glass for BeeBee.

I watched as BeeBee took several long gulps. Her hair was wadded into a messy bun at the nape of her neck. Dark circles showed under her eyes. The poor thing looked wearier than any seventeen-year-old that I'd ever met.

The empty glass clinked on the table. BeeBee declined when Sam offered a refill. "I thought maybe I could ride to work with you today," she told us. "I can finish telling you about Eva."

"Of course," Sam smiled.

"We would love to hear more about your sister," I agreed. I still felt on the edge of a cliff, hung between wanting to know everything and wanting to be spared the pain of the truth that BeeBee carried.

Minutes later, with a few more topped off mugs of tea and coffee, we all piled into Sam's SUV. After the wreck at the beginning of the month, the insurance determined her little yellow Juke as a lost cause and totaled it. With the new car, Sam upgraded to something with a little more space yet still sporty enough to suit her, a cherry-red Jeep Renegade.

BeeBee got into the backseat; I climbed into the front. Sam adjusted the AC to combat the warm and muggy morning air.

"What time are you taking Landon on a tour of homes?" I asked.

"After lunch sometime. Gladys is scheduled to work the front this afternoon." Sam answered. "During lunch I'm going to get the colors stripped from my hair so that I can change it to something new next week."

"I want to change my hair," BeeBee piped up from the back. "Regina made me dye it this weird caramel color."

"What color is your hair naturally?" I asked.

"Very, very dark brown. Eva's was black."

Sam nodded, looking at her in the rearview mirror. "Come with me at lunch. I know we can find one of the girls to fit you in."

"Really?" Her mouth tilted upward.

Sam nodded while I asked, "What color are you going to choose? Natural, or something different?"

"The darkest brown they have, I think." After a few seconds of thought she added, "But I might put a thin pink streak in it, to remind me of Eva."

"That's sweet," Sam said. We were nearing the turn-off into the main part of town.

"Where did I stop last night?" BeeBee asked.

"The woman, the one who decided to buy Eva and you together." Even saying aloud that someone bought children made me cringe.

"That's right." BeeBee dropped her gaze to the floorboard, her eyes taking that far off look again. "They gave us showers. Fed us. Set us up in a shared room with lots of other girls, but the beds were soft and the blankets warm. For a time, it seemed things would be okay." She shook her head ruefully. "Turns out, they just wanted to make sure we were healthy enough to work. At first, we were only made to clean. The work was hard, scrubbing floors, bathrooms, washing load after load of sheets. They taught us a few skills as we got older. Some girls learned to dance. Others, like me, learned massage." Her voice broke. "The first time I refused to *finish* a massage for a client was the first time they beat Eva." BeeBee drew a shaky breath. When she spoke, steel reverberated from her tone. "I decided then that I had to get her away. If I could escape with her I would, but all that mattered was that Eva be far away from those evil people."

Sam pulled up into the parking lot behind the Ooey Gooey Goodness Bakery. The drive which normally felt long from the beach had flown by. Silence reigned as Sam killed the engine.

"Let's take a break and find some cookies. Then you can tell us the rest if you feel like it," I suggested to BeeBee. She gave a nod and opened the door. Sam and I shared a pained look. "I know," I said first. "Some people should just be shot."

"Or drawn and quartered," she said. "Children, Piper. They were children."

"Come on." I whipped my key from my pocket and we caught up with BeeBee at the back door. I flipped on the light switch and made my way to the cookie jar where we kept a few cookies back for ourselves, always adding in the leftovers from the display case at night. Sam brought over a napkin and I piled on several Butterscotch Oatmeal Cookies. She sat down with BeeBee at the table while I pre-heated the oven and pulled dough from the walk-in fridge. We worked and nibbled in quiet until several batches of cookies were baking.

"I got her out."

BeeBee's statement caused me to freeze, cookie halfway to my mouth. I placed it on the napkin, dusting off my hands. "That's amazing!" I said.

Expression sober, eyes sad, she said, "Yeah. I hope so. It wasn't easy."

A knock sounded on the back door and BeeBee shook her head as if in a daze. Sam unlocked the door to let Victoria inside; BeeBee and I cleaned off the work table.

"Morning," Victoria smiled.

"Good morning," Sam answered. I waved and BeeBee gave a little nod.

I looked to BeeBee and she gave a tiny shake of her head. I understood; she would finish sharing Eva's story later.

"How did things go at the college?"

"Eh."

Sam raised an eyebrow.

"Not so good?" I guessed.

"It isn't that," Victoria shrugged. "It ended up being a huge college fair. You know, where tons of different places all send people with information booklets and they set up tables and give away rubber bracelets and water bottles and lanyards."

"Sounds like you scored some swag. How is that bad?" Sam asked.

"My scholarship is to the college here, in Seashell Bay. Mom says I can't go away to culinary school until I get the basics all taken here with the free college money." Victoria sighed as she tied on her apron. "But Millie found an art school that she really wants to go to. In Chicago."

"When does college start?" BeeBee asked, seamlessly falling into the conversation.

"At the end of August. Millie would have to move at the beginning of August to get a place in the dorms."

"I'm sorry to hear that." Sam gave her a quick hug. "I know we will all miss Millie if she goes, but it'll be especially hard for the two of you."

"You know what that means?" BeeBee asked, hands on hips.

Victoria shook her head.

"That means we have to make this the best summer ever before Millie leaves, plus we get to plan a going away party." She smiled.

"That's right!" I chimed in, eager to cheer up Victoria. "You can bake all of her favorites and we can do a send-off surprise party here at the Ooey Gooey."

"She would love that," Victoria licked her lips. "And it does sound like fun."

"It's settled then," Sam clapped her hands. "I'll take care of decorations." Sam loved a good party. "I better get out front and make sure we are ready to open soon."

I nodded, turning to Victoria. "And you and I have lots of cookies to mix because I've been slacking this morning."

The oven timer buzzed. Victoria crossed her arms and pursed her lips as if the sound completely contradicted my claims of laziness.

I raised my hands in defeat. "I didn't say I did nothing. I just admitted I haven't done as much as normal." The teen laughed and slipped on a pair of oven mitts. Fresh cinnamon smells leapt from the oven as she removed the tray of Cinnamon Bun Cookies.

BeeBee said goodbye and slipped next door to help Flo.

Victoria and I mixed, baked, and chatted easily about the classes she would be taking in the fall and the changes we would need to make to her schedule at the bakery. A constant hum filled the room as mixers buzzed and the walk-in fridge made running noises. The sounds were a comforting background noise, until a tremendous banging on the back door broke the spell and scared me to death.

The spoon I had been scooping cookie dough with went flying. Victoria jumped and caught her hand in the mixer. Sam even came rushing through the swinging door.

"What in the world is that noise?" Sam asked, eyes darting around the room.

More banging, the door shaking with the violence, reverberated through the room. Muffled yells could be heard as well.

I motioned Victoria back away from the door. Sam took one look at Victoria's hand and pulled her to the sink to wash blood from her injured fingers.

Flipping open my pocket knife, I clutched at the handle as I approached the door. Maybe the person on the other side would go away if I didn't unlock it. Then again, I thought as the banging commenced, maybe they needed help.

Knife at the ready, heart hammering in my chest, I flipped the lock and opened the door swiftly, keeping my foot poised to slam it shut.

CHAPTER 5

Heavy rain and earth-shaking thunder took me by surprise. I stepped back, dropping my knife. It clattered across the floor. Lightning cracked across the sky, lighting up the figure hunched under his coat. "Griff?!" I swung the door wide and my boyfriend stepped inside. Water slid down his coat, dripped down his nose.

"BeeBee's missing!" he looked between us all with wide eyes. "She isn't anywhere at the house."

"Oh…" I picked up my knife and slammed the door shut against the weather. I leaned my forehead against the door. Shuffled my feet. Did we really forget to tell Griff? I gulped. "Umm, about that." I turned to face Griff.

"Do you know where we should look? Have you heard from her?" Griff kept talking.

"Griff!"

He quieted and looked into my face. "BeeBee is fine. She rode with Sam and me to work. I'm so sorry we forgot to tell you."

"Busy morning. I assumed Piper texted you, she probably thought I did," Sam looked to me and I nodded. "BeeBee woke up early and came to the bakery. She's over at Flo's now."

Griff dragged a hand down his face.

"We're really sorry! I didn't mean to worry you," I hugged him, wet clothes and all. "Thank you for coming to get us and find her though. It means a lot."

"Two dozen."

I stepped back and cocked my head. "What?"

"Two dozen cookies is the going price of giving a man a heart attack," he gave me a gentle nudge toward the counter. "Go on, start bagging them up. I've got work to do after all."

"You're incorrigible," I rolled my eyes. "Two dozen of anything or something specific?" I asked him as Sam handed me a to-go box.

"I've been knocking in the rain for a long time," he tapped his foot.

"We never heard you," Victoria said.

I glanced over to see Sam bandaging her finger with supplies from the first-aid kit. "You okay?" I asked.

"I'll be fine," she nodded.

"I'm sure you couldn't hear over the rain," Griff said. "Still, I think two dozen cookies with nuts and chocolate will cover the heart attack factor."

"Honestly, I didn't even hear the rain, much less the knocking. Didn't know it would be storming today at all." I placed an assortment of nut-filled, chocolate-oozing fresh cookies into the box, licking my fingers after I closed it up. Mini Chocolate Chip Sandwich Cookies with Chocolate Hazelnut Cream Filling. Yum – I might have to eat the ones that I didn't give to Griff.

"It started about ten minutes ago," Sam said. "The storm. Moved in out of nowhere. Instead of a sunrise over the tops of the buildings, I looked up from the counter to see a looming black cloud rolling in. The bottom dropped out of the sky right after. We had a few of the business crowd stop in, but not many customers are going to come out in this mess. I better get back up there in case I'm wrong though."

Griff took his cookies and jacket. I wished him luck with leak calls and inspections today and told him to be careful in the weather. Locking the door back, I leaned against it. "Alright. Now, we clean up this mess and try again." Cookie dough smeared the cabinets where I had tossed my spoon in fright. Victoria's mixing bowl had overturned when she jerked her hand free.

"This all needs to be thrown out now, right?" She asked me as she surveyed her station.

"Yep. We can't serve people part of your finger," I winked. "Not even if we discount it."

"What's going on with Sam's mom?" Victoria asked as she scraped the contents of the mixing bowl into the trash can.

"What do you mean?"

"The posts going around social media. Haven't you seen them?"

I frowned. The newspaper article must have been photographed and shared online. Sam wouldn't be happy to hear that. "I saw the newspaper with the mohawk. I'm sure it will die down soon enough."

Victoria rinsed the bowl, shaking her head. "No. That isn't what I'm talking about. Hold on, I'll show you in just a second."

I crossed the kitchen and stored my finished bowl of cookie dough in the walk-in fridge. When I turned, Victoria had finished loading the dishwasher and held her phone out for me to take.

More pictures. No mohawks. This time, Deidra did not have a mohawk. She also did not have on a top, though thankfully creative caption blurred out the full image. WIFE OF THE MAYOR IS LIFE OF THE PARTY this headline read. I noticed the photo still showed a teenage Deidra. Maybe she did some questionable things in her younger days; it still seemed someone had a very personal agenda to make Deidra look as bad as possible though. Why else dig up things from eons ago? And where were they getting these pictures anyway?

"Do you mind if I take your phone out and show Sam?" I wanted to be ahead of any other bearers of bad news.

"Of course not; go ahead."

"Thanks." I pushed through the swinging door, relieved to see the café mostly empty.

"Hi, Piper." Barbara, one of our regulars held up a cup of coffee in greeting, her other hand holding onto a bag of goodies. "Sam just told me how great the summer sales have been for the Ooey Gooey Goodness Bakery and Flo's Flowers. Congratulations."

"Thank you," I smiled, keeping the phone behind my back.

"I always love it when small businesses help each other out," she said. "Have you girls thought about coming back to another yoga class at the spa?"

"Maybe," Sam made a noncommittal noise.

Barbara laughed. "It gets easier," she promised. "Well, I have to run. Today is a mess and if I'm not back soon my husband will send a rescue party."

A cacophony of noise - pounding rain and rumbling thunder, car horns honking, tires splashing through puddles - all poured into the bakery as Barbara opened the door to leave. I could see the streets had small rivers of water flowing down the sides as the rain fell too fast for the drains to keep up.

"A mess is right," I said to Sam as the door shut. "And unfortunately, the weather isn't the only one."

"What else? Is Victoria's finger not okay after all?" Sam glanced the direction of the kitchen.

"She's fine. I'm not sure about the rest of us. Look at this," I pressed the phone into her hands.

CHAPTER 6

I worried about the havoc Deidra might wreak when she saw the newest glamor shots of herself going viral on the web. Sam had just left out the back door to get BeeBee and visit the hair salon after looking at the post.

Just like the first, Sam had never seen this picture before. "I know everyone has a past," she had said, blinking her eyes as if trying to un-see the photo, "but this craziness isn't like my mother at all. I can't imagine her ever leaving the house without lipstick, much less being in public sans a shirt."

I continued to mull over the sudden media interest in Deidra's past. "Well, Mina. What do you think?" I fluffed the little palm leaves as I poured a bit of water into the dirt for the plant.

"Ummm…Piper?" Victoria stared at me from the counter. "Who you talking to?"

Woops. I hadn't heard the swinging door open. Caught talking to the potted palm, great. Maybe I'm losing my mind. "Nobody." I shook my head. "What's up?"

"Nothing really. I was wondering, can I have my phone back?"

"Yes, I'm done. Do me a favor though? Try not to show anyone else those photos of Sam's mom." I retrieved the phone from my apron pocket and returned it.

"No problem." Victoria disappeared back to the baking.

~

"Whoowee," the door opened, the sound of the bell overhead drowned out by the storm which hadn't slackened. "Looks like we're in for a real frog strangler. Must be some big tropical storm." Gladys plopped her umbrella in the makeshift umbrella bucket that I'd set up by the door.

"And hello to you," I laughed.

"Good afternoon," Gladys continued to wipe her feet on the mat. A useless attempt, considering the amount of water it had soaked up today, but I wouldn't try to stop her. "Did Sam already leave?"

"Yes, she should be at the hair salon by now. I'm not sure how well the plans for house shopping are going to hold up in this weather though."

"House shopping?" Gladys asked as she joined me behind the counter. "Is Sam moving?"

"No." I explained Sam's plans for the day.

Gladys gave a little smile. "Good, good." She poured herself a cup of coffee. "Too bad about this weather though. Maybe she and Landon will have to cozy up somewhere dry, what do you think?"

I rolled my eyes. Gladys and her matchmaking never failed to catch me by surprise. "I wouldn't count on it," I told her. "BeeBee is with Sam; she's getting her hair colored, too."

"Maybe I should color my hair?" Gladys twirled a finger through a tight gray curl. "Not blue though; then I'd look like one of those blue-haired old women. Hmm," her forehead creased. "Maybe blonde. Or dirty blonde!"

Seeing that my opinion wasn't at all needed, I extricated myself from the hair color discussion before it was too late. "Since BeeBee is out with Sam, I think I'll go check on Flo."

Gladys waved one arm at me, still muttering to herself about hair. I took that as a sign that she didn't mind manning the cash register alone for a bit. Weighing my options, I decided darting down the sidewalk and into Flo's from the street side promised a bigger chance of staying dry than going out the back and hoping she heard me bang on the back door. Before I got across the room, Gladys called me back.

"What did Deidra come in here throwing a fit about?" she asked me.

"She was just…wait a minute, you were nowhere near here. How did you now Deidra came in throwing a fit yesterday?" My brows drew together. I crossed my arms as Gladys shuffled guiltily.

"Mina told me," she shrugged.

"Mina. This Mina?" I pointed to our potted palm.

Gladys nodded.

"Listen, I know you like to talk to Jack and Drew," the palm trees at her home. "And maybe I slipped up and spoke to this plant today; I admit, she's cute. Still, you can't expect me to believe she told you about Deidra."

"Not in so many words," Gladys shifted her eyes from me to the door. "Hello!" she greeted as a bedraggled group of teens flooded the café, along with about a gallon of water sloshing off of them. "Come in, come in. Who wants coffee?" Gladys latched on to the excuse to ignore me.

With a sigh, I resigned myself to picking up this conversation another time. Back on track to my current destination, Flo's, I exited and hurried next door.

"Hi," I greeted.

"Come on in," Flo smiled. "What brings you over today? I hope it isn't for another batch of break-up flowers?" She raised her eyebrows, eyes twinkling merrily beneath.

"Very funny." I chuckled, recalling Flo's confusion when Griff and I came in to buy first-date / last-date flowers for Kendra. "Actually, I came to check on you. Need any help while BeeBee is gone?"

"How sweet!" Flo beamed. "Thanks, but no. This weather is keeping customers away for the first time in weeks. I hate to admit it, but I'm thankful for the break. I'm nearly caught up on arrangements to make." She indicated a lineup of beautiful bouquets and vases behind the counter. "When I finish, I'll work on balancing the books. BeeBee plans to be back later this afternoon."

"That's good to hear. I do hope this bad weather moves on though." I glanced back out the storefront windows. Gray skies as far as my eye could see. "I don't think I've seen a storm this bad since I moved to Seashell Bay. What did Gladys call it?" I chewed on my lip thinking. "A frog strangler?"

Flo snorted. "I haven't heard that term before. Guess it makes sense; as fast as the water is rising out there, a drowned frog or two wouldn't be surprising."

I chuckled but the image of a little cartoon frog splayed out with his tongue lolling from his mouth popped into my head, chasing the chuckles away. Poor frogs. Poor us; if it got any worse that would be flash flooding. "I guess I should get back to the bakery," I told Flo.

"One minute." She finished tying a loop of ribbon around a vase and then beckoned me closer. Lowering her voice, she whispered, "Speaking of Gladys, I received an order of flowers to be delivered to her."

My mouth dropped open. "Really?"

Flo nodded. "I'm only telling you this to confirm I can deliver these to the bakery, of course." She wiped the grin from her face, all business as she discreetly spun a short vase so that the card faced me.

"Of course, of course," I bobbed my head, leaning to get a look at the sender's name on the envelope. *Frédéric.*

"Anyway," Flo settled the vase back amongst the row of completed arrangements. "I thought you could let me know when Sam is back...I mean when a good time to deliver the flowers to Gladys would be."

I smiled. "You bet. Keep your phone handy; I'll shoot you a text."

Back at the bakery, I grabbed a kitchen towel and dried off the spattering of rain from my arms and face. Even with the awning, you couldn't go outside without getting a little wet. The group of teenagers still sat at two tables by the window. I grabbed the coffee pot and refilled their glasses while Gladys rang up an order for a young woman at the counter.

"These cookie sandwiches are legit," one of the teen boys nodded at me as I poured his coffee.

"Thank you. Can I get anyone anything else?"

"Your number," one of them wise-cracked. The girl beside him slapped his arm.

Saving my eye roll for when my back was to the table, I smiled politely and left them to their snacks. "Gladys," I said as the customer left the counter. "I'm going to help Victoria in the kitchen. Let me know if you need anything."

"You bet. Here are two orders that came in today for parties."

I took the two small slips of paper and thanked her, heading through the swinging door. I made a mental note to order professional order forms with our logo. It was one of the things we couldn't afford right away and I'd been forgetting to put them in the budget the last few months. Maybe Millie could design something.

"Victoria," I called. Her head poked out of the fridge. "Do you know if Millie is coming in today?"

"Yes." Victoria disappeared back inside then came out, four bowls of dough balanced on her arms. I rushed over to shut the door and help with two of the bowls. "Thanks," she said. "Millie should be here soon. She had a phone interview with that art school today."

"What is all this?" I looked at the bowls of dough. Recognizing two as chocolate chip cookie dough, I peered more closely at the other two.

"Gladys told me that we almost sold out of the Mini Chocolate Chip Sandwich Cookies, so those two are to make more."

"Great, I'll whip up extra hazelnut filling. What about the others?"

Victoria held up one bowl, Sugar Cookie dough, to make Mini Sugar Cookie Sandwiches. I thought we could make a light, summery filling flavor for those, but I'm not sure what yet. The other bowl is also Sugar Cookie dough," she nodded to the fourth bowl. "I'm going to mix in strawberry jam and lime zest to make Strawberry Limeade Cookies."

"Genius!" I patted her on the back. "Why don't I concentrate on both of the fillings. You can get the Mini Chocolate Chip Cookies in the oven first."

"Okay, cool." Victoria never had to be told twice. She set to work scooping tiny mounds of cookie dough onto parchment-paper lined pans.

Millie came in from the café right as I started on the Lemon Whipped Cream Filling for the Mini Sugar Cookie Sandwiches. Squishing sounds came from her soaked shoes as she walked. Her pant legs, too, were soaked up past the ankles.

Victoria stared at her drenched friend. "Holy cow, Millie! Did you walk here?"

"Nope. I may have to walk home though." Millie leaned her elbows onto the stainless-steel work island in the center of the room, head drooping. "I nearly hydroplaned on my scooter more than once. The street out front is three inches deep in water on the sides of the road."

"I'm so sorry, Millie." I looked between the girls. "You two know Sam or I are happy to give you a lift home if things don't dry out some." I held up a hand to curtail their protests. "I won't have you in danger. We'll see how the storm plays out but you have a ride if you need one."

Tension leaked out of Millie, her shoulders sagging in relief. "Great. It was kind of scary, especially when cars passed and sprayed more water over me; as if the road wasn't hard enough to see already."

"Thanks, Piper." Victoria continued pulling sheets of cookies from the oven and placing them on the cooling racks.

"Millie, how would you like another art project?" I asked.

"As long as it doesn't involve creating a water feature for the flooding, count me in."

I described the type of order form we needed. "I'd love you to put your creative touch on it to really represent the Ooey Gooey Goodness Bakery. Our logo, plus whatever your heart desires."

Clapping gleefully, Millie assured me she could do it. "Thank you for this," she said. "You and Sam hired me to clean. I never imagined I would also get to do so much extra-fun stuff with my art, as well. I'm so lucky!"

"You aren't lucky; you're talented. See if you can have something ready for me on Monday, can you?"

"Absolutely!" She stood and stretched her arms overhead. "I'll start working on it right after I wipe down tables and clean up trash up front."

A high-pitched whirring noise sounded. For a moment, I thought I might be losing my mind. When Victoria looked up and glanced around the room, I knew she must here it, too. The noise grew louder.

"Do you think that is the severe weather alert system?" Victoria's voice trembled a fraction.

"No..." I cocked my head to the side. "It sounds like it is coming from the back door." In confirmation, a sudden clattering sound rang out. The door knob twisted. Finding it locked, the person on the outside stopped trying. We waited. The whirring noise revved up again, similar to that of a dentist drill.

Victoria's eyes widened even more. "What do we do?" she asked.

I snaked my hand in a drawer, pulling out one of the cans of pepper spray Gladys had insisted we each have as part of our "supplies" earlier in the month. I might not have carried it on my person all the time like she wanted; still, I kept it handy.

"We find out who it is," I said. "Get ready to holler at Gladys in the café if I need you to."

CHAPTER 7

I wrenched the back door open and stepped back. Rain peppered my face. His back turned to me, I experienced a feeling of déjà vu as, for the second time in one day, Griff stood in the pouring rain outside the door. This time he wasn't alone.

"Hey!" I yelled over the roaring rain. "What the heck are you doing? Are you crazy?"

Hearing, Griff turned. Skirting a ladder, he stepped inside and shut the door.

"Here," Victoria called. She tossed a kitchen towel our way.

I caught it and held it back. "You can have this," I waved the towel. "After you tell me what you are doing. Why is someone on a ladder out there?"

"I tried to call," Griff said. "We're putting up a little canopy. You shouldn't have to stand in the rain to unlock your back door." Not only a building inspector, Griff also ran a few crews of guys for small repairs and installations to bring things up to code.

"Griff! It is storming out there." I stomped a foot. "Surely a canopy could have waited."

"It's raining today. Which means it might still be raining when you leave to lock up." He shrugged. "You needed a canopy."

"I highly doubt that safety protocol gives permission for canopy installation during inclement weather."

Griff shrugged. "I won't tell if you don't."

I tried to be angry at the infuriating man but the truth was I could barely contain a smile. Growing from the warm-fuzzy feelings in my belly, the smile persisted and I grinned. "You are crazy," I told him.

"Always," he promised. "We should be done in a few more minutes and then out of your hair." Griff squeezed my hand, waved to BeeBee and shouldered back out into the rain.

Victoria whistled as she ambled away from the swinging door and back to the counter.

"I don't want to hear it," I told her, earning myself a giggle.

"Yes ma'am," she saluted.

I edged my phone out of the cargo pocket on my hip after she turned away. There it was: one missed call. I tapped the button on the side a few times to turn the phone up to full volume and put it back.

An hour later, Sam came bustling inside with BeeBee trailing behind. "We have a canopy." Sam made it a statement rather than a question.

I answered anyway. "Your brother helped install it. In the rain. Thankfully, nobody blew off the ladder or got struck by lightning."

"At least, we assume not," Victoria piped up.

"True. Wouldn't have been able to hear them if they did."

"Well, there weren't any bodies," Sam reassured me.

"Lovely." I gave a wry smile. "Now, let's see the new hair." Both girls wore hoods to protect from the rain, BeeBee's an extension of a cozy hoodie sweatshirt; Sam's hood attached to a designer Burberry raincoat. I wouldn't be at all surprised if Sam had bought them today after the freak rainstorm began. It seemed unlikely they would have been laying around in her new car.

"You first," BeeBee told Sam.

Sam shrugged out of her raincoat, hanging it on a hook to drip. I made a mental note to put a dry towel down back there before one of us slipped and fell.

"Wow, I didn't even know you could have hair that color." Victoria stepped closer, gazing at the light purple hair.

I circled my finger in the air. Sam spun obediently. I ran my hand through it, lifting it to see through to the bottom layers.

"It's all the same color," Sam answered my unspoken question.

"Very pretty," I told her. "Kind of makes you look like a magical fairy which is perfect because we have a magical cookie order for more of your unicorn masterpieces."

"The color is lilac," she said. "Okay, your turn BeeBee."

BeeBee flicked the hood back from her head. Black as crow's wings hair highlighted the delicate Asian features of her face. "Beautiful," I told her. "But I thought you were getting brown and just one pink stripe?" On the left side of her head, two deep blue, about an inch wide, ran from top to tip.

"I decided on black before we got there. Then, Sam convinced me to go with blue."

"It's the color of human trafficking awareness," Sam explained. "I looked it up."

"Two blue stripes…" I looked back to BeeBee.

"One for Eva. One for me." BeeBee smiled.

"Who's Eva?" Victoria glanced around the room.

"You know what," I slapped my hands on my thighs. "I just remembered that Flo has a delivery to make now that we're all here." As planned, my announcement distracted everyone including Victoria. I'd bought BeeBee a little time to choose whether or not she shared with anyone else about her sister.

CHAPTER 8

Trying to look nonchalant while trying to crowd six people behind the counter in the Ooey Gooey Café isn't exactly possible.

"What gives?" Gladys asked seeing Victoria's furtive motion for Millie to join her, Sam, BeeBee, and me beside Gladys at the cash register. "Is the kitchen flooded? Did someone break in? I know I've got some supplies here…" Gladys reached for the zipper on her trusty fanny pack; the fanny pack that contained pepper spray, panic buttons, and a plethora of other gadgets that I knew of, to say nothing of anything Gladys had added but failed to mention.

Right on time, Flo opened the door and carried a short vase with a plump, round bouquet of white daisies, orange roses, and pink lilies.

"Hi, Flo." Gladys greeted. "You coming to join this crowd behind the counter, too?" Gladys eyeballed us.

Victoria smothered a giggle.

"Not at all, Gladys." Flo strode forward purposefully. "I'm simply here to make a delivery." She smiled and placed the vase on the counter.

Gladys looked over the top of the flowers at her. "For Piper or Sam?" she asked twitching a thumb our direction.

"Neither."

"Oh?" Gladys peered at our little huddle again. "Then who?"

"Why don't you read the card and see," I motioned to the arrangement.

"This better not be a bouquet of prank flowers," she frowned. "The kind that squirt water. I'd be upset, Flo, since you didn't tell me we could buy prank flowers."

"For goodness sake, Gladys." Flo crossed her arms. "I wouldn't sell something so childish as prank flowers. My flowers are about beauty and communication."

"Too bad," Gladys mumbled as she searched the arrangement. Spying the card at last, she pulled it from the plastic pitchfork-looking holder. "It's for me!"

"Open it," Sam urged.

Gladys opened the card, reading silently.

Before I could so much as attempt a peek over her shoulder, Gladys stuffed the card back in the envelope. "Piper, Sam."

"Yes?"

"Yeah?"

"Could I have the next few days off?" she asked.

I looked to Sam. Shrugged. She nodded. "Sure," I didn't mind if Gladys took time off. Though I would have like to ask her why, I didn't get the chance.

"Thanks!" Gladys hauled the vase of flowers out the front door and down the sidewalk. We watched her get into her car and drive away.

Millie spoke first. "That was an odd reaction to flowers."

We all agreed.

CHAPTER 9

I stretched my hands above my head, and pointed my toes, stretching my legs out to the corners of the bed. Sunday. Daylight leaked into my bedroom around the edges of the curtains. The bakery wouldn't open until one and I didn't have to go in early since Sam and I stayed late to do the baking last night. She and Landon had rescheduled house tours to Monday, thanks to the weather.

Wait a minute! Sunshine.

I untangled my legs from the sheets and hopped over to the window. Sunshine beamed. Not a cloud in sight, thank goodness.

My phone beeped from the nightstand. Unplugging it from the charger, I plopped back down on the bed to read the new message.

Sam: You up?

Me: Yep.

Sam: Can one of the girls help at the Ooey Gooey today?

Me: No prob. What's up?

Sam: Mother. Mandatory Lunch. Something about dinner wardrobe.

Me: Ick.

Sam: Griff has to be there 2.

Me: Double ick. No worries, we will handle the bakery.

Sam: K. See you at church?

Me: Yeah, see you then.

I looked at the time on my phone. Plenty of time left before I needed to get ready. My phone beeped again as I tucked the corners of the sheets back into place. Wondering what Sam had forgotten, I stared at our conversation thread for half a minute before realizing the notification was for a message from Victoria.

Victoria: How soon can we do going-away party for Millie?

Victoria: Like, Friday?

Victoria: She leaves next weekend for art school. ☹☹

I waited a moment to see if she would send a fourth text. When none came, I responded.

Me: We will make it work for Friday. Millie can work the register today. You and I will talk plans in the kitchen.

Victoria: TY TY TY TY! ▯

Me: Welcome!

Bed made, messages all answered, teeth brushed, I grabbed a notepad and headed to the living room. Party planning meant one thing: a new list. Finding a purple gel pen in the cute mason jar full of writing utensils, another new treasure I purchased when refurbishing after my apartment got shot to pieces not long ago, I started jotting down the things I would need to find out from Victoria. Number of people, invites or open, favorite desserts, theme or favorite color, allergies, name of the school Millie was leaving to attend? The list went on. Satisfied that I had captured most of my thoughts, I stuck the spiral notepad into a purse. Church today meant I'd give the regular cargo pant wardrobe a break and wear a dress instead.

Time for breakfast. I whipped up some sausage balls, oozing with sharp cheese and tanging with spicy seasonings, plated a handful, and carried them with a glass of tea back to the couch. I didn't get lazy mornings very often; I planned to take full advantage of my lounge time. Flipping on the news, I bit into the moist, delicious sausage ball as I watched reports of the damage from yesterday's storm. Seven inches of water measured in most areas. The worst part of the forecast predicted that more would soon follow. Hurricane Loretta charted a course for Florida with building strength. Whether the hurricane would also make landfall here, or only send another deluge of water remained undetermined.

Thank God that Griff installed that canopy. Looks like we may need it soon after all.

I paused as I picked up the remote to flip channels. Deidra's face splashed across the screen. A tableau of smaller images dotted the sidebar, all of Deidra as a teen. Wincing, I turned up the volume.

"Teenage miscreant becomes town menace?" The nasally voice on the television posed the question. "Sources say these scandalous photos of Deidra Lowe, first lady of Seashell Bay and wife to Mayor Lowe, are only the beginning of an unveiling of her past, and present, sins."

Clicking the television off, I looked down at my empty plate. Good thing I had already polished off breakfast; now I'd lost my appetite.

~

The church sanctuary filled up quickly. Of course, I arrived several minutes early, so finding a seat wasn't a problem. Sam and I attended services more regularly now that we took Sunday mornings off from the bakery. Today, however, Pastor Dan had mentioned that a special guest would be introduced and hinted that we should be there.

"Did you save us a seat?" Sam whispered. The choir and instruments began their first notes as she and BeeBee slid into seats beside me without waiting for an answer.

Worship music and singing lasted for half an hour. As the last chords were sung, Pastor Dan ascended the steps to the platform. "Good morning, good morning." He smiled, displaying large white teeth. "Today's service is going to be a tad different than our normal Sunday morning. Of course, that means you all get a break from me preaching."

The congregation laughed as a body. One or two peopled hooted out *amen.*

Pastor Dan laughed right along with everyone. When the room quieted, he grew serious. "I am pleased to introduce a new member of our community, of this church, and the head of a brand-new focused ministry." Stretching an arm out to the side, he waved someone up to join him from the front row.

Landon jogged up the steps and shook Pastor Dan's hand, enveloping him with the other arm in that universal male hand-shake / back-slap version of a hug.

"Brothers and sisters, this is Landon." A smattering of applause sounded before the introduction continued. "Landon, why don't you take a few minutes to explain your role and our churches role for the new ministry program."

"Thank you, Pastor." Landon waved to the congregation. Dressed in khaki pants and a navy polo shirt, he presented a very professional image. "A few of you may remember the fundraiser that local businesses and Sandy Shores Evangelical Church participated in several earlier this year to raise money for Breaking Chains. I work with Breaking Chains, identifying victims of human trafficking and reaching out, giving them opportunities to get free and receive help."

A murmur rippled through the chairs.

Landon continued speaking. His voice carried strong and clear I noticed wryly, thinking of my own fear of public speaking and the struggle it had brought me weeks ago. It still felt like yesterday. I shuddered, relieved that it wasn't me standing behind that podium with a microphone. I tuned back in to the words being spoken.

"I've spent years operating on my own, or in a small group with other members of Breaking Chains. The past few months, I've realized that one of the things missing from my life is one of the same things missing from the lives of so many victims. Connection. Roots. Somewhere to call home."

Glancing at Sam, I saw that she was smiling and nodding. Reaching over, I squeezed her hand. She squeezed back. On the other side of her, BeeBee studied her fingernails. She remained attentive to Landon's speech; I could tell by the slight angle of her head, ear up and to the front of the room. I imagined any reminder of her previous life was difficult. I nudged Sam and nodded my head toward BeeBee.

Sam took my hint. She clasped BeeBee's hand and we sat there, linked together hand-to-hand, as we listened to Landon's plans unfolding.

"I'm proud to say that I've found my own home, here in Seashell Bay. Not a house, mind you. I'm still looking for one of those; see me after church if you have a spare." Everyone laughed as he pointed a finger out at the crowd of people. "But really, I found some great people. Connected with them. Am looking forward to coming to know the rest of you as well. I found a true home, at last. And so, I asked Breaking Chains if I could begin an extension of their relief and recovery division right here. They agreed and Pastor Dan graciously invited me to use this church and all of you, wonderful people, as the home base of operations. You will all be on the ground floor of building this ministry."

A loud clapping sounded this time. BeeBee, Sam, and I broke hands and joined in.

"It is our goal with this ministry to provide that very same connection and spirit of togetherness that I found here to aid those who are rescued from various human trafficking situations, to help heal them emotionally and give them opportunities to thrive physically. I'm going to turn things back over to Pastor Dan now. We have pamphlets in the back for you to sign up if you would like to receive more information, volunteer time or resources, or make suggestions for ways you think this ministry could operate to meet those goals."

CHAPTER 10

"Did you know?" Church let out early and I walked down the steps beside Sam.

"Know what? That Landon would be working at the church?"

I nodded.

"Nope," she shrugged. "But maybe he had planned to tell me yesterday while I showed him different houses and apartments."

"Maybe so." I looked around. BeeBee and Landon were a few steps behind us.

I looked out at the ocean, close enough to be visible although the sound of the waves breaking was lost in the distance. The water showed signs of the storm; darker, rougher, and with spots too small to see in detail but that I imagined were little bits of debris and seaweed floating on the top.

Griff materialized at my right shoulder. "Did Sam tell you about lunch?"

"She did. Will I see you after?"

"You bet. Unless you want to come to lunch and see me now?"

"No way. I'm going to sit this one out," I shook my head multiple times. "Deidra on a normal day, that I can handle. Deidra after the media smear I saw this morning, I'm not coming within two blocks of that ticking time bomb."

Griff and Sam each grimaced. "Trust me," Sam pushed hair behind her ears. "I've been trying to think of a way out all morning. Ever since that headline on TV."

"I saw it. There is good news though."

We had stopped walking, waiting for BeeBee and Landon to catch up. "And what would that good news be exactly?" Sam wanted to know.

"Your hair is lilac. She hasn't seen it yet so that will distract her at least through to the dessert course."

Griff burst out laughing. "Thanks, Sis. You're always taking one for the team." He play-tapped her on the chin.

Pursing her lips, Sam prepared a retort but Griff was saved from her barbs by BeeBee and Landon.

"Lunch?" Landon asked.

Sam shook her head. "Mother's house."

"Same." Griff tipped his head at Landon, then BeeBee, then hugged me goodbye. He and Sam crossed the parking lot to their respective vehicles.

"That leaves you two." Landon smiled.

"Bakery," I shrugged.

"Same." BeeBee laughed. "Technically, it's the flower shop for me."

"Tell you what though. You can bring us lunch to the bakery." I winked.

"That's fine by me." Landon agreed. "We can have whatever you want."

"What about Victoria and Millie? Or Flo?" BeeBee looked to me.

"Maybe pizza for everyone?" Landon swiveled his head between us, gauging our reactions.

BeeBee grinned.

My stomach growled. "Sounds perfect! Get three or four mediums and bring them around back to the kitchen."

"Deal."

BeeBee and I hopped into my truck and made for the bakery. Flo and she would only be working in the back today, not open for customers.

"I'll text you when the pizza gets here," I told her as she hustled to the back door of Flo's Flowers and I unlocked the kitchen door for the Ooey Gooey.

She gave a nod, then disappeared inside.

By the time I had my apron tied on, Victoria and Millie had arrived.

"Millie, would you mind opening up the front and running the register this afternoon?"

"Absolutely not," Millie smiled. "Do you want me to take any cookies up to add to the display case?"

I pulled a couple of boxes from the counter, baked fresh yesterday evening. "These need to go in. Thank you."

The swinging door barely whooshed closed behind Millie when Victoria started spewing ideas. "We need to have so many cookies. Or a cake. Can we have both? Oh! And we should totally invite

Millie's parents, too. Piper, how are we going to do all of the regular baking plus all of the extra baking, yet somehow keep it a secret?"

"Well, first, we don't have a meltdown." I interrupted, worried the girl would soon have herself hyperventilating. "Deep breaths."

"Okay." Victoria inhaled through her nose, closing her eyes. Before I could count to four, her eyes popped back open. "Drinks!" The word came out in a panicked whisper. "What will we do for drinks. The bakery just makes food. And coffee. But Millie doesn't drink a whole ton of coffee you know."

"Alright, you sit. I'll bake." I guided her to the island in the center of the kitchen. "And while you are sitting, I want you to fill out all the things on this list that you know. The ones you don't know, you and I will brainstorm later." I plopped the notebook in front of her. "And Victoria, we have a massively giant fridge. We will buy drinks." I fished a pen from the junk drawer in the corner and handed it to her. "Now, get started. We will throw Millie an epic going away party, don't you worry." I laid a reassuring hand on her shoulder.

Throwing me a grateful look, Victoria got down to business. For a time, the scratching and scribbling noises of the pen competed with the sounds of ingredients being measured into bowls. Or not measured, as often happened to be the case when I baked. Sometimes, you just had to feel the right amounts.

A knock sounded at the back door. I hurried to unlock it. Landon entered. Pizza boxes were stacked up to his chin.

"Somebody order a pizza?" He raised his eyebrows.

"Get in here, you goofball. That's a whole lot of pizza." I steered him toward the island. Millie, so engrossed in party planning notes that she didn't hear him, jumped when five boxes of pizza dropped onto the table a few inches from her face.

"I'll text BeeBee." I reached for the notebook. "Let me hold this and you can grab Millie from up front if there are no customers."

"What if there are customers?"

"I'll go up front while Millie eats." Landon moved toward the swinging door as he offered. "Then I get to eat all of the leftover pizza that y'all don't finish."

Victoria asked if he had any idea how much pizza teenage girls could consume in one sitting and I laughed out loud. Landon went up front, shaking his head; Millie joined us immediately. BeeBee and Flo came through the back door within a minute of my text. I passed around napkins and we all dug in with enthusiasm.

"Does anyone think we should leave some pizza for Landon?" BeeBee asked after ten minutes of chit-chat and pizza. Several boxes were getting bare.

"If you insist." I winked and went to relieve Landon. Natural charm oozed from Landon; he had a whole cue of people in line along with a growing stack of cookies balanced on the counter beside him. I watched curiously as the next customers, a sweet married couple that spent an hour each Sunday afternoon together here at the Ooey Gooey Goodness Bakery, moved forward and pointed out their requests.

"One Snickerdoodle Surprise and one Oatmeal Raisin." Landon pulled not one, but two of each cookie from the display case. One of each he bagged and handed across the counter to Ed and Mary. The other two he added to the leaning tower of cookies that were stacked dangerously close to his elbow.

After the line dwindled, I cleared my throat.

"I know you're back there," Landon turned. "And I'm guessing you've been wondering about this little stack of cookies."

"It doesn't look so little from here." The stack wobbled precariously. I hoped nobody in the café sneezed; I feared the slightest breeze would send the stack cascading to the floor.

"You mind?" Landon handed me a large to-go bag. I took the bag and held it just below counter-level. In a giant swoop, he put all of the cookies inside.

"And what are these cookies for?"

"Everything everyone ordered sounded irresistible. I made the obvious choice and decided not to resist." Landon shrugged. "Besides, now you can consider your debt for the pizza paid."

"I got the better end of that deal." Pizza was expensive, especially the ooey gooey stuffed crust pizza that Landon had bought.

"Sam and I didn't know you were starting a branch of Breaking Chains here. Are you excited?"

"Definitely. I've got to tell you, Piper, I didn't realize what I'd been missing out on until I reconnected with you and met all of your friends."

"What do you mean?"

"I've been so wrapped up in work that I didn't take time to form relationships. I had buddies in our teams, of course. That was all I did though; spend my time in seedy places, seeing the worst of humanity, stressing myself out about fixing it."

"It sounds like you were busy trying to take care of everyone but yourself."

"Yeah." He ran a hand across the back of his neck. "When I saw how close you and Sam, even Griff, all were I got a little jealous. Then, when you and Sam came to find Griff and I, it all clicked. You didn't care that you put yourselves in danger. You had each other's backs no matter what. I knew that I needed to make some changes in my life."

"Getting to spend more time with Sam didn't make the decision to uproot and move any harder did it?" I laughed at the sheepish look that crossed Landon's face. "Go on to the kitchen. They may have eaten your pizza by now."

~

"She's infuriating!" Sam's voice exploded into the relative silence of the bakery as she and Griff came through the front door a little before three in the afternoon. She brushed past Mina, the little palm swaying in the breeze of her wake.

I looked around. A few customers watched Sam, then dropped their gazes and spoke in whispers. Others merely glanced up in surprise and then munched happily on their snacks unfazed.

Sam dropped her voice to a harsh whisper as she approached the counter. "I need chocolate before I do something I regrets."

Opening the display case, I stepped out of her way. I raised my eyes to Griff in question and was surprised to find his countenance equally stormy as Sam's tone. "Want to talk about it?"

Before either of them answered, the bell above the door jingled. "Griff, I'm so sorry." The leggy woman rushed up to the counter, her knee length pink dress swishing around her knees. I'd only seen her from a distance before but I'd hazard a guess that this was Kendra.

"I had no idea your mother planned to ambush you like that, truly. I apologize and wanted to let you know that I will not be accepting any more invitations from her." Kendra gathered herself, standing taller. "You left before I could explain."

My head spun, trying to catch on to missed events. Sam continued to examine cookies. Griff rubbed both hands over his face like he was trying to wake up from a bad dream. Giving up on being brought into the loop, I extended a hand. "Hi, I'm Piper. Welcome to Ooey Gooey Goodness Bakery."

"It's so nice to meet you!" The woman gushed and shook my hand. "I'm Kendra. Thank you for sending those sweet flowers to dinner with Griff. I've been wanting to come and say hello but work has kept me tied up."

"Hi, Kendra. Can I get you a cookie?"

Sam stood then. "Here, have one of the sandwich cookies." She handed over a Sugar

Cookie Sandwich with the Lemon Whipped Cream Filling.

I leaned down and pulled out a Triple Chip Chocolate Cookie and offered it to Griff. He smiled, tossing the whole cookie in his mouth at once.

"I take it that lunch was less enjoyable than expected?" I raised my eyebrows.

Sam wiped her mouth with a napkin. "You could say that. You could also say having your fingernails removed one at a time isn't the best way to get a manicure." She crumpled the napkin up into a tiny ball.

"There's pizza in the back. Landon brought it."

The words weren't long out of my mouth before Sam escaped to the kitchen. I turned back to Griff and Kendra. "Well. Which of you would like to fill in the blanks?" I gestured to an empty tabletop next to the counter. I would be able to hop up and help customers if needed, but until then curiosity chewed at my insides like Bugs Bunny on a carrot.

"Mother," Griff's lips curled in distaste, "didn't invite only Sam and I to lunch. She also invited Kendra and Garrett."

"Garrett?" I tilted my head. The name sounded familiar. "You mean Garrett like hospital-flowers-sending Garrett? The one Sam is supposed to go to the mayoral dinner shindig with?"

"The one and the same," Kendra nodded. "And Deidra made it sound like I would be a part of that day too – as Griff's date." She held up a hand as my mouth dropped. "Griff and I made it very clear that would not be happening, that we would not be seeing each other. Deidra invited me to lunch on the pretense that she and Mayor Lowe were interested in my new business."

"Let me guess, somehow the business never came up?"

Kendra nodded. "You got it."

Griff sighed. "That isn't the craziest part of it."

"Shoot." I noticed Grandpa Rex making his way toward the counter, two grandkids in tow. "Save that thought." I joined the trio and asked Timmy and Tommy if they had been playing in the mud puddles.

"No m'm," the freckle-faced one answered glumly.

"Can't get our Sunday clothes messy." His brother frowned. "Momma doesn't like messy."

"I have to agree with your mom on that one." I ruffled their hair. "Now, tell me what you two would like today."

After bagging up several Domino Doubles, I waved goodbye to the cheery family and sat back down with Griff and Kendra. "Where were we? That's right, as always, you said things were even worse than the surprise dining companions." Where Deidra was concerned, worse than imagined seemed to be the common theme.

"She also insisted on a wardrobe fitting."

"A what?" I sputtered.

"A wardrobe fitting." Sam spoke from behind me, having come out from the kitchen without my notice. She pulled up another chair. We all scooted round to make more space. "Mother ordered outfits and hired a tailor to come after lunch today and take measurements so that the clothes could be fitted and fixed before Thursday."

"The dinner is this Thursday?" I wouldn't touch the subject of matching outfits yet. No way.

"Yes. And, obviously, since I declined Deidra's less than courteous insistence that I be present, you still have to schedule your own fitting." Kendra delivered the news with a somber expression.

I wanted to laugh. One look at Griff and Sam confirmed the truth of it though. Griff would take me as his date, but I would have to conform to Deidra's version of presentable. "I'll get more chocolate." At this rate, if another bit of bad news came our way, I'd have to close the Ooey Gooey due to us eating all the stock.

"I should really get going." Kendra stood, smoothing down her skirt. "Piper, how much do I owe you for the cookie?"

"Nothing." I waved off her cash.

"Fine. But when I get my business up and going, I would love for you and Sam to cater dessert at the grand opening."

I smiled.

Sam nodded. "We would love to. What is your business going to be?"

"A seafood and burger joint on the outskirts of town. I'm signing the papers this week to take over ownership." Kendra's entire face brightened. She waved her hands around as she described her vision. "The plan is to shut it down for a month, renovate, and reopen under a new name: The Seawitch's Seafood & Pool."

"That's why you saw me with Kendra at that seafood and burger place." Griff explained. "She asked me to give it a look before she made an offer, see what work would need to be done to bring it up to code. We looked at the lot behind it too, to make sure a small pool and splash pad zone could be added."

"But Deidra?" Confusion lingered over how and why Deidra had become involved.

"She heard from a friend of a friend or a rumor, who really knows, that I took Kendra to lunch. Not having the full story, she latched on to the idea that she could secure a match with an up-and-coming lawyer for me."

"And unaware that I had left behind the law career. Too ugly." Kendra frowned. "Too stressful. I want to create an oasis of fun for people who need to unwind. Somewhere to bring your kids for a playdate without having to eat a greasy over-processed kid's meal."

"That's going to be amazing." Impressed by her passion and goal, I felt myself warming up to Kendra. The little green monster retreated back to the dark corners of my mind, realizing she wasn't a threat, just another target of Deidra's scheming.

"Thanks. And I plan to make an elegant and unique menu for adults plus a really special menu for the kids. Theirs will include lots of sea creatures and mermaids. What do you think of The Seaweed Sandwich as a choice?"

"Kids will eat it up." Sam winked. "Really, that is a fantastic idea. We can theme our desserts in a similar fashion."

I jumped in, too, ideas popping into my head like crazy. "Madeleines with little sugar pearls inside. Starfish cookies. It'll be a blast."

Kendra clapped her hands. "I'm so excited! Even more so, now that I've tasted more of your delicious desserts."

"Where's Gladys?" Griff asked after Kendra left.

I slapped my forehead. "We forgot to tell you? She got mystery flowers from Chef Fabio, I mean Frédéric, and asked for the next few days off."

"Are they really mystery flowers if you know who they're from?" Griff raised an eyebrow.

"The note was a mystery." Sam smacked him on the arm. "And the need to take off for several days is odd; she's already part-time help."

"I'm sure Gladys will tell you when she's good and ready." Griff stretched. "I think I'm going to go home and watch the ball game." He kissed me on the cheek and hugged Sam.

I didn't even ask what ball game, who was playing or anything else. A sports fan I am not and I didn't plan to start now; a fact I felt certain Griff knew. "See you tomorrow."

"You aren't planning to come over tonight?" Sam followed me to the counter.

"No. Victoria and I have work to do." I filled Sam in on the partial game plan for Millie's going away party.

"What do you need me to do to help?"

"You and BeeBee could shop for the party supplies, plates, cups, drinks and whatever. I think Victoria is almost done filling in the blanks on my list." I pulled the notebook from my apron. "I'll get her to finish it and you and BeeBee can shop sometime this week."

"Great. That's right up my alley."

"Don't I know it."

CHAPTER 11

Tuesday morning, a loud thud registered through my groggy dreams and I jerked awake. Images of bullets tearing through my home flashed through my mind. Shaking them off, I listened. Monday had passed in a monotonous drizzle, both at work and in weather. Today, wind and rain drummed outside. I shuffled to the curtained window and peeked out. An empty trash can slammed up against the wall, again and again, trapped between it and the air conditioning unit. Having identified the culprit responsible for my early wake-up call, I decided it was now time for breakfast.

I realize many people would simply go back to bed at three in the morning, but there was a little dish I'd been wanting to try. Flipping on the light in the kitchen, I grabbed a stick of butter from the fridge. Walnuts and honey from the pantry, pears from the bowl on the table. Brown sugar from the canister on the counter and a little nutmeg from the spice cabinet completed my line of ingredients.

I know. I know. Baked fruit is supposed to be for fall and winter. With the storm brewing outside, comfort food was calling my name. Using a food processor, I chopped the walnuts to a very small size, mixed them with melted butter, and pressed them into a miniature pie pan. See – sensible sized breakfast; it's not like I was making an entire pie plate of Pear & Walnut Crumble. Slicing and coating the pears with the honey, brown sugar, and nutmeg was next. Then top it off with a little walnut and brown sugar, place foil over the top, and it would be ready to pop in the oven.

I dressed while I waited for my breakfast to bake. Digging my raincoat from the back of my closet, I wondered briefly where my umbrella might be at. In the end, I decided against hunting for it. I always felt like I got more wet struggling to close it and get in the truck than when I just went without an umbrella.

Beep.

I started toward the kitchen then realized that sound was from my phone, not the oven timer. Reversing my steps to the bedroom, I picked up the phone and tapped over to my messages.

Victoria: Can you give us a ride to work? Storm is supposed to get worse.

Me: Absolutely!

Victoria: TY

Me: Send the address.

The oven timer buzzed at last. While the crumble cooled, I plugged the address into my navigation then texted Sam to let her know I would be picking up Victoria and Millie for work. I didn't want her to worry if we were a few minutes late.

Deliciousness oozed from my Pear & Walnut Crumble as I cut into it with a fork. Tasty; too bad I didn't have time to savor it. Victoria and Mille were at her aunt's house a ways out near where Gladys lived. I needed to leave soon to make up for the extra time that driving there and back to the bakery in the heart of town would take.

~

"Griff must have sent someone over yesterday afternoon to install a canopy for Flo." No surprise that I hadn't noticed. Yesterday might have been the busiest Monday we'd seen all summer. I walked into the kitchen and blinked in the bright lights. Sam had indeed beat us to work.

"Yeah, I remember him mentioning it." Sam closed the walk-in-fridge and placed several bowls of dough on the counter and island, juggling not to drop them before she got them settled.

"I'll go turn on the lights and make sure everything in the café is ready to open." Millie squeezed past Sam and I to the swinging door.

"Do you want me to mix new dough or bake the mixed dough?" Victoria slid into her apron and looked between the two of us for instructions.

"Why don't you mix? I'll help Piper get cookies on pans." Sam passed me a few sheet pans.

Victoria fist-pumped the air. "Awesome."

"Did Landon find any houses or apartments he liked yesterday while you showed him around?" I knew they had spent several hours looking, trying to fit in as many viewings as possible in case the storm interfered with future tours today or tomorrow.

"One or two. He wanted to look at them again before deciding."

"House or apartment?"

"One of each."

I tried to picture Landon in a cozy little house. Failed. "Did y'all have a nice time?"

Sam's face lit with pleasure. "We did! Landon is so easy to talk to, funny; I really like him." Her smile drooped slightly.

"What's that face for?" I paused from scooping dough, watching her face closely.

"I hate that I have to go to the dinner at the country club with Garrett when I might've had a chance to enjoy myself if Landon were escorting me." She groaned. "Now I'll be doubly miserable."

"Sunday at lunch, was that the first time you met Garrett?"

Sam rolled her eyes. "Yes, though from what I could tell he's been a frequent guest of at the house. It's odd."

I laughed. "Odd that someone could be friends with your mother? Yes, yes, it is."

Sam smirked. "No. More than that. Garrett looks strangely familiar, but I know I've never met him until this weekend. I feel like I should be able to place him though."

"I'm sure you'll think of it." I shrugged. "You never know, maybe he just has one of those faces."

"Maybe." Sam took one full tray to slip into the oven as I resumed scooping dough onto another. "Have you taken care of your Thursday night wardrobe fitting yet?" She hip-bumped me as she returned to the island.

"What do you need a wardrobe fitting for?" Victoria threw a quizzical look over her shoulder.

"For the big schmoozing-dinner Mayor Lowe's supporters are throwing on Thursday evening." I turned back to Sam. "Speaking of, no I haven't been fitted and you haven't told me what we have to wear either." I narrowed my eyes at Sam. She loved clothes. Granted, she preferred picking them out herself; still, the fact that she hadn't described in any way the apparel chosen for this event smelled suspicious.

"It's one of those things that is indescribable; you'll have to see it yourself."

"Fine. Where do I have this fitting?" I pursed my lips. "It seems unlikely your mother is going to welcome me to her house and call back her special tailor."

"I'll call and set up the appointment with Vinny."

"Vinny?" I raised my brows.

"Vincent Von Vaughn. Tailor extraordinaire, at least according to him."

Victoria snorted and I laughed out loud. "You're kidding me, right?" I looked hard at Sam. "That can't be his real name."

"I assure you; it is."

"And he likes to be called Vinny?"

"Hates it." Sam winked. My sides split with laughter. I couldn't wait to meet this tailor, Vinny.

When I stopped laughing, I told Sam to call him. "Set it up for tonight, unless you're busy. You are definitely coming with me."

"Wouldn't miss it," Sam promised. She stepped out the back door to make the call. I caught a glimpse of the darkening sky.

"I better check the weather report." I rooted around in my pant pocket until I felt my phone. Pulling it out, I was surprised to see a message from Gladys.

Gladys: Back at the bakery tomorrow if that is okay?

Typing quickly, I responded.

Me: Sounds good. Everything alright?

Gladys: All is good. Been very busy.

Me: Okay. We will see you tomorrow.

Gladys: Will Sam be there tomorrow? And girls?

Me: Yes. We should all be here.

Gladys: Good.

I frowned. Why would Gladys need to know we would all be here? Her rushed leave of absence and silence about the flowers had me worried. What if Chef Fabio, sorry Frédéric, had broken things off with her and she was too embarrassed to confide in us? What if she had been home with nobody but Jack and Drew for company. My phone beeped again.

Gladys: One last favor?

Me: Yes?

Gladys: Almond Truffles.

I grinned at the screen. That was a dessert, not a favor. And since she hadn't requested something drowning chocolate in chocolate, I could safely assume she was not in emotional turmoil.

Me: They will be awaiting your taste-testing skills.

Back to business. I pulled up the local weather station and skimmed the radar map. And gulped. Hurricane Loretta had increased to a category 5 storm. Landfall in Florida was imminent. The wind and rain that Seashell Bay and other such towns up and down the coast could expect to get as part of the fallout was frightening.

The back door rattled. Sam came back inside, shutting the door with a heave. "Things are really starting to pick up out there."

I turned the phone to face her. "Change of plans. You and BeeBee are staying at my place tonight. Griff too if he wants."

"Why?" Her eyes roamed the article, eyes widening.

"Because I'd feel better without you on the edge of the ocean if it decides to roar up as part of the hurricane and come inland, that's why."

"Sounds reasonable to me." Victoria spoke from behind the stand-mixer. "I'm glad we are a little further inland during times like this. Is the storm really supposed to get bad?"

I nodded grimly. "It may make the storm earlier this week look like mere mist."

"When should we expect it?"

"The weather apps predict it will start by two this afternoon." I looked over at Sam. "Do you need to go home and get clothes?"

"Nah."

I raised my eyebrows in disbelief. My friend wasn't the type of person to wear the same outfit two days in a row – even if all she did was sit on the couch in it – and yet she expected me to believe she would be fine to not have a change of clothes after baking and working all day in the ones she wore. Not buying it.

Reading my mind, or perhaps the not-so-concealed doubt flashing across my face, Sam said, "I have a few clothes in the car. They should work and if I have to stay longer than a day," she shrugged, "well, there is always shopping."

Shopping. How could I not have factored shopping into the equation?

The oven timer buzzed and I moved to grab a couple of oven mitts.

Sam surveyed the kitchen. She and I had successfully cleaned out the bowls of dough. Everything from them was either baking or awaiting its turn in the oven. "I'm going to help Millie out front." She pushed through the swinging door.

"Shoot!"

"What's wrong?" Victoria asked.

"Nothing. I just forgot to tell Sam that Gladys would be back tomorrow."

"Oh, cool!"

I smiled. "That reminds me, are you ready for your next baking challenge?"

"What do you mean?"

"How well do you know your way around a truffle?"

CHAPTER 12

After explaining the basics of a truffle – actually, several styles of truffle - to Victoria, I left her to handle capturing the almond flavors and truffle style in whatever way she saw fit. Finding Sam and Millie chatting in the café, I joined them.

"Just the two people I needed to see."

"What's up?" Sam leaned against the counter.

"Gladys is coming in to work tomorrow. For whatever reason, she wanted to be sure we would all be here."

"Assuming the hurricane doesn't blow us away." Millie glanced out the front windows at the darkening sky.

While we were all looking outside, in strolled one of our local firemen. His boyishly handsome face seemed to make him entirely too young for such a dangerous job. I'd guess eighteen or nineteen at best. I didn't know him but soon gathered that Millie did.

"Hiya, Millie." The fireman winked and tugged on his suspenders as he approached.

Sam waggled her eyebrows at me, turning her back to the strapping man making his way to the counter. "Millie, looks like this customer is all yours."

"O-kay." Millie took Sam's place at the register with a puzzled look on her face.

Sam and I stepped back. I fiddled with the coffee pot. Sam folded napkins. And we listened. Shamelessly.

"Good morning. What can I get for you?" Millie asked, polite as ever.

"What do you recommend?"

"Everything is good. What did you get last time?"

I raised my eyebrows at Sam. So, he'd been in before. I didn't recognize him.

"I can't remember. What's your favorite?" The hunky firefighter smiled at Millie.

Millie's brows crinkled thoughtfully. "I guess this week my favorites are the Cinnamon Bun Cookies."

"Sounds great. I'll take six."

Millie retrieved the cookies from the display case, long blonde ponytail bouncing. As she bagged them up, the fireman interrupted. "You can leave two of those out," he held out cash to pay for his order.

"Okay." Millie placed two cookies on a napkin and accepted the wad of bills. She counted change back and handed it to him. "Have a nice day."

"I hope so." He sent another drool-worthy smile Millie's way before he left.

"So?" I sidled up next to Mille.

"Huh?" She met my grin with confusion.

"Who's the hunk?" Sam tossed a thumb over her shoulder toward the closing door.

"The fireman?" Mille's expression cleared. "Oh, he's a customer that never seems to know what he wants."

"I think he knows what he wants." I tapped my pointer finger on the counter beside the two cookies still sitting on a napkin.

Millie looked down. "Oh no! He forgot his other cookies." Panic washed over her face. The young fireman was nowhere in sight on the sidewalk.

Sam leaned around me and slid the small rectangle from beneath the napkin. "I think Piper meant this."

Millie picked up the piece of paper and flipped it over.

I waited. I did. An entire two seconds I waited before I peeked over her shoulder to read the hastily scrawled note.

Sweet treats for a sweet girl. Enjoy. Davy.

A phone number followed the signature. I shot Sam a thumbs up; she couldn't see the note, but our instincts had been right. Mr. Handsome Fireman Davy was flirting with our little Millie.

We waited for Millie to speak.

Sam, nearly as impatient as me, finally prodded her. "Well? What's it say?"

Millie handed over the paper. Sam read it. "Are you going to call him?" she asked.

"What?" Millie snapped out of her speechlessness.

"Millie," Sam placed both palms on the counter and leaned forward. "You can't tell me you didn't see that boy flirting with you."

"And he bought you cookies," I added helpfully. A man who knows the value of keeping sugar in a woman's life might be worth a closer look at. Lucky for me, I'd already found such a man.

"Are you sure? I mean, he was probably just being nice." Millie twirled a loose piece of blonde hair by her ear.

"Honey." Sam shook her head. "You said he comes in and never knows what he wants, right?"

Millie nodded.

"Let me guess: he always orders whatever you recommend?"

"Yeah, now that I think about it, that sounds right."

I jumped in, taking over for Sam. "When was the first time he came in?"

"The day I accidentally flipped the fire alarm and set off all of the sprinklers." Millie ducked her head, face reddening in embarrassment over the time she snagged the fire alarm with the broom handle and didn't realize it. "He didn't buy any cookies that day."

"After that, he started coming to buy cookies though?"

Millie smiled. "Yes. I remember thinking that even though I goofed things up for you, at least some good came out of it because he must not have heard of the Ooey Gooey Goodness Bakery before that day."

"He could buy cookies at the grocery store," Sam told her. "He came back here because he met you. Today's exchange could have told me that alone; if you need further proof, a note and a phone number should really be enough." She handed the paper back.

We didn't have time to discuss it further; Victoria popped up behind us from the kitchen with a tray full of truffles. "Who wants to try an Almond Crunch Truffle?"

My hand shot into the air. Sam and Millie's followed swiftly behind.

Smiling, Victoria held out the tray with one hand, grabbing her own truffle with the other. "I haven't tried them yet," she admitted. "Plus, there's another tray in the kitchen that I made completely different."

I raised the powdered-sugar-coated chocolate ball up in the air. "A toast to truffles."

Three truffles tapped my own. "Cheers," Sam grinned.

I bit down directly in the center of the truffle. Tasty! I studied the layers of the truffle in my hand as I allowed the other half to roll around in my mouth, chewing slowly to discover each little surprise. Working my way outside to inside, I detected powdered sugar and cocoa powder, a coating chocolate for a crunchy outside shell, a soft brownie-like textured chocolate middle filled with chopped almonds, and a hint of almond extract.

"That is one good truffle!" Sam tossed the rest of hers into her mouth.

Millie, remaining somewhat lost in thought, continued to nibble on her own and nodded in agreement.

"Are you sure you've never made a truffle before?" I tilted my head at Victoria. Natural talent is one thing, but this girl was skilled.

"I'm positive. Eaten them, of course, but never made one." She smiled. "Until you explained them, it always seemed too complicated."

"You said you made others?" I finished eating the delectable little bite in my hand.

"Yep. Come on, we can go try those now." Victoria spun toward the kitchen.

Following, I promised to bring one out for Millie and Sam to try.

A clap of thunder sounded. I glanced over my shoulder before the swinging door shut. Looked like the downpour was beginning early. Yikes.

~

Victoria's White Chocolate Almond Truffles had been to die for, we all agreed. After sufficient taste-testing, we put the remainder of both types of truffles away. If Gladys came tomorrow and we didn't have any, she would be one upset lady.

"Uh-oh. Not good."

I looked over at Victoria, worried that a cookie disaster might be in progress, only to find her phone the object of her distress. "What's the matter?"

We had been mixing up and baking extra cookies to have on hand tomorrow, in case the storm caused any electrical problems this evening. If we already had cookies baked, we could still open for business.

She grimaced, shaking her head, and handed me the phone rather than answering.

Uh-oh was right. Another headline, another unflattering photo. This time, Deidra of the present, not Deidra of the past, carousel-ed across a banner on social media. The post, submitted by screen name TheTruthWillOut, boasted the heading: A Rat by Any Other Name Would be as Hideous.

The photos…oh the photos! First up, Deidra tripping in the gopher hole at the courthouse; someone had caught it in full-on digital color, down to the irate red of her scowling face. Second spin, the banner photo showed flooded streets dotted with floating gopher traps. A few of the traps even had deceased rodents attached. Yuck! The final photo on the reel showed Deidra smiling, holding an umbrella. Tiny caption at the bottom of the post in bright red letters claimed: *Town menace strikes. Deidra determined to destroy anything that she doesn't like. Poison being detected entering public water mains. Is this from illegal quantities of poison used on gopher holes with no concern for groundwater? What secrets will the next storm reveal? Stay tuned to find out.*

"This is bad. Very, very bad." I gave the phone back to Victoria.

~

As the rain picked up that afternoon, customers dwindled. By four it was evident we might as well close up Ooey Gooey Goodness Bakery for the day. Before we did, I pulled Sam aside for a pow-wow. Millie went to the kitchen to get a head start on cleaning.

"This is insane." Sam scrolled through the loop of photos. "Now we have to worry about contaminated water supplies? No wonder someone is going after her; she thinks that rules don't apply if she wants to get something done."

"At least she can't blame you for this one." We were seated at one of the round tables in the café. Only two other people remained, finishing up the last bites of a shared pie slice, and I didn't worry about them overhearing our conversation. I could barely hear our conversation. The torrential rain drowned out most sounds; I couldn't imagine how loud it would be when we actually went outside to leave later.

"What makes you think that?"

"The angle this photo was taken from," I tapped the photo of Deidra, legs splayed wide, one heel sunken in a gopher hole. "There isn't any way you could have taken it from that direction or that far away considering she tripped trying to usher your patriotic-haired-self off the courthouse lawn."

"Reason and logic will not stop my mother from blaming whomever she wants."

"Fine, I'll give you that. But at least there is a chance she admits it couldn't have been you, no matter how small."

"I still can't figure out what makes her think I have something to gain from ruining her image.

This is all because the first picture included us both with wilder hair." Sam leaned forward, resting her forehead in her hands. "I wish I knew who kept posting all of these things."

"You know what Gladys would say, right?"

Sam groaned without looking up.

"Time to investigate."

"How? Where?" She sat up, rubbing tension from her neck. "If there were a way to track the person behind the account 'TheTruthWillOut', don't you think Mother would have found it by now?"

"We start with who would hate your mother enough to try and ruin her."

Sam arced a thin eyebrow at me in disbelief.

"Okay, let me clarify. We figure out who, out of the admittedly long line of people who hate your mother, would have access close enough to her to take or discover these new and old photos."

"You mean, like her assistants?" Sam tapped her long fingernails up and down on the table.

"Exactly. They would be a smart place to start. Didn't she fire two more recently?"

"I'm sure. It's really much too difficult to keep up with." Sam sighed.

"Where do you think we can find the names of the last three or four assistants?" I rubbed my temples. Obviously, it wasn't like we could approach Deidra for the information.

"We could ask the current assistant, I guess." Sam shrugged.

"Unless the current assistant has it out for Deidra and gets suspicious of why we are asking questions."

"Easy." Sam smiled. "I'll tell her that I'm looking to hire my own assistant."

Lightning cracked outside. Our customers scurried out the door. I watched as the man attempted to hold an umbrella over his wife and keep it from blowing away at the same time. "Obviously we aren't doing anything today."

"Agreed." Sam nodded and stood. "Let's get this place closed up and go check on Flo and BeeBee."

"Yeah. If they don't plan to close early, maybe there is something we can help them with to get them finished sooner."

Sam took one look at the rising water in the street. "I definitely hope Flo plans to close early."

Flo did indeed decide to close early. She and BeeBee were washing down the flower cutting station when we knocked on the back door. "Come in, come in."

Crossing the eight feet between the back door of Ooey Gooey and the back door of Flo's Flowers had Sam and I both looking like drowned rats. "We'll just stand by the door, so you don't have to mop everywhere we drip." I looked down at myself. Oh well; I'd be wetter than this by the time we got to the truck. Maybe I should have reconsidered the umbrella.

"We wondered if you needed any help getting finished with orders?" Sam held her hands out. "It is getting pretty bad out there and we closed the bakery early."

"Millie and Victoria are waiting for a text whenever we get ready to take them home; they'll lock up the bakery and meet us at the truck. Until then, we're all yours." I smiled.

"That's very sweet!" Flo tossed a damp paper towel in the trash and pulled a dry one from the roll by the sink. "We actually planned to call it quits early today, too."

"Do you need a ride?" It might be a tight fit to get everyone in my truck but I trusted it to handle potentially flooded roads much better than any car that sat much lower to the ground.

Flo shook her head. "No. I don't live far from here. It will take me less than five minutes to get home." Rain pounded harder on the roof, driven by furious winds. "Okay, maybe less than ten minutes," Flo amended her estimate. "BeeBee can go ahead if you girls are ready."

I glanced at Sam; she gave a barely perceptible shake. We stayed on the same wavelength most of the time and today was no exception. "No. We'll wait until you leave. I'd feel better knowing we all got out of here together."

Flo finished drying the counter. "Sounds good. I only need to give the shop out front a look, turn the lights out and lock up. Should be ready to go in no time."

"No rush," Sam assured her.

Flo had been right. In no time at all, the four of us huddled beneath the new canopy outside the back door as Flo turned the key in the lock. Across the way, Victoria gave me a thumbs up from below the bakery canopy; she had locked up and they were ready. I clicked the unlock button for my truck, the lights blinking in the gray light. For the middle of the afternoon, visibility was slim. Sheets of rain blew sideways and trash gusted through the back lot. The dumpster lid banged, blown open and pummeled by the wind.

"Text me when you get home."

"What?"

"Text me when you get home," I yelled louder. When Flo nodded that she understood, we all took off running to the vehicles. Doors slammed in concert, one after the other, as we all piled into my truck. Sam's door was the last to close. I looked over at her in my passenger seat and chuckled. Her pointy-heeled stilettos were clutched in her hand.

"At least I didn't try to run in them." She pursed her lips.

"But only you would have worn them to begin with on a day when the worst storm of the season had been forecasted." I looked down at her bare feet. "Did your extra bag of clothes include rainboots, by any chance?"

Sam looked down at her bare feet, then out the window in the direction of her car which we couldn't even see through the curtains of rain; she groaned.

"You didn't get your clothes out of your car, did you?"

Slowly, she shook her head.

"I have them."

Sam and I turned to stare at BeeBee scrunched behind Sam's seat. Two large bags, one an army-green duffle and the other a quilted animal print tote, covered her entire lap and part of Victoria's beside her.

Sam clapped her hands together. "You're amazing."

"When in the world did you grab those?" I knew there was no way she'd had time; I mean, Sam was the last one in the truck after all.

"Just now." BeeBee shrugged.

"What?!"

"I dashed over and got them on the way to the truck," BeeBee said matter-of-factly. "I knew I needed mine and Sam's bag happened to be in front of it in the backseat so I snagged them both since you said we were going to your place for the night."

"Good grief you're fast." I eyed her in wonder.

"Oops. Does that mean I left my new car unlocked?" Sam chewed on her lip.

I rolled my eyes. "Let's get home and get dry." Flo had left the parking lot already, so I pulled out into the road, windshield wipers set to the highest setting or what I like to call *see how long they can go this fast without flying off* speed.

Victoria's mom called with a change of plans. I drove both Victoria and Millie to Victoria's Aunt Sophie's home. It happened to be closer to downtown and a greater distance from the beach than Victoria's house; Millie would stay with them tonight as well. From there we continued on to my apartment. I stuck to the main highways to avoid washed out roads. We only passed one wreck – a Corvette sideways in a ditch.

Street signs swayed precariously from traffic light poles. Lines in the road blurred, making lanes hard to distinguish. My knuckles gripped the wheel, clenched white, as I tried to avoid the same fate as the Corvette on the flooded roads.

"Home sweet home." I sighed as I maneuvered the truck into the only parking spot that I could find close to my apartment door. "Ready to make a run for it?" I looked at Sam, then at BeeBee. Both nodded.

"One, two," I grabbed the door handle. Sam reached back and took her tote bag from BeeBee. "Three!" We each hopped from the truck and dashed through the rain. Grateful for my cozy apartment being on the ground floor, doubly thankful it had a covered awning, I searched my key ring for the right key and in we went.

CHAPTER 13

"Scoot over." I wedged myself between the end of the couch and Sam later that night, placing the tray of ooey gooey Oatmeal Butterscotch Cookies on the coffee table in front of us. BeeBee sat on the other end of the couch. The couch was new. A light tan color, Sam and I found it at a discount furniture store – boy was that an adventure – along with the new side tables and a taller coffee table, when we went shopping to redecorate my apartment after the shooting.

Reaching for a cookie, BeeBee said, "Not that I'm complaining, but I thought you said you were making supper?"

"She did." Sam paused the Cookie Cake-Off on TV and snagged two cookies at once. "This is Piper's version of baked oatmeal."

"Guilty." I shrugged. "You are welcome to go raid the fridge if you want anything more though; it won't hurt my feelings a bit."

"Nope. Baked oatmeal is fine with me." BeeBee winked and munched on her Oatmeal Butterscotch Cookie, holding a napkin below her chin to catch any crumbs.

"BeeBee, would you like to finish telling us about Eva?" Sam put a hand on BeeBee's knee. It was the first time we had all three been alone together since she left off on the story Saturday.

"Yeah, I think I would. I didn't expect it, but I've actually felt a little better since talking about her. Like she's with me again, not just a figment of my imagination."

I nodded. "You said that you got her out?"

"That's right." BeeBee leaned back on the couch, closing her eyes. "Mrs. Clark. I think that was the woman's name; it's been so long ago." She sat back up. "There was this one woman who came in to get foot rubs. I don't think the poor lady had any idea what other businesses were being run in that massage place. She came in every week for three months and boy did she love to talk. Over time, I could see that she was lonely. She only had a cat and a little bird for company."

I laughed, picturing Granny, Sylvester, and Tweety-Bird in my mind. "That must have been a well-behaved cat to live with a bird."

"Probably. Anyway, I started putting together a plan. One day, I snuck the keys out of her purse and hid my sister in her car." BeeBee took a long drink from the tea glass in front of her. "Gosh was I nervous! If they caught us outside, we would have been in huge trouble. I still don't know how we managed but I got Eva out the back door and hid her under a blanket in the backseat of Mrs. Clark's car."

"Maybe this is a dumb question," Sam interrupted, "but why not just reach out to Mrs. Clark to help both of you?"

BeeBee cast sad eyes down to her lap. "Too afraid. If she didn't believe us it would do no good, if she talked to the owners about what I said, they would hurt us, maybe even hurt her." When neither Sam or I spoke further, BeeBee resumed her story. "Once Eva was hidden, I went back inside just in time to magically *find* Mrs. Clark's keys under the massage table. She thanked me, handing me an extra tip, and left. One of the older girls snatched the tip from me and sent me to clean the bathrooms."

"That's it?" I gaped. "Wouldn't Mrs. Clark have brought Eva back when she discovered her? You really never saw her again?"

A single tear rolled down the side of BeeBee's nose. She flicked it away. "I never saw either of them again. As soon as the woman in charge of us realized Eva was missing that night, they packed us all up and shipped us out under the cover of darkness."

"Why?" Sam's brows furrowed.

"To minimize their risk. They moved us around often anyway, probably so we couldn't make friends and spill to the clients. If someone ran away though, the move was immediate."

"I guess they didn't want the person coming back with the police or something." I picked up another cookie and chewed thoughtfully. "And you've never tried to find Eva?"

"No. I couldn't."

"We can now."

BeeBee and I both looked at Sam, who swiveled her head between us.

"What do you mean?" BeeBee frowned.

"We can look for her."

"How?" Desperation hung heavy in the word. BeeBee's fists tightened, her knuckles turning white, like she was holding on to something for dear life.

"Yes, please explain."

"BeeBee, do you know what city you were in when you helped Eva to escape?" Sam clasped her hands together, hopeful.

"Umm…" BeeBee squeezed her eyes shut, rubbing her fingers in circles over her temples. "Fair-something, maybe?"

"Fairhope?" I guessed.

"Fairchild?" Sam shook her head. "No that isn't it, sorry."

"Fairfield?" I tried again.

"That's it!" BeeBee bounced up. "Fairfield."

"What about any other details?"

BeeBee closed her eyes, brows bunching together in concentration. "The sign on the way out of town." She opened her eyes. "The population sign on the way out said 10,998. I remember seeing it in the bright headlights and thinking it would be much less than that with us gone. I also remember thinking the only good thing would be not smelling all the smoke from the factories around there anymore."

Sam clapped her hands. "See? Now we have a name and a place to start."

BeeBee sank back deeper into the couch. "I don't know. It's a long shot."

"Yes, it is," I admitted. "Still, it is a shot and Sam's right; I think we should take it, don't you?"

"Let's do it. Let's find my sister." BeeBee's smile could have lit the room if the storm knocked out the power.

Which, at this point, was still possible. According to my weather app, things weren't likely to lessen until the wee hours of the morning.

Sam's thoughts must have been running along the same line as mine. "How does the storm look?" she asked, peering at my phone.

"Bad. The rain isn't expected to let up for hours still." I pulled up my contact list. "I'm going to call Griff. I thought that he would be here by now. And what about Landon?"

Sam shook her head. "He said he would be fine in the hotel; he's in a lower level room and they expect rain to be worse here than wind anyway."

I nodded to Sam as I heard Griff answer the phone. Holding it closer to my ear, I smiled into the mouthpiece. "Hey! Where are you?"

"On my way. Should be there in ten minutes."

His response was short and voice tight. I glanced over at the rivers of water flowing down my window pane and imagined he was probably trying to concentrate on the road. "Great. Drive safe and we'll see you in a minute." We disconnected and I said a silent prayer that he would arrive here safely, glad that he hadn't been stubborn and remained at the beach house.

"Griff is on his way. Why don't we make a quick game plan for tomorrow while we wait?"

"By game plan, she means list." Sam joked to BeeBee.

"Three lists." I stuck my tongue out at my best friend. "One for each of us. Sam, is there anything you still need to get for Millie's surprise going away party?"

"Nope. All of the decorations are bought and in the back of my car. We still need to do the baking tomorrow though."

I started writing. "I'll put that on my list and share with Victoria. I'll also need to check the Ooey Gooey for leaks, storm damage, or flooding."

"What can I do?" BeeBee nibbled on another cookie.

I stretched my legs out, resting the heels of my feet on the vintage aqua-painted coffee table. "I don't know if flowers are like cookies but if Flo has some old flowers that aren't going to get used before they die, you could put together a few small table arrangements to bring."

"Sure, I can do that."

"Sam, you start researching Clark's in Fairfield. Let's see if we can track down anything about Eva. BeeBee, maybe you can describe your sister to Millie. She's a fantastic artist. I wouldn't be surprised if she could make us a decent sketch to work with and if she can't, she'll know someone in her art class that can."

"Okay. For the flowers, is the party Thursday or Friday night? I can't remember."

"Friday night," I answered.

"Piper!" Sam batted me on the arm with the back of her hand. "We never did go do your fitting. That's tonight."

"Oh no! I completely forgot, with the storm and everything."

Sam looked at her watch. "We've still got time." She raised an eyebrow at me.

BeeBee's eyes grew to be the size of golf balls. "You two are seriously considering going back out in this mess?"

Knocking sounded on the door. I whisked my feet to the floor and jogged to the entry. Checking the peephole first, I opened the door and let Griff inside. He greeted me with a soft kiss. I laughed as water ran down his hair onto my face and we pulled apart.

"Quit making out and get in here," Sam hollered from the other room.

Griff scowled and I rolled my eyes. With a last peck on the cheek, I turned and led Griff to the living room.

"Cookies for supper?" He took two cookies and the chair caddy-cornered to the couch as I wiggled back into my spot by Sam.

I raised my eyebrows. "Nothing better."

"Maybe some hot chocolate." Sam ducked as I attempted to hit her with a throw pillow. "I'm just saying," she pointed out the window. "On a night like this, hot chocolate would have been appropriate."

"You know where the kitchen is."

"Too late; we have to go."

I groaned.

"Go? Go where? It's a disaster out there."

"To see Vinny." Sam pulled a face. "We forgot that Piper's fitting for the country club dinner is tonight."

"No way; neither of you needs to go anywhere." Griff crossed his arms.

I crossed my arms right back. "Hello. My house, my fitting, my decision. Wouldn't you agree?"

"I know I agree." Sam narrowed her eyes at her brother. "Last time I checked, we invited you to this party to for your safety, not the other way around."

"Fine. That may have come out wrong, but it doesn't make me wrong. Driving conditions are only worsening." Griff splayed his palms on his knees, leaning forward. "Be smart and make the right decision."

"Plus," BeeBee chimed in, holding up the nearly empty platter of cookies. "If you two leave who is going to bake more of this deliciousness?"

I looked at Sam, sharing a silent conversation like we often do, and knew the decision was done. "We will stay as long as Vinny agrees to reschedule."

Griff breathed a sigh of relief as I spoke. He looked to Sam. "You are easily as gifted in the powers of persuasion as Mother; use them. Call and get him to change the appointment, please."

Sam leaned over and fished in her purse on the floor until she came out with her bedazzled gold phone. I looked at my plain gray phone case; some days, I'm surprised we're friends. We all stayed quiet as she dialed and spoke to Vincent Von Vaughn.

"He's coming over."

"He's what?" I yelped.

"He's coming over," Sam repeated. "Vinny is coming here to do your fitting. Says he is too booked to reschedule and too killable to not get an order done for Deidra."

BeeBee coughed and spluttered, choking on a cookie. "Too killable?"

"He must have been reading all of the social media outrage over Deidra poisoning the gophers." Seeing she had no idea what I was talking about, I pulled up a recent post and passed my phone over to bring BeeBee up to speed.

"Unexpected, but fine. At least you don't have to drive in this mess." Griff stood and wandered into the kitchen.

I heard the clank of ice cubes in a glass. "So," I turned back to Sam. "When will Vinny be here?"

"He says between six and seven."

A look at my watch told me it was nearing five p.m. "Good. Plenty of time to finish watching the Cookie Cake-Off." A brand-new series on the Foodie Network, Cookie Cake-Off pitted five contestants against each other this week to build a three-layer cookie-cake with a beach theme. It was like this episode had been filmed just for us.

CHAPTER 14

At half past six, Sam's phone rang. "Hello?" she answered. "Yes. Yeah. Okay. Yep, that's the one. Be right there."

I gave her a questioning look.

"Vinny is here." She sighed as she stood to her feet and extended an arm to help me up from the couch. "And he needs help bringing in his bags."

"Bags? Please tell me he didn't invite himself to our impromptu slumber party?"

Sam laughed at the appalled look on my face. "No. His bags of fabric and pins and tools for measuring."

Griff rose from his chair. "If you three want to find a place for him to set up, I'll help Vinny bring in his stuff."

"Thanks, Griff." I led Sam and BeeBee to my bedroom where we scooted furniture and tidied up. Thankfully, I was a fairly neat person, so the room didn't need to be cleaned seriously or anything.

Hearing shuffling in the hall, I poked my head out of the bedroom door. I stifled the urge to laugh as I watched Griff plodding down the hall with garment bags and hat boxes and who knows what else towering above his head.

"Come on, come on. What, do you think I have all night?" A perturbed voice floated toward me from behind Griff.

Like a rabbit popping out of a hat, a head appeared to go with the voice. I jerked my head back inside the bedroom and leaned against the wall, widening my eyes at Sam as I tried to compose myself after my first sighting of Vincent Von Vaughn. "You," I hissed, stabbing a finger at Sam as she hid her Cheshire grin behind one elegantly manicured hand.

"Me?" She squeaked.

"You didn't tell me that Vinny was a dwarf!"

A masculine throat cleared behind me but the warning came too late. Griff took a step back as Vinny elbowed past his knees and entered my bedroom.

"My name, in case you care, is Vincent Von Vaughn, and I happen to have dwarfism but am not a dwarf; I do not spend my days picking through rubble singing terribly ridiculous tunes in hopes that I might find a diamond behind a clump of dirt."

My lips parted but words eluded me. The crimson in my cheeks burned brightly. Talk about not judging a book by its cover – don't judge a person by their name either. I had fully expected some English-Lord fancy-pants aristocrat to trot in with a hoity-toity attitude.

"Now, Vinny," Sam smiled. "Don't be hard on Sam. She didn't realize the preferred term is people of short stature."

"The preferred term would be my name, rather than that atrocious shortened nonsense you insist upon using, Miss Samantha."

BeeBee snickered from a chair in the corner.

"Though," Vincent looked me over, "perhaps pulling diamonds from dirt is my specialty after all. I think I can work with this." He gestured to me with a flick of his wrist as he spoke.

Miffed at being referred to as *this*, I held my tongue anyway; after all, I'd basically just called Vinny a midget. "Where do we start?"

Vinny unzipped a long garment bag. Waiting was torture as he rooted around in it, removing layers of fluff and plastic before finally pulling out the garment itself. "Here we are, here we are."

I gaped that Vinny could look so pleased with himself as he held the atrocity up for view. And an atrocity was a kind name for it. "Are you serious right now?" I looked from him to Sam. It had to be a prank. *Please, let it be a prank.*

Sam smiled.

Vinny glared.

I turned to Griff, my last hope. "Griff, this isn't what I have to wear to the dinner is it?"

Sympathy softened his grim nod. "Don't be too disappointed. Just remember, we'll match."

"Look," Vinny snapped, giving the outfit a good shake. "I don't have time for this. Let's get started so that I can get home before the parking lot floods and my car floats away."

That got me moving. I snatched the suit from Vinny's hand and fled to the bathroom to try it on. *Maybe I could accidentally flush it down the toilet.* Too soon, I had to face the music. Feeling like a giant squash, I marched back into the bedroom. One shoulder-pad studded sleeve kept slipping down; the suit jacket was too big. The skirt fit in the waste but the bottom hem reached to an odd length between my knees and shins. And the sheer yellow blouse beneath the wide jacket, well I'm certain the entire outfit should have been illegal.

BeeBee choked on her glass of tea.

I narrowed my eyes at Sam, watching as she struggled to keep a straight face. Griff, thank goodness, had vanished from the room and wasn't here to witness my humiliation. No doubt he escaped to the safety of baseball game or horror show on television; he had, after all, already endured his fitting another day.

"Please explain to me why we are wearing suits that look like they came from the '80s?"

Sam threw her hands up. "How should I know? Evidently Mother still thinks this style is power-dressing to the fullest. We have to look 'smart and chic' to help Dad remain popular with the voters."

"That makes no sense; isn't his second term almost up anyway?"

"Yes," she nodded before plopping down on my bed. "But evidently my mother has him convinced that the rules don't apply. She thinks that with a little extra schmoozing, the people will keep him in office."

"Enough chit-chat." Vinny clapped his hands together like a teacher with an unruly class. "Now we make this into something presentable."

I gasped in shock and jerked away as Vinny flipped the bottom of my skirt up so that it came three inches above my knees instead of four below. "What the?"

"Don't worry." Sam put up a hand to calm me. "I asked Vinny to bring our suits into this century a little. By the time he's done, you won't recognize it."

"O-kay," I drug out the word the same way I wanted to drag my feet about this fitting, feeling unconvinced. My concerns were not alleviated when Vinny whipped out a pair of shears longer than his forearm and began chopping off the skirt material above my knees. "Won't that be pretty uneven?" There went all those mental pictures I had of tailor's meticulously measuring with a long floppy measuring tape, exacting every stitch and thread.

"You got jokes, do ya?" Vinny sneered and continued snipping away.

Disregarded skirt material pooled at my feet. I looked up at Sam but she was talking to BeeBee. *Oh well. It isn't like this outfit could get any worse, even if it ends up with an uneven hem.*

As the last of the fabric hit the floor, Vinny turned away and opened one of the smaller boxes that Griff had carried in. As if to confirm I had been too quick to judge yet again, from the box he pulled a sewing tape measure and box of pins. Awfully long pins. I cringed at the thought of those sharp objects near my poor legs.

For the next hour, Vinny worked swiftly. His small hands made for nimble fingers. Not a single poke or scratch from a pin hit me the entire time. By the time we finished, I was beginning to have hope. The shoulder pads were gone from the jacket, Vinny had even allowed me the honor of yanking them out by hand, and the whole suit would of course be taken in at the seams to allow for a more form-fitting style.

"The color is still hideous but I guess it is what it is." I handed each of the carefully pinned pieces of clothing back to Vinny to stow in the garment bag, grateful to be in sweats and a t-shirt again.

"Don't worry," Sam winked. "With a few accessories, we can tone down the yellow or at least accent it enough to appear tastefully cheery."

"Really?" I crossed my arms. "I highly doubt you can do anything with a necklace to make me look less like a squash."

"I may be the Tailor-Extraordinaire," Vinny turned to me with both hands fisted at his hips. "But Samantha is the Accessory Angel. If she says she can make you an attractive squash, she can do it." With that he began stacking all of his bags and boxes again, the tower extending over his head.

"I'll go get Griff." I rolled my neck, stiff from trying to stand up straight and tall, trying to get the kinks out as I walked down the hallway to the living room. "Hey." I leaned against the door frame. "Tell me truly: do you have to wear a yellow suit?"

Griff grinned. "Not a full yellow suit. A bright yellow shirt with dark blue slacks."

"She couldn't even go for tan or black slacks?" I grimaced. "Anyway, if you don't mind, I think Vinny is ready for some help carrying things back to his car."

Griff clicked the TV off and stretched. "That's fine. The Bay Bears were losing anyway."

My eyebrows scrunched down as I tried to figure that one out. "The who?"

Griff laughed, tugging me into step by his side as we walked down the hall. "Minor League Baseball; so close they are practically local. You really don't know a thing about sports, do you?"

"Not a bit."

"Don't worry, there's time."

"Nope. I'm hopeless." I shook my head.

Griff just laughed. He and Vinny made quick work of the boxes and garment bags. Soon we were ducking rain and waving goodbye from my tiny front porch. I had to wrench hard on the door to slam it shut, the wind trying to suck it from my hands the whole time.

"Wow!" I slid the lock into place. "It's getting worse out there."

"I think we should go check the weather report." Sam turned into the living room with the rest of us following. Sam turned the TV on and found a news report as we all settled back into our places. The hurricane in Florida had dropped to a Category 4 storm before making landfall. Still, it destroyed countless homes and businesses and reports showed that it hadn't died out yet. After three or four minutes, the weather report switched over to local coverage. Both tropical storm warnings and hurricane watches were in place for counties all around us. It appeared Seashell Bay was still in the area most likely to receive winds of 96 to 110 mph.

"How long can this possibly last?" BeeBee hugged one of my throw pillows to her chest.

Griff answered first. "Typical hurricanes last only 12 to 24 hours. As for the fallout wind and rain Alabama will see, well I'm not sure on that one."

"I hope that Vinny makes it home okay." Sam chewed on her lower lip.

"You and Vinny are chummier than you let on, aren't you?" I watched my friend as she worried.

"He's been making special occasion outfits for Griff and me since I was a little girl." She smiled fondly. He scared me at first because he was different. Then, he offered to put whatever kind of buttons I wanted on my Easter dress one year."

Griff laughed. "I'd forgotten those. You picked frogs."

Sam nodded. "And even though he knew Mother wouldn't like it, Vinny put those tiny green frog buttons all over my dress. Even where buttons weren't needed."

"Your mother didn't fire him?" I raised my eyebrows in surprise that such a prank had been let go.

"Oh, she tried." Sam rolled her eyes. "Nobody else lasted long when Mother threw fits over the garments. She called Vinny back before Christmas that same year."

"And Vinny doesn't actually mind you calling him Vinny?"

"He hates it; he's also given up on changing it." Sam smirked. "I'll text and make sure he made it home before we go to bed."

We agreed on another cooking show, a contest for appetizers and main courses this time instead of all baking, for Griff's sake. As the judges were about to announce a winner and settle the bets between the four of us, the TV went black, along with the rest of the apartment. Power outage.

Glancing at my phone, I saw that it was after nine. "I guess that means we go to bed. Sam, help me get blankets and pillows from the closet. We can make a pallet in my room. Griff, you can have the couch in here."

"I won't need a blanket," he spoke, clicking the flashlight on his phone to bright. "And these pillows will be fine. Y'all go ahead to bed; don't worry about me."

I leaned over and kissed Griff on the cheek. "Night."

"It's not so dark in here that I can't see the PDA," Sam joked. "And don't stick your tongue out at me; I'd see that, too.'

I stuck my tongue out anyway, then followed Sam and BeeBee out of the room, careful not to bump into any furniture in the glow of our cell phones. Though we might have been able to squeeze the three of us into my full-size bed, BeeBee opted for a pallet on the floor, insisting she was more than comfortable. Sam and I piled into the bed.

"BeeBee," Sam shined a light on her face to show it was she who was talking. "I reached out to Landon and he has a few ideas on how to look for your sister."

I could hear BeeBee's breath hitch. At last, she said softly, "Thank you."

"Okay, okay." I swatted at Sam's phone to break the thick emotion curling into the room. "Put the light down you're creeping me out."

Sam started making scary faces into the light of her phone. Soon, the three of us were making shadow puppets on the ceiling with our cell phones and giggling like middle-school girls at a sleepover.

CHAPTER 15

Wednesday morning was a mess. I awoke to the sounds of a startled BeeBee getting stepped on by Sam on her way to the bathroom. Minutes later, the alarm went off and we all groggily attempted to share the one bathroom to get dressed. Griff opted to skip the shower and left for work. I think three women before makeup and breakfast probably frightened him away; smart man.

At the bakery, chaos continued. The power had indeed gone out, ruining the freezer had defrosted, leaving water running everywhere and, on top of that, Victoria called to tell me that she and Millie would be late. Good thing we pre-baked lots of cookies yesterday.

"It's not a problem," I promised again as Victoria apologized on the phone. "You can't do anything about flooding; we'll see you when you get here."

"Who was that?"

"Victoria." I explained to Sam while I hunted through the junk drawer for a few emergency candles. "The street that her aunt lives on is completely flooded. Evidently, apart from the influx of rain, a tree knocked out a fire hydrant and water ran freely into the street all night."

"How awful!"

"Do you need me to stay here and help out instead of going to Flo's?"

"Thanks, BeeBee, I appreciate it but you go ahead. We started out with just the two of us when we opened; we'll be fine."

"Besides," Sam added as she retrieved the mop from the closet. "Gladys should be here today. Isn't that right, Piper?"

"Yeah. I forgot. She should be here by the time we open."

"Okay." BeeBee looked skeptically at the darkened room, took the bag of Cranberry Muffins that I handed her, and let herself out the back door.

While Sam mopped, I checked on all of the dough. "Most of this is still pretty chilled. I don't think we lost any of it." I put a few bowls further back in the walk-in fridge, where it was cooler. "We might if the power doesn't come back on soon though."

"Maybe it will come on before we open."

The flickering candle on the work island whooshed out, extinguished by the air from the closet door when Sam put the mop away. I sighed. "We can hope."

Weak light filtered into the café through the front glass as I unlocked the door two hours later. The rain had lessened but not stopped completely. Sam joined me.

We both jumped as a wet thwack sounded on the pane of glass. Papers and trash had been blowing in the street and now one was stuck to the front window. I moved to go get it but stopped when Sam tugged on my arm.

"Do you see this?"

I leaned down, struggling to make out the image in the darkness. "No."

"I think it's another picture of my mother."

"Let me go get it off the window and we'll see what it is for sure."

Holding the soggy paper beneath Sam's cell phone flashlight, I tried to smooth out the creases but only succeeded in tearing a hole in the center of the article. So much for reading it. Two things were clear, however: one, that was a picture of Deidra and she was not a teenager any longer; two, she was walking up the steps of an adoption agency.

"I don't understand." Sam drew in a shaky breath.

Even my own hands wobbled as I tried to make sense of the scene. The headline, the only remotely legible part of the soggy paper, read: SECRET LIFE OF MAYOR'S WIFE?

Folding up the paper, I led Sam to the nearest table. She sank into the chair, unseeing; her gaze drilled into the floor but she wasn't looking at it. She had gone quiet.

Hurrying, I stuffed the newspaper under the counter and poured a mug of strong coffee. "Drink this." I wrapped her hands around the mug, insistent.

Behind me, the bakery door burst open, the bell jingling loudly and the storm howling a greeting of its own. Sam and I jumped. The coffee mug slipped from her loose grip and shattered on the floor; the sound of breaking glass lost in the racket of the storm. Coffee sprayed across the shins of my jeans. I gasped as the hot liquid plastered them to my legs.

"It's raining cats and dogs out there!"

I turned.

Gladys stood patting Mina on the head. She folded her umbrella up and dropped it into the umbrella holder by the door. "My, my! What happened here?" Gladys put her hands on her hips, surveying the broken shards of glass and puddles of coffee.

I shook my head. "Morning, Gladys. Just a little accident."

"You girls should really be more careful."

"I'll get the broom." Sam folded the newspaper and carried it away with her.

"I take it that the electricity is out here, too?"

"Yep." I mopped coffee up with a handful of napkins.

Gladys nodded. "I thought it might be. What's the plan for today; are we open or closed?"

"We have plenty of cookies baked to be open."

Sam joined us, broom in hand. The shards of coffee cup were soon scooped into the dustpan. "I'm not sure how many customers will stop in with no lights."

"I can take care of that." Gladys flipped the collar of her raincoat up to cover her neck. She went back outside, shielding one side of her face from the rain with her hand. She reached into her backseat and emerged with a box so large that it threatened to topple her over.

Flipping the hood of my jacket over my head, I hurried out to help. The large box was cumbersome; I don't know how Gladys loaded it into the car by herself. The contents clanked and rattled as they swayed against each other while I walked. There was no lid. I hoped whatever was inside wouldn't be too damaged by the rain.

Sam held the door open as Gladys and I came back inside.

"What is all of this stuff?" I sat the box down on a table with a thump.

"Supplies."

Sam and I exchanged nervous glances. Sometimes "supplies" were questionable with Gladys. Though, admittedly, that panic button she gave me had come in handy not long ago. I just hoped these supplies didn't require a fanny pack.

"What kind of supplies?" Sam leaned closer to the box.

Not answering, Gladys pulled out a jug of liquid and handed it to me.

Squinting at the label in the low light, I read the words aloud. "Tiki fuel?"

Gladys merely continued unpacking the box. Two large lanterns came out next. Three candles. A box of matches. A small radio. Baggy full of batteries, all shapes and sizes. A deck of cards. A

Swiss Army knife. An odd little can covered in duct-tape and marked *cooking*.

So interested in what Gladys had brought, neither Sam or I remembered to ask her where she had been for the last two days. The more important question seemed to be where all of this stuff came from.

"Where did you get all of this?"

"What are these?" Sam held up the lanterns she had been handed.

"Kerosene lamps. This is my Dark or Disaster Emergency Box." Gladys surveyed the mound of supplies on the table and the floor with pride. "You girls should really think about having one. Let's light the lamps first." Gladys took one of the lamps from Sam and took it to the counter.

"You just keep this box of stuff ready all the time?" Sam looked again at the various items, putting down the second lamp and holding up the bag of batteries for inspection.

"You bet. I learned the hard way though." Gladys reached for the jug in my arms. I handed her the tiki fuel. "Must have been about forty-three years ago. Snowstorm hit Texas and dropped more than ten inches of snow in places. We only got five or six inches where I lived but that didn't matter. For Texas, an inch of snow may as well be a blizzard."

"I didn't know you were from Texas." Sam put the batteries down and came back to the counter.

Carefully, Gladys poured oil into the base of the lamp through a small hole. A little splashed onto the counter. "Most of my life. Anyway, that snow wreaked havoc. Between increased car wrecks from people who couldn't drive in a little bit of white, to overwhelming the power grids as everybody cranked the heat up to the eighties, there was a blackout that lasted three days. Can you bring me the matches?"

After several strikes, it became clear the soggy matches weren't going to light the wick.

Slipping into the kitchen, I grabbed the lighter I used on the candles earlier. "Here, let me." I pushed the button and flame shot out. I held it over the wick until the little white fibers caught.

"Harold and I, we found ways to stay warm." She chuckled. "Lucked out and had enough jerky in the house to last us for food. The well out back was good enough for drinking water. After power came back on, we went to the store for supplies and I've kept the habit."

Gladys placed the glass tube back on top of the wick. "You can control the flame by turning this." She demonstrated turning the little dial knob.

Sam gasped and grabbed Gladys's hand.

I looked at her, puzzled. The flame hadn't gotten very big; she couldn't be alarmed by it, surely? But Sam's eyes weren't on the flame or the lamp at all. She held Gladys's hand into the light staring at it. Or, more specifically, at the large diamond ring, flame twinkling brilliantly off of it, on a very important finger.

CHAPTER 16

"Is that what I think it is?" I reached over and pulled the ring-studded hand toward me.

"Hey now! This isn't tug o' war." Gladys slipped her hand away from Sam and I.

"Spill it." Sam crossed her arms.

"Frédéric and I eloped." She said it nonchalantly.

My eyes widened and bulged in shock; I probably looked like one of those big-eyed stuffed animals. We waited.

"Don't look at me like that. I planned to announce it to everyone at once later today." She moved back to the supplies and began gathering up more things.

"No, no, no. We are not done discussing this." I stepped in front of her.

"What's to discuss?"

Sam gawked. "How about the fact that we don't even know your new last name?"

"I kept my own last name. Frédéric and I agreed it would be easier than changing mounds of paperwork to change from Gladys Hall to Gladys Duval."

"Then the flowers you received…?"

She nodded. "The flowers were a proposal. The card simply said *'marry me?'*"

"I don't know what to say."

"Congratulations." Sam hugged her.

"Yes, we're very happy for you." I hugged Gladys in turn then we busied ourselves getting the rest of the bakery as well-lit as possible. Sam found some window markers and wrote cutesy messages like 'come cozy up to a cookie' and 'seeking shelter, come on in' on the front windows in giant letters.

I didn't bring up Gladys's elopement again. She seemed happy and that should be good enough for me. Still, I would have felt better about it if Sam and I had spent any time around Frédéric. Gotten to know him outside of his Chef Fabio persona, perhaps.

My phone dinged. A text from Victoria.

Victoria: Almost to the bakery.

Me: Okay. I'll unlock the back door. Be careful.

Victoria: K, thanks.

"Victoria and Millie are almost here." I glanced up at Gladys and Sam "I'll be in the kitchen."

Not five minutes later, I opened the back door to the two drenched girls. Watching a monster-truck worthy maroon vehicle drive away, I raised my eyebrows. "Nice ride."

"Thanks. It used to be my uncle's truck." Victoria hung her dripping raincoat on a peg. Millie did the same. "My aunt doesn't like to drive it much but she couldn't bring herself to get rid of it when he passed away."

"That would be hard."

Victoria shrugged. "It definitely came in handy today. Who knows, maybe she'll let me buy it from her eventually."

"You're going to have to save up a lot longer than it took us to get scooters." Millie looked around. "No power here either?"

"Nope."

"Us neither." Victoria shook her head. "And I don't know when the road will drain. There's nowhere for the water to go and the rain isn't slacking."

"It's a mess." I pointed to the sopping wet floor by the door. "And it's making a mess, too. Since we can't bake without the power, would you two mind mopping and seeing what you can find in the storage closet to keep people from slipping on wet tile when they come in the door to the café?"

"Sure thing!" Millie's blonde ponytail bobbed less enthusiastically than normal, stuck together in a tangle of wet hair. She took off to find the mop.

Victoria rummaged around and soon had two oversized turquoise kitchen towels spread out on the clean dry floor in front of both the café and kitchen doors.

Sam joined me in the kitchen. "I got a call from Landon."

"Is he okay?"

"He's fine. He and Pastor Dan and some other church members are setting up a temporary shelter at the church for anyone with severe storm damages. Landon called because they thought if we had any of the day-old cookies or pastries, we might sell them at a discount to the church to set out for snacks. Some of the women are making sandwiches for lunch to give out."

"Have we had very many customers today?"

"About half our usual amount. Still, considering the weather that isn't bad at all."

"You're right. It sounds like we can well afford to get rid of some of the goodies though. I'd rather donate them to help people than for any to go to waste. Text Landon that he can come pick them up."

Sam pulled her phone out.

"And please ask him to let Pastor Dan know these are a donation. He doesn't need to worry about paying for them."

"Will do and I completely agree."

Half an hour later, Landon came inside. The bell over the door announced his arrival. Gladys and I were at the counter.

"Do you have some cookies ready for me?"

"They're in the back. Go on through. Sam should be done boxing them up by now."

"Thanks." He nudged my shoulder as he passed and smiled at Gladys.

"Maybe I shouldn't have eloped."

My mouth dropped. I turned to Gladys, shocked at the out-of-the-blue statement. "What?"

"I'm just thinking out loud. If we had done a ceremony, at least I would have gotten to throw a bouquet." A sly grin slid over her face. "Then we would have at least known if you or Sam were going to be the next to get hitched."

CHAPTER 17

"See you later." I waved. Sam had decided to go with Landon to help set up the food and serve.

"My money is still on you and Griff, no matter how much time Sam spends with that boy." Gladys waggled her eyebrows at me.

"You're impossible. Nobody else is getting married right now."

She only smiled bigger. "I'll remember you said that."

"Whatever," I mumbled under my breath. Louder, I told her the new plans. "I'm going to the local news station to give them an announcement that needs to be posted to let people know food and shelter are set up at Sandy Shores Evangelical Church." I waved the printout that Landon had given me from Pastor Dan. "Millie can help you up front since there isn't much to be done in the kitchen with no ovens going."

"You best be careful out there. Those flooded roads are no joke."

"I will. I promise."

Walking through the kitchen when there is no electricity, I decided, is depressing. There were no fresh cookies waiting to be tested, no heady aromas of chocolatey goodness to inhale. I certainly hoped the power came back on soon. If we couldn't bake again soon, the Ooey Gooey Goodness Bakery might become the Boo Hooey Sadness Closed Bakery.

I took my time driving to the local news station. Street conditions were as bad or worse than Gladys had warned. Twice I had to detour around the main route due to flooding. One intersection sported several stalled cars whose owners never should have tried driving through water so deep.

My circuitous route eventually led me to my destination. There were few other vehicles out and about. KDOP Channel 17 News was located in a large rectangular, white brick building. The news station shared the space with the one and only local radio station as well as the Seashell Bay Press, the town newspaper.

Stepping into the lobby, I took a moment to look around. Slate gray tiles covered the floor, with pale blue walls creating a soft atmosphere. Oceanscapes dotted two of the walls. A single receptionist sat at a small but sturdy wooden desk. She talked rapidly into the headset hooked over her ear while simultaneously typing on the laptop before her. Beyond the reception desk, three metal doors lined up in the back wall. Sam usually did the small amount of advertising for the bakery; I craned my neck to read the nameplates next to the doors.

"May I help you?"

So intent on my task, I hadn't heard the receptionist end her phone call. She was looking at me askew. I guess squinting for five minutes over her head at the doors might make me look a little bit nuts. "Yes, please. I need to talk with someone with the Seashell Bay Press."

"Name?"

"Piper Rivers."

"No, the name of the person you need to see." She said it slowly, like she feared I might not be too bright.

"I don't know. Someone who can publish an announcement for me."

"You don't have an appointment then?"

Her put-out tone reminded me of Missy, the local news anchor. Maybe condescension was a requirement for the media profession. "No, ma'am. No appointment."

"Take a seat." She flicked a wrist toward a row of hard plastic chairs by the door. Purposefully misunderstanding, I inched past her desk and seated myself in one of the plush, comfy wingback chairs nearer to the wall with the doors.

"Excuse me!" The receptionist glared. Fortunately for me, her phone rang. Pushing the button on her headset, she turned and began speaking.

Luck was on my side. While the receptionist had her back to me, the center door flung open and Kendra walked out. She stopped short seeing me and I took the opportunity to catch the door before it shut again.

"Hey, how are you?"

"Good." She smiled. "What are you doing here?"

"Posting a notice about the food and shelter for victims of the storm or disaster relief workers who came to help."

"Wow, that's great. I feel so terrible for all of the people whose homes have flooded."

I nodded sadly. "It's terrible."

Kendra looked at her watch, a beautiful charm bracelet type. "Sorry, I've got to run. Too many errands."

She and Sam had one thing in common: they made nearly sprinting in high heels look as easy as a stroll on the beach. I hurried into the newspaper offices, shutting the door softly behind me so as not to alert the receptionist.

Okay. I made it in but still had no idea who would be the best person to speak with. My eyes roved around the room. Rows of cubicles greeted me; small square colored blocks all linked together with tiny rectangular windows at the top. I shuddered. Thank goodness the bakery continued to provide a steady income and an outlet for all of my creative energy. The thought of being stuck in thirty square foot space all day, staring at a screen for hours and hours nearly made me hyperventilate. My gratefulness for being able to pursue my passion increased tenfold in that moment.

Seeing offices in the back of the room, I decided starting there made the most sense. Pushing away from the door, I straightened my back and walked confidently between the rows of cubicles. *Act like you belong and nobody questions it.* Advice I'd gotten from Sam once upon a time in our college days when I asked how she could be so self-confident all of the time. A lesson I'm sure Deidra foisted upon her at a young age.

Deidra's name was suddenly a whisper nearby. I stumbled, nearly twisting an ankle. Had I spoken aloud? Darting quick glances, I saw that nobody in the room was paying a lick of attention to me. The whispers quickened, burning like wildfire through the room.

"Did you hear?" A brunette tapped on the orange cubicle wall. "There's another big story coming."

"About the storm?" A girl with glasses popped her head up to look through the small window at the brunette.

"No. The mayor's wife."

I kept walking. They weren't giving any details away so far and goodness knows I didn't want to be swept up in the middle of anything concerning Deidra. I wonder where they were getting the story though. Slowing my pace, I lowered my lashes and surveyed the room. The only people I saw were seated at cubicles. No other person. It must have been a phone call tip. Or someone who already left. My thoughts flitted to Kendra of their own accord. *No, surely not.* Shoving the thoughts aside, I brought the slip of paper up in front of me and knocked on the glass office door labeled Editor.

A balding, slightly overweight man sitting at the desk inside waved his hand in the air without looking up. I took that as permission to enter.

"Hello."

"Who are you?" Finally raising his head, Bill, according to the name on his desk, shot me an impatient look.

"I'm Piper Rivers." I stuck my hand out to him. "Nice to meet you."

Rather than shaking my hand, Bill glanced back at the papers on his desk, moving a few sticky notes around. His computer, I noticed, sat covered in dust at the side of his desk and surrounded by dirty coffee mugs. *Not one for technology or tidying up evidently.*

"What do you want?"

I smiled, determined not to let his rudeness upset me. "I'm here to place an announcement in the paper."

"Where do you work, Pippy?"

"It's Piper." My nostrils flared and I inhaled deeply. "I co-own the Ooey Gooey Goodness Bakery. I came to place an announcement…"

"Did you bring any cookies?" He eyed me as if there might be some tucked away somewhere.

"No, sir."

"Of course not. If you want to advertise cookies you have to buy an advertisement slot just like everyone else. Down the third row, second cubicle." Bill waved dismissively and dropped his gaze to the papers on his desk once more.

"Excuse me, Bill." My forceful tone snared his attention. Maybe I should have counted to ten like Sam sometimes does but it was too late now; I could feel my blood pressure rising. "If you would be so kind as to let me finish, you would understand that I am not here to purchase an advertisement or to advertise and sell cookies."

Bill narrowed his eyes, leaning back in his large leather chair which creaked and groaned in protest.

"I am here to place an announcement about storm disaster relief efforts and aid. I believe Pastor Dan called ahead to let someone know to expect it. Unfortunately, I don't have a clue who that person would be." I tried to calm my face which I'm pretty sure was currently running its own advertisement of my frustration with journalistic persons of any kind. "Now, if you could please tell me who the public service announcement needs to go to, I will happily leave you to your obviously busy day." My pulse raced. I half expected Bill to kick me out of the building. My moment of self-righteous anger fled; heaven forbid he find out I snuck my way inside rather than waiting in the lobby.

"Danny sent you?" Bill started laughing. The laughing turned into wheezing and he reached for a coffee mug.

I cringed, hoping he lucked out and grabbed a fresh one.

After a few gulps, he seemed to have it together again. "Danny and I were in high school together. I haven't seen him in a long time. Guess that means I ought to get myself to the church, that's what Danny would say. Always was more into God while the rest of us boys were more into girls."

Noticing the lack of a band on Bill's ring finger, I thought that Pastor Dan must have caught the blessing on both counts but refrained from pointing that out. No reason to lose this newfound goodwill. "That's right. He asked me to personally deliver the announcement so that it could be in tomorrow's paper first thing in the morning."

"Best let me see it." He extended a chubby palm stained with blue ink. "Danny never could properly punctuate a paper to save his life."

Trying hard to conjure up an image for Danny the schoolboy in place of Pastor Dan, I handed over the folded rectangle of paper. And waited. Bill attacked the page with his blue pen – there goes my notion that all editors bleed red onto articles – and eventually nodded, satisfied.

Pulling a bright orange sticky note from the pad, Bill scrawled a note across and stuck the note to Pastor Dan's announcement. "Now it can be printed in my paper." Bill shoved the paper back at me. "Take this to Amy. Sixth cubicle."

"Thanks." Bill ignored me, already engrossed in slashing someone else's article to pieces. At least, that's what it looked like to me. I'm sure to him it was an act of heroism making something worthwhile out of a mess of text. Before I left, I thought of one more thing that he might be able to help me with. "Bill, may I ask you a question?"

"Make it quick."

"Do you know who has been feeding the media information and photos about Deidra Lowe? I'm a friend of her daughter and…"

"Get out!" Bill looked up, his face turning red.

I flinched, the anger rolling off of him palpable.

Banging a meaty fist on the desk, he raved on. "I've already told that woman and her whole team of lawyers that this paper will print news no matter who you are and our source is confidential. Get out and don't come back!"

Yikes, guess I found another person not part of Deidra's fan club. I backpedaled out of the office and spun away only to find the entire newspaper staff poking their heads out of their cubicles, staring at me. "Amy?" I squeaked, embarrassed.

One platinum-blonde haired woman with a mohawk at the end of a row of blue cubicles raised her hand. Everyone else sat back down. Hushed and not-so hushed whispers followed me as I made my way to Amy.

"Bill told me to give you this." Asked would have been too polite a description for receiving orders from that bull of a man. "It has to be in tomorrow morning's paper, please, so that people know where they can go for food and things if the storm damaged their homes."

Amy blew a large purple bubble with her gum. Biting it, she popped the bubble and sucked it back in her mouth. She scanned the page. "Shouldn't take me but three minutes to make the corrections."

"Thank you."

"What'd you do to tick the ol' man off?"

"I'm sorry?"

Amy smacked on her gum. "Oh, come on. We all heard him yelling. It'll be our butts he chews the rest of the day thanks to you riling him up. May as well tell me why; it's the least you can do."

I bristled. Being told I owed her for her boss being volatile didn't particularly put me in the mood for sharing. Still, maybe to get some info I had to give some; Amy might be more forthcoming about details on where the Deidra smear campaign was coming from.

"I only asked a question. Your boss misunderstood and thought I was a friend of Deidra coming to harass him about the articles the paper has been publishing lately."

Smack. Smack. Bubble. "And you're not?" Amy crossed her arms.

"No, not at all. In fact, Deidra hates me. The problem is, my friend Sam is getting blamed and she had nothing to do with those photos." I sighed. "I wish there was a way to figure out who the source is."

"This Sam – guy or a girl?"

"She's a woman." My eyebrows drew together in confusion.

Amy relaxed, uncrossing her arms. "Well, good luck on your little mission. I can tell you the notes are coming from a guy but that's all I know."

Surprise coursed through me. "I guess that narrows down fifty percent of my search." Giving a small laugh, I pushed a little further. "How do you know it's a guy?"

"Handwriting." Bubble. Smack.

Strongly tempted to snatch the gum right out of her mouth, instead I waited for more information.

Sure enough, she leaned forward, eyes gleaming at the opportunity to give up the next juicy secret. "I'm the one who gets all the handwritten junk to fix before printing. Definitely a guy."

"Why do you think that?"

"I don't think it. I know it. You can just feel it." Bubble. Pop. "That's not all. He's most likely schizophrenic, too. The letters were oversized and he crossed out extra letters a lot." She nodded, like this made all of the sense in the world.

O-kay. My hopes for a decent clue came tumbling down – my bubble burst, as it were. Obviously, there wasn't going to be any enlightening information here, after all. I thanked Amy, made sure she had the announcement, and wound my way down the aisle of cubicles to the wooden door I'd entered through.

Scooting past the receptionist, I escaped back into the rainy day outside. *My goodness, how long can a tropical storm last?* Puddles were unavoidable. I splashed my way to the truck and decided to check in at the church. At this point, it was closer than the bakery. A quick detour wouldn't hurt and I could let Pastor Dan know in person that

the announcement should run on schedule
tomorrow.

~

"Piper!"

I turned to face the kind woman, as sweet as
her voice. "Hey, Nora. Things are bustling in here."

"You bet. We have three different volunteer
organizations bunking in the basement. Disaster
relief teams from all over the state, would you
believe it?" She shook her head in wonder, a hand
over her heart. "And then, of course, we have those
who were scared to stay in homes along the coast
and sought shelter before the storm or whose home
is too damaged to live in right now."

"Oh boy! Did Sam and Landon make it back
with the goodies from the bakery?"

A wide smile lightened Nora's face. "They
did! You girls are just too kind. I think you'll find
them in the kitchen if you want to check in."

I hugged her. "Thanks, Nora."

Picking my way through the crowd of
people was tedious. I glanced at my watch. Worried
that they might need me back at the bakery, I went
out a side door. Rain persisted. I would be well and
truly drenched before I got back to work. I pulled
my hood tighter. *Should have bought one of those
plastic rain jackets like Sam's.*

Planning to circle around and enter the kitchen from the outside, I stopped short when I heard arguing coming from the corner of the building. My heart stuttered and I automatically slowed my breathing. The last time I'd walked blind into an argument between strangers, I'd ended up stranded in a pit and nearly buried alive or shot. Neither had appealed to me then and while I suspected that was a one-time scenario, I still preferred to look before I leaped. Moving slowly forward, I listened.

"You've got to stop this foolishness, son."

"Oh, I'll stop it all right. All of it."

"Just give me the album and come home."

"I won't."

An album. That didn't sound too bad. I chastised myself for being so paranoid. Some punk kid arguing with his dad about a rock band or something, probably. I continued on the path toward the voices; maybe I wouldn't interrupt them too much.

"Dad. Dad!" Panic laced the voice this time.

Gasping for breath, the second voice grew weaker. The words were hard to make out. "Wade. Don't. Please. Don't stay here. Forgive."

"Dad!"

I raced around the corner, concern for the man who sounded in pain overcoming caution. A figure draped in a black rain slicker knelt over an older man who lay collapsed on the ground. As I watched, the hand clutching his chest slid to his side.

"Is he okay?" I shouted, running now. The figures were right in front of the kitchen door.

Bolting upright, the man in the rain slicker whipped his head to me, then back to the man on the ground. He hesitated.

"Should I call 911?" I reached them only to be shoved aside as the man in the black slicker took off running. His hood slipped and I thought he looked familiar but with the rain and the man on the ground I didn't have time to worry about him. Punching numbers in my cell phone, I called 911 and stumbled to the kitchen door. Banging on it for help, I returned and knelt by the man. I picked his head up out of the mud and felt for a pulse. Nothing.

~

By the time the ambulance arrived, it was far too late. It would have been too late even if the roads hadn't been flooded and they had arrived five minutes earlier. Landon and Sam had rushed out of the kitchen after I banged on the door but there was nothing they could do either. The man was dead.

I tried to pay attention as they took my statement; first, a police officer, then a detective whom I'd never met. Instead of hearing the questions, I kept seeing the man's arm drop from his chest and hearing it splash into the mud at his side, again and again.

"Are you sure there is nothing else you can remember about the man?" The detective, a wiry black man in a three-piece suit, asked again.

Who wears a three-piece suit in Alabama during a tropical storm?

Detective Johnson cleared his throat, summoning me back from my thoughts.

"Nothing. For a second, I thought that he looked familiar but I don't know a single person named Wade." I brushed loose strands of wet hair out of my face. We stood under the awning at the back of the church; beyond it, the rain trickled steadily down but the fierce beating drops were at last lightening up. Before the police arrived, I had asked Sam if she knew anyone named Wade. She didn't.

"Thank you for your time, Miss Rivers." He flipped his notebook closed. It disappeared into the inside pocket of his navy-blue suit. He motioned to one of the cops, passed on some instruction as they walked, and then disappeared around the corner to the parking lot.

"Come on, let's get you inside." Sam appeared, tugging on my arm. I followed her in a daze. Landon held the door open and Sam settled me at a table in the kitchen. She settled a napkin of cookies in front of me and I reached for them mechanically, my body switched into autopilot mode as my mind processed the last hour.

About halfway through the second Chocolate Chunk Brownie Cookie, the sugar spiked in my system and the fog cleared from my brain. "Thanks, Sam. Can I get a glass of water?"

She filled a cup at the sink and handed it to me.

Pastor Dan tapped on the door frame and came in from the hall. "I've come bearing gifts." He held up a large towel.

Grateful, I accepted it and wrung some of the excess water from my hair into the towel before wrapping it around me. Truth be told, the chill from the air-conditioning made my already soaking wet clothes freezing. "I've really got to go home and change clothes so that I can get back to the bakery."

Protests immediately went up and I covered my head with the towel until everyone quieted down. "Look, I'm going to freeze to death sitting here dripping all over the floor. I'm going home to change and back to work. Nobody tried to kill me. I happened to be in the wrong spot at the wrong time, that's all."

"Again," Sam muttered.

Ignoring her, I continued. "There is no reason I can't work and work is where I need to be."

"You've had a shock, dear." Pastor Dan shook his head and kneaded his hands together. "You shouldn't be driving. Roads are dangerous enough with the flood conditions but if you drive distracted, they could turn deadly."

"He's right." Landon held up a hand when I started to argue. "I'll drive you. Sam and I finished setting up the food. I planned to drive her back to the Ooey Gooey anyway; now, I'll drive both of you."

"Fine." I frowned. "But we're still taking my truck. I don't want to leave it here."

"That sounds fine to me."

~

We made it to my apartment and the bakery without incident. Once at work, time whizzed by. Griff came by, taking Landon with him to help photograph damages, pass out masks and gloves to be used during cleanup, and help pump water from homes. I did not envy the work ahead of them.

Midafternoon, the power in the bakery blinked back to life.

"Thank God!" I closed my eyes and listened happily to the hum of the large walk-in freezer as it kicked on. After recounting the day's events several times, I wanted to move on to brighter topics.

I put Victoria to work mixing batters for the next day while I double-checked that the ovens still worked fine. Hours of busyness followed. A sense of contentment floated around the kitchen as we made much progress in little time. Customers continued to trickle in; not our usual crowded café but that was to be expected with people dealing with their own storm cleanup. Victoria and Millie were probably needed back at their homes to help as well.

Whispering my plan to Sam, I texted Flo to ask if she thought they could close fifteen minutes early.

"I brought the flowers." Flo and BeeBee ducked in the back door of the bakery not long after my text. "You didn't say what they were for so I didn't put them in a vase."

"They're perfect." I took the tiny bundle of white roses. I checked my phone. Sam texted me the all-clear. "Okay, everybody to the café."

Single file, we made our way through the swinging door and into the front of the bakery. Sam ushered everyone to seats. Landon and Griff were already seated. Sam must have texted them to get back here, too.

Standing beside Gladys at the counter, I addressed all of our friends. "Our community still has a long road ahead to get past the damage from the tropical storm but I for one am ready to celebrate. We are all safe, the bakery and our homes are okay, at least as far as we know, and on top of that, Gladys has some special news." I presented the flowers to Gladys.

"Thank you, Piper." Gladys held the roses to her nose, inhaling. Letting out a breath, she smiled. "Well, I'm very glad you are all here because I wanted to tell you together. Of course, Sam and Piper found out a little early but they don't actually know everything yet."

Sam sat up straighter, eyebrows pulling together in a sharp v.

I moved around the counter and took a seat next to Griff. *What else could Gladys have to tell us?*

"Flo, thank you for not reading the card in my flowers. Honestly, I don't know how you do it. I'm so nosey, I would insist on writing every message personally just to stay ahead of anything juicy." Gladys winked. "But since you didn't open it, I can tell you all now that the beautiful bouquet delivered to me last week contained a proposal."

Gasps went up around the room. I waited, one leg jiggling over the other knee, dying to know what could be a bigger secret than marriage.

"That's right." Gladys nodded, meeting eyes around the room as she continued. "Frédéric, or Chef Fabio as you may know him, proposed and I accepted. We are married." She held her left hand up in front of her. "As happy as I am to share that news with you, I've been delaying the rest of it."

I leaned forward, staring intently at Gladys. Sensing my nervousness, Griff reached over and squeezed my hand.

"Frédéric and I will be leaving on a month-long cruise a few weeks from now."

CHAPTER 18

"What?" Surely, I must have heard her wrong. Leaving for an entire month? I knew Gladys had been a little restless, bored at home and tired of vacuuming to pass the time; that was why she volunteered to work part-time at the bakery, after all. But this? First an elopement and now a month-long trip? I didn't know what to think. *Maybe an extremely late-onset mid-life crisis?* Shaking the mean thought from my head, I fixed a smile on my face and joined the others in congratulating her.

After all of the excitement died down, the questions began. As everyone begged to know where the cruise would go, what excursions they would take and so on, I slipped out of the café back into the kitchen, busying myself at the sink.

Griff followed me. Stepping up behind me at the sink, he wrapped his arms around my shoulders.

Leaning back, I relaxed into him, exhilarating in the feel of solid muscles holding me up.

"What's the matter?"

I tilted my head back to look up at him. "I don't know. It just feels too fast."

"Gladys, you mean?"

Nibbling on my bottom lip, I nodded. "Oh! I almost forgot. Will you go grab Sam? There's something I meant to tell y'all."

Leaving me with a trail of kisses from cheek to ear, Griff let me go to search out his sister.

Placing a plate of Chocolate Oatmeal Cookies in the center, I sat down at the big stainless-steel island. My wait was short. Griff returned right away with Sam and Landon both in tow.

"What's up?" Sam flicked her long lavender hair over one shoulder. She and Landon sat at stools across the table from me while Griff straddled the one by my side.

"I forgot to tell you that I got some interesting information when I dropped off Pastor Dan's announcement at the Seashell Bay Press."

"Really?"

"Yeah. First, it sounded like your mother is threatening to sue the paper, maybe all of the media in town, for printing and showing the pictures and articles about her."

Sam rolled her eyes. "No surprise there."

The swinging door opened and I paused as the rest of the group filed through.

"I'm taking off." Flo waved bye, congratulating Gladys one last time.

Victoria hung her apron and Millie's on the pegs by the back door. "I think we're going to head out, too. I just got a text that my aunt is on her way to pick us up."

"I'm going with them." BeeBee put a thumb over her shoulder. "I'm going to see if I can help clean up limbs or water and stuff."

Nodding, Sam smiled at the girls. "Okay. See you all in the morning."

"Let one of us know if you need a ride." I didn't know if the streets would be back to normal tomorrow or if the flooded areas would take longer to recede.

"Thanks."

"Bye."

Millie grabbed her purse; Victoria snagged a cookie for the road and they left.

"Well. Do you girls want to come on a cruise?"

I smiled. "I think we should probably let you and Frédéric spend that trip together alone."

"Imagine the fun we'd have though." Sam sighed. "Unfortunately, Piper's right; plus, we really need to stick closer to the bakery for a while."

"Agreed." I gave a nod. It had been nice focusing on the baking and our brand this month. Trips and catering were fun, don't get me wrong, but they were taxing, too.

"Phooey." Gladys crossed her arms and leaned against the counter.

"You don't need a girls' trip when you have a new husband." Sam waggled her eyebrows.

"I guess that's true. But we may need a girls' trip to pick out my sexy cruise wardrobe." Gladys winked.

Landon choked on his bite of cookie, coughing and sputtering. Sam and I erupted into laughter.

Griff shook his head at the bunch of us. "Okay. Okay. Piper, did you learn anything else at the newspaper office today?"

"As a matter of fact, I did." I explained about my odd conversation with Amy. "I don't know how much stock to put into her 'feeling' about the male handwriting though. Oh! And I ran into Kendra, too. She was on the way out when I went in."

"Hmmm."

We all turned to Gladys.

"I'm surely not the only one thinking it's suspicious that a few minutes after Kendra leaves, there is gossip about a new Deidra story?" She put her hands on her hips, clucking her tongue. "Pretty interesting timing."

"What would Kendra have to gain from slandering our mother?" Sam cupped her chin in her hands, leaning on the table as she thought.

"And where would she get the photos?" I pointed out another big issue: access.

"Didn't you tell us that Kendra was at lunch at Deidra's on Sunday?" Landon glanced from Sam to Griff and back again.

"Yes..." Sam frowned. "And she arrived before we did, right?"

Griff confirmed, slowly nodding. "But what? You think she had time to snoop around the whole house and find a jackpot of scandalous photos in the time it took for mother to greet us or snap orders at the staff?" He stood and went to the fridge for a glass of milk. "It doesn't make sense."

"Deidra's been trying to set Kendra and you up. Maybe Kendra got mad that you declined." Gladys ticked off possibilities. "Maybe she's been to the house more often than you think. Maybe she's really a cat-burglar and snuck in during the dead of night to steal those pictures and who knows what all."

I rolled my eyes. "I think we're getting carried away. Sam, did you ever find time to talk with Deidra's assistant about names of past employees who were let go."

"As a matter of fact, I did. Let me think."

It seemed like ages ago we made the plan to solve the mystery of the scandal starter.

"I wrote it down in the notepad of my phone!" Sam swiped the screen and started tapping apps. "Here it is; the last three people Mother fired. Janet, Holly, and Trip."

"Trip?" Griff raised an eyebrow.

"Your mother actually hired someone named Trip?"

"Evidently, that one was a huge mistake and Trip didn't last the day. Seems the current assistant heard rumors that your mother entered to win a trip except that Trip turned out to be a male stripper who showed up at the office when she was down an assistant."

"I don't want to know." Griff ran a hand down his face, closing his eyes as if to block out the thought of Deidra and a male stripper.

I hoped it worked better for him because I was struggling to stop seeing the image my imagination tossed out for that one. I couldn't decide if it made me want to laugh or cry.

Gladys, on the other hand, appeared unfazed. "I'll interview Trip if you want."

"No!" Sam and I barked at the same time.

"Spoil-sports."

"Your husband might not understand your interest in a boy-toy." My deadpanned statement had Landon and Griff both choking this time. Poor guys. They might have nightmares for weeks after tonight's conversation.

Gladys harrumphed and stood to leave. "Well, I think I'll go on home. My money is still on Kendra though; maybe I'll dig into her."

Uttering any protests would be useless. Besides, Gladys pestering Kendra had to be better than her trying to track down a male stripper. "Goodnight, Gladys."

"See you tomorrow." Sam called out. "You will be able to work the afternoon so that Piper and I can get ready for the dinner, right?"

"I'll be here." Gladys stuffed a napkin of cookies into her purse as she left.

"You know what we need?"

"A list?" Sam guessed.

"Always. But I was going to say the beach."

Griff hugged me. "That is a good plan."

Landon stood, pulling Sam to her feet with him. "I agree. Let's go."

Piling into my truck, we made the short drive to the nearest public beach. With some scrounging, I was able to find an old blanket under the seat. I carried it with us over the dunes. The sun hung suspended in the sky; not quite sunset but not quite bright as day anymore. The tropical storm might be over but it had left its signature scrawled in mounds of seaweed across the sand. My beloved ocean, normally a crystalline blue and turquoise, yawned a deep navy swirled with brown, the waves extra rough and the tide up even higher than normal for this time of evening. Plastic bottles bobbed along the surface.

Landon and Griff, with the help of some large broken limbs, scraped a section of the beach clear of seaweed.

Sam grabbed two corners and helped me spread the blanket flat in the clean spot. We plopped down, letting our feet hang off, toes digging into the sand. It was a tight squeeze when Griff and Landon joined us. A very pleasant, tight squeeze.

For a time, we allowed the rhythm of the waves to relax us. Renewed clarity and energy seeped through me with each deep breath of salty air.

"Back to business." I leaned away from Griff and fished my phone out of a pocket. "Sam, which of those assistants are you going to get in touch with and which should I?" I plugged the name and contact information for Janet into my phone as Sam gave it to me.

"Speaking of contact information," she looked at Landon. "How is the search for Eva going?"

"There are a few promising leads, actually."

"Tell us." I crossed my legs on the blanket. Griff, too, shifted to see Landon better.

"Well, I don't want to tell BeeBee yet. No sense in getting her hopes up."

We all nodded.

"I searched for Fairfield in our database, specifying parameters that kept the search in the closest states only. We have hits for reported human trafficking in all of them except Georgia, so that didn't narrow it down much."

"Where's the part that gets promising?" I prompted, impatient as ever. In the wake of the storm and the Deidra disaster, we needed some good news.

"The good news is that Fairfield, Alabama has a huge industrial side of town. Thinking about the smoke and factories that you told me BeeBee described, I decided to concentrate most efforts there for now and assume the traffickers have mostly been moving around the state rather than crossing state lines." Landon rubbed his hands together. "There were four addresses for the name Clark. Only two of them have been in the area for over a decade."

"So that's good news?" Sam raised her eyebrows.

"I hope so. Tomorrow, I plan to dig even deeper. If I can't find anything online, I'll call them myself."

"Please, let us know the moment you find out anything."

Landon promised he would.

Sam stretched. Landon's gaze followed her and I noticed Griff's mouth tighten. I kissed him on the cheek. For Sam, purely distraction, a complete sacrifice on my part. *Ha, right!*

Leaning his forehead into mine, Griff looked into my eyes as if he could stay there forever.

I shifted, uncomfortable with the attention. Goodness knows what my hair looked like. I could feel the oily sheen on my face from sweat and salt. I broke eye contact; ducking my head, I looked at my phone. "We should probably all go home. There's lots to do tomorrow."

Sam groaned. "Let's just skip tomorrow."

"She's right. We all have early mornings." Landon rose.

The trek back to the truck was a quiet one. Sam and Landon walked ahead, whispering together. Griff tucked my hand in his, circling his thumb over my thumb. "They're good together, you know?" I nudged him with my hip. "You may have to tone down the overprotective brother vibe."

"Or not."

I rolled my eyes.

CHAPTER 19

Thursday morning, after shutting the alarm off, I remained in bed not moving. I listened. Silence. No drip-drop. No pitter-patter. No whooshing, pounding, thumping wind and rain. I hurried to the window, peeking out just to be certain. The storm had well and truly moved on. Obviously, the sun still hid below the horizon being four in the morning and all, but I had high hopes for a bright and cheery day.

Until I remembered. Dinner. "Urgh." I groaned, leaning my head against the cool glass of the window pane. Dinner at the Seashell Bay Country Club with Mayor Lowe and Deidra. Sam was right; we should skip today and move on to Friday.

Friday! Yikes. The party. I forgot to make sure Victoria had everything she needed for desserts. At least Sam finished getting the supplies. I think. Another sigh escaped me. My mind zipped in a thousand directions. So much for a bright and cheery day.

~

At the bakery, I raced in a dozen directions. Due to a few flooded roads remaining, there was actual traffic this early in the morning as people left early to make it through all of the detours. Thanks to the unusually congested route, I arrived late to the bakery and yet, managed to be the first person there. Not a good sign.

Pre-heating the ovens, pulling dough out of the fridge, carrying boxes of baked cookies to the display case; the tasks that normally brought me joy seemed to be never-ending this morning. A car horn beeped out back. Cracking the door open, I saw Sam in the dim parking lot light struggling to carry boxes and bags and…were those balloons?

"Is Gladys here yet? Or Millie?" Sam puffed, out of breath and about to lose the juggling battle.

"Not yet." I kicked the door stop in front of the door, propping it open. Just in time, I caught two boxes as they toppled from the stack in Sam's arms. "What is all this stuff?" Somehow, she had made it all the way across the parking lot without catching her heels on a rock or in a pothole even though she couldn't possibly see past the stack of packages. *Amazing. It's like high-heels are her superpower.*

"Party supplies."

A resounding thud sounded as we placed everything on the island table.

"Quick – we have to hide it before everyone gets here." Sam opened the supply closet.

"Don't you think Millie will see it when she goes in there for cleaning supplies?"

"Shoot."

"Where do you think we're going to hide balloons?"

Sam tapped her long fingernails on the table. "Flo's Flowers!"

I considered it. "That's actually pretty brilliant. Anybody who sees the balloons will assume they are going on a flower arrangement that Flo is making."

"Exactly."

"Okay. You take those to Flo; I'll try to hide the rest of this in the pantry." Surveying the mound of purchases again, I had to ask. "Don't you think this might be a little much for one going away party?"

"It's not for one going away party."

"Then…?"

"Half of it is for a belated congratulations / engagement / wedding party / thing for Gladys." Sam grinned. "No friend of mine is getting married without having a party. No reason we can't do both at the same time."

"Good idea, except one thing."

Sam's lips turned down in the tiniest frown. "What's that?"

"You didn't tell me, so now I don't have a present for Gladys."

Sam's face lit up. Too late for me to take it back. And as expected, the next words from her mouth were predictable. "That means we get to go shopping before dinner tonight!" With an added bounce in her step, another unfathomable thing at this time of morning, she clasped the balloons and went to stow them next door.

With some serious speed and stacking skills, the other boxes were put away before she returned.

The door barely shut behind Sam before her phone rang. "It's Vinny." She moved to take the call in the café.

I scooped tiny balls of dough onto pans and slid them into the oven. Once the racks were filled, I set about making something new. Today would be experiment day. Olive Oil Rosemary Baby Bundt

Cakes. By the time I had sprayed the miniature Bundt pan, Victoria and Millie were knocking on the back door.

Flipping the lock, I opened it and let them in.

"BeeBee already went to Flo's." Millie, seeing me looking around outside, spoke up.

Victoria knelt in front of the oven. "Sorry we're late. Looks like you didn't really need much help."

"No problem. Did y'all still have issues with the roads?"

Millie nodded her head up and down, blonde ponytail swaying wildly. "We had to take a really long way."

"Our scooters wouldn't have made it through most of the water. Some of the shallow places might have been fine but we figured it'd be best not to risk it."

I agreed with Victoria. "A few minutes late is far less expensive than an accident or injury."

Sam tiptoed through the swinging door.

"Why are you being weird?" I tilted my head at her.

"What?"

"You look like you're sneaking. Why would you be sneaking in our own bakery?"

Victoria and Millie shrugged and nodded. "You look like my mom when my little brother first goes to sleep, like you don't want your feet to touch the floor or an explosion might sound."

"Maybe I tiptoed a little. The reason though is that I didn't want Gladys to notice me slip away. She's here and I need you to need her for something."

I quirked a brow. "You're making no sense."

"Frédéric brought her to work today. If you hurry up and call Gladys back here for something then I can invite him...you know..." She faltered, unable to say more with Millie right there.

"Gotcha. On it." I whisked out of the kitchen with Sam trailing behind before the girls could ask questions. *Now they probably think we're both nuts.*

"Piper, you remember Frédéric?" Gladys stood up from pointing out different desserts and greeted me.

"How are you?" Smiling, I shook Frédéric's hand.

"Je vais bien." He inclined his head. "I'm doing fine. Merci."

"Gladys, I need you in the kitchen for half a minute. Do you mind?"

"Of course not." Patting Frédéric's arm, she followed me.

Now, what to tell her needs her attention. I racked my brain for ideas as we walked through to the kitchen. She would know that it wasn't to taste test; typically, we brought those into the café for whoever was working the counter.

"What did you need?"

I looked around, hoping inspiration would strike. Sadly, inspiration seemed to be taking the day off. "I...forgot?"

"Happens to me all the time." Gladys turned to leave.

"Wait!"

Eyebrows rose expectantly as she paused. I blurted the first thing that came to mind. "I wondered if Frédéric knows any savory dessert recipes. I hoped you could ask him, save me the embarrassment."

Suspicion passed over Gladys's face. Her hands moved to her hips.

"I could Google them, of course. But he's a real French chef and all." I gestured helplessly, sinking. *Come on, Sam, hurry it up in there.* Timid

215

and embarrassed wasn't my style; Gladys knew that and had to be wondering what was up with my odd behavior.

As if hearing my mental plea, Sam stuck her head through the door. "Hey Gladys, I think Frédéric is about to leave if you want to tell him bye. If you and Piper are done?"

"All done." I spun on my heel and disappeared into the pantry before Gladys could get a word in.

For the rest of the morning, avoiding Gladys became my main objective. Easier said than done. The fourth time that I ducked into the pantry, or was it the fifth, Gladys cornered me.

"Strange. You're alone."

"What?" The comment puzzled me. My guard dropped.

Gladys crossed her arms and that teacher look she was so good at fell into place. "You've spent so much time in the pantry today that I felt certain I'd catch you in here making out with Griff. But no, it's only you in here."

I snatched an open bag of dark chocolate chips off the shelf. "You caught me. Bad cravings today." She looked unconvinced. I tossed back a handful of the dark chocolate morsels, talking with my mouth full. "It's that time of the month." I rubbed a hand across my lower abdomen.

"Oh!" Understanding dawned on her face followed by a most sympathetic expression. "Score one for getting old, no more of that time of the month."

Sam calling my name broke up the uncomfortable moment in the pantry. Stepping out into the kitchen, I sighed as Gladys made her way back to the café. "Yes?" I searched for Sam.

She stood by the back door. "We have to go early. Vinny called. He needs us to pick up the outfits for tonight."

~

"Has there been any sign of that new story about your mother yet?" With the Seashell Bay Press employees abuzz yesterday with rumors of a new article, I expected another front-page headline. The hectic morning left no time for checking out the paper or social media.

Sam scrolled her phone as I drove. "Nope. I don't see a thing yet. The announcement about food and shelter at the church looks great though."

"Excellent." Silence stretched as we drove. "Have you asked her about the adoption clinic photo yet?"

Sam's head swung side to side. "I'm not sure I even want to."

"Why not?"

"Two reasons, really. First, she'll probably flip her lid if I bring it up. Second, what if I was adopted? Do I want to know?"

"I think I would be too curious not to know."

"This is it." Sam pointed to a house on the left.

Signaling, I turned in. "Vinny works from home?" I changed the subject. Sam would figure out what to do when she was ready.

"No. He has an office on the East end of town. He said he wasn't going in to work today when he called."

I rang the doorbell, noting the camera feature and giving a little wave.

Hacking and coughing sounded before the door even opened. "Achoo!"

Involuntarily, I stepped back out of the germ range of sneezes. Vinny held a wad of tissue to his nose and trumpeted into it.

"I guess you're a little under the weather."

Vinny glared through puffy eyes.

"I mean, not you're little. Or below the weather." I stuttered. "Sick. You look sick."

Vinny eyeballed Sam. "Your friend is a real smooth talker isn't she." Leaving the door open, Vinny waddled down the hall, blowing his knows every few seconds.

I waved an arm toward the house. Sam entered and I followed behind. Far behind. Vinny and I obviously weren't meant to be chummy which was fine; the excess snot kept grossing me out anyway.

"Your clothes are in the purple bag." Vinny stood in front of a pile of garment bags and boxes. There were various garment bags and boxes lined along the wall behind the sofa like sentinels. The purple garment bags lay across the coffee table, hanging off both ends.

"Thanks, Vinny." Sam gently swooped the garment bags into her arms.

Making haste, I retreated into the hallway. Two steps. Only two steps before Vinny called me back.

"Where are you running off to? Someone has to carry all the rest."

Wary, I re-entered the living room. "The rest of what?"

Jerking a thumb at three black and one golden garment bag swinging from the trim above a door across the room, Vinny used the other hand to blow his nose yet again. The man housed a mucus factory behind that flat nose. "Deidra's order. It's only right you deliver them, too. After all, my considerate nature and willingness to make a house call during a hurricane is how I ended up with this bloody cold."

"It was not a hurricane." I matched Vinny glare for glare. "It was a tropical storm."

"Grab the bags, Piper." Sam let out a long sigh. "We have to see Mother tonight regardless. Might as well get on her good side by bringing the rest of the clothes."

CHAPTER 20

The rear-end of the truck slid sideways as I slammed on the brakes. "Holy cow!"

"The storm must have been even worse here than we realized." Sam leaned forward in the seat, staring out the windshield at the massive tree laying across her parents' driveway. "Maybe that's why Jerry abandoned the guard house, to find someone to cut up the tree."

"Maybe." It had been odd to find the gate open and the old guard not at his post. Coming up on the tree, the storm was my first thought, too. I got out of the truck. I needed to see if driving around this mess would be possible. Something didn't seem right. There were no broken tree limbs. Not a single limb from any of the surrounding trees. Only this one solid tree, directly across the drive.

Sam's door slammed. She would probably ruin whatever heels she had on in all of this mud.

I picked my way through the branches and around the end of the tree. "Uh-oh."

"What's wrong? Are we going to have to walk all the way to the house?" Sam asked.

"We're going to have to walk all right. And we need to be careful."

Sam drew close but stayed on the other side of the downed tree.

"Why?"

Crouching, I found my way back to her. "This wasn't the storm. This tree has been cut down."

"Like, on purpose?"

"Yeah. I don't know why. There's no room to drive between the other trees. We've got to walk."

"Okay. I guess we should take the bags?" Sam began unbuckling the straps on her heels. Deidra would have a fit when she showed up with bare, muddy feet.

"Isn't there a golf cart or something at the house we can use to come get them?" Really, I thought we should burn the bags so we didn't have to wear the crazy yellow outfits tonight.

"Probably." Shoes off, Sam started walking forward. "Why do you think they cut the tree down?"

"That's what worries me. The tree seemed perfectly healthy. The chainsaw was still sitting beside it; the motor was cold."

Sam frowned. "It was cut down but not cut up?"

"Yep." My mouth pulled into a grim line. "Someone blocked the driveway with no intention of unblocking it."

Moving faster now, we held to the cover of the tree line and jogged toward the house. My eyes roamed the grounds. No movement that I could see, nothing to indicate anything was wrong but nothing to indicate everything was fine either.

Sam left the shade of the trees to go up the porch steps.

Pulling her back, I jerked my head around the side.

Sam gasped as she noticed what I did. An arm lay sticking out of the hedges next to the house. Both hands flew to her mouth, her eyes round with fear.

A finger to my lips, I shushed her. Whispering, I told her to stay put. "I'll be right back."

Stooping so low that I nearly crawled, I inched forward. With every snapping twig or rustling leaf beneath my foot, my gut clenched. My movements slowed the nearer I came to the bushes and the prone arm. I told myself that slow and quiet was necessary if I didn't want anyone in the house to know we were outside, it's hard to say. If I were honest with myself, I just really didn't want to pull those bushes back and find out who lay among them.

Steeling myself, I drew a bracing breath and reached my hand forward. Pulling back the lower branches, I peered through the leaves. "Son of a!" I fell backward as something leapt out at me.

Hearing my cry of alarm, Sam rushed forward, brandishing one of her shoes as a weapon.

A small grayish brown frog hopped away.

My chin sunk to my chest in relief. "False alarm," I whispered. We sat silently. I counted to five but my yelp seemed to have gone undetected. "Okay. Here goes." Latching on to several branches again, I pulled the curtain of green hedge back.

"It's Jerry." Sam rested a hand on my shoulder as she peered beneath the foliage. Jerry, the kind-hearted guard from the guard shack. "Is he…?"

As I watched, his chest rose and fell in small breaths. Blood trickled from a spot behind his ear.

"He's alive but he's been knocked out." I kept my voice low and dropped the bushes back into place.

"Thank God," Sam exhaled. "Now what?"

Before I could answer, my ringtone pealed out the Pink Panther theme song on full volume.

I fumbled with my pocket in my cargo pants but couldn't get the button undone. The music played on and on. I finally jabbed the side button through the fabric, silencing the ringer, and jerked the flap, button flying off. The screen continued to show an incoming call. "Gladys?" I whispered.

"Piper, I have those recipes for you." Her voice coming through the speaker in my ear sounded loud enough to wake the dead. I cringed.

"Gladys it isn't a good time." I whispered, sneaking a glance at the window above us. Did the curtain just twitch? "Send police to Deidra's house."

"What? What? Piper? I can barely hear you. Do you want the recipes?"

"No," I growled a little louder. "Send the police to Deidra's house."

"What did that crazy woman do now?"

Gravel crunched behind us. I sprung around but froze when I saw the gun.

Sam lifted her hands into the air.

"Drop it." A command, no doubt about it.

I let the phone slip from my grasp as told, hearing Gladys still on the other line, yelling my name. I hoped she hung up and called 911 fast; this didn't look good.

"Hey, baby sister."

CHAPTER 21

I couldn't wrap my head around what I was seeing. Or hearing. Illogical. Ludicrous. Insane. At the prodding of the gun, Sam and I were marched into the house.

"Mother!" Sam lurched toward the dining table. Deidra Lowe sat at the head, dripping with jewelry like royalty and trussed up like the Thanksgiving turkey.

"Of course, you show up with her instead of someone who could actually get me out of this ridiculous situation." Even tied to a chair, Deidra's high-and-mighty attitude didn't waver. "We're never going to make it to the country club on time at this rate. And you, young man, are no longer invited. You'll never dine anywhere but the inside of a prison for the rest of your life."

"Shut up!" Garrett waved the gun. "You're right about one thing: you won't be makin' it to the country club on time. And neither will baby sis' here either."

"Why do you keep calling me that?"

A crazed grin spread across Garrett's face. "You mean Mommy-Dearest here never told you about me? She wouldn't have, now would she."

Gone was the polished speech and fancy clothes. This man could have been Garrett's homeless twin. Dirty, tattered jeans, stained with mud, a ripped dress shirt, half-tucked in and half loose; he looked like he'd been caught in the storm. And maybe he had. Maybe he'd been hit in the head and lost his mind.

Head whipping between Deidra and Garrett, lingering longer on Garrett and the gun, Sam choked out, "I don't understand."

"Garrett," I spoke softly, hands out in front of me as I stepped toward him. "Maybe, if you put the gun down, you can talk to us. Tell us what's going on."

"I'm going to tell you all right. I'm gonna tell everybody every single shameful secret this woman has." He sneered at Deidra.

She stiffened and lifted her nose higher in the air. "Don't listen to him, Samantha."

"I said be quiet. One more word from your lying mouth and I duct tape it shut." Garrett waved the gun back at me. "You. You're going to tie up blondie here. I'd prefer to do it myself, among other things," he stalked forward and rubbed a finger down Sam's neck and along the collar of her shirt, "but then you might try to escape."

Sam shuddered.

"What do you want me to tie her up with?" Anything to get him away from Sam.

Garrett dropped his hand from her and turned to point to a pile of rope across the room. It lay on a long, black rain slicker. Something clicked. My eyes jerked to the back of Garrett's neck while he was still facing the rope. There it was. An oddly shaped white blob of a birthmark on the back of his neck. Sam had described it to me once after Sunday lunch. That was what struck me as familiar when I saw him running away from the old man. I didn't put it together that the man in the raincoat was Garrett because I heard him called Wade.

"Okay. I'm getting the rope." I kept my hands up and moved slowly across the room, one small step at a time, hoping to put him at ease. A twitchy trigger finger we did not need. *At least this time it isn't my fault we're in the middle of a crazy mess.* Not much consolation but still, the thought spurred me on to find a way out, if only to point that out to Sam later. For now, I'd keep it to myself; I doubted she would currently be amused.

"Hurry up." Garrett scowled, yanking the top two buttons of his collar undone. Sweat beaded on his forehead. I began to think he might be as nervous as we were. There might be hope for us yet.

I edged between Garrett and Sam. Grabbing her hand, I led her away from him.

"What are you doing?" More a roar than a yell, Sam flinched and shut her eyes tight as Garrett came up behind us.

Turning, I talked to him like I would one of Grandpa Rex's grandboys. "It's okay, Garrett. I'm taking her to the end of the table to tie her up by Deidra, exactly like you asked me to. That way, you can watch them both easier." Garrett's face clouded and I could practically see the squeaky wheels grinding in there, trying to process that information. Spinning, I pulled Sam further away while he remained preoccupied.

I grabbed a chair, dragging it a little bit closer to Deidra. Making a big show of sitting Sam up straight in it, I leaned close to her ear and whispered. "He's Wade. From the church dead guy."

She raised her eyebrows but stayed otherwise impassive.

"Get on with it."

Gathering the rope, I wound it around Sam, weaving it in and out of the carved wooden design on the chair back.

"You better make it tight." Garrett narrowed his gaze at me.

At least the gun was finally lowered to his side, no longer waving around the room.

"You bet." I tugged on Sam's hands, pulling them all the way to one side of her chair and kicking Deidra's foot under the table. She glared at me. I bumped her again, this time gaining her attention lower. Sam's hands were within reach.

One sharp nod. The only acknowledgement Deidra gave. I hoped she understood.

As expected, Garrett marched down the table the moment I stepped away from Sam and checked the knot. It was as tight as a fishing line hung on a log.

Garrett grunted, jerking me by the elbow and, as I allowed him to lead me to the other side of the table, I almost smiled. He hadn't noticed that Deidra could now reach Sam's hands with her own. With a little luck, plus some discreet wiggling, one or both of them would be free soon.

Since I had used the last of the rope on Sam, Garrett held on to me while he tried to decide what to do next.

"Are you going to tell us all the secrets now?" Sam's voice cracked through the silence like a whip.

Garrett scowled. "Impatient, aren't you."

"Kind of bored, actually." Sam exaggerated a yawn. "I'm not a big fan of being tied up and held against my will. I have better things to do."

While Sam was buying time, I scanned the room through lowered lashes. Other than getting my hands on a chair, there wasn't much hope of securing a weapon. The only things Deidra had in the dining room were expensive, delicate little teacups in a magnificent display case, so large I doubted I could even push it over if given the chance, and a silver spoon collection in a shadowbox on the wall that I would have to stand on tiptoe to reach.

A sharp tug on my elbow interrupted my scheming. "Sit down." Garrett shoved me roughly into a dining chair. Turning, he glowered at Sam. "You have better things to do? That sounds familiar." Hatred filled his eyes as his gaze moved over Deidra. "She always had better things to do, too."

"What do you mean?" Sam tilted her head.

"She got pregnant before she got married. But she had better things to do than raise a kid.

Better life to live than be the wife of some broke cashier."

Deidra's mouth tightened in a thin line. She didn't blink, didn't speak, staring at Garrett with contempt.

"Is it true?" Sam look at her mother.

"You bet its true." Garrett snapped. His fingernails digging into my shoulder now.

Deidra remained silent. No denial. No laughter, no protest; only a stony face and rigid posture.

"And you think you're her son?" I looked up at Garrett, drawing his attention back to me with the question, giving Sam and Deidra more time to work the ropes.

Garrett squeezed my shoulder tighter. The gun pointing at my chest as he waved it admonishingly. "I don't think; I know. I have proof. Now, shut up. Nobody is talking to you."

Yep. Must be Deidra's blood; he inherited her unfathomable annoyance with me and he doesn't even know me.

"Can you show me?" Sam lowered her lashes, turning her mouth down at the corners in a tiny pout. "Can you show me your proof that our mother abandoned you?"

"You wanna see?" Garrett dropped the gun back to his side. He let go of my shoulder, taking small steps toward Sam. She was playing him and the maniac couldn't even see it, so hungry for sympathy and belonging.

"Please." Sam nodded. Eyelashes batting. She deserved an Emmy.

Placing my hands flat on the table, I eased up out of the chair. Just a few inches. Slow movements. Move. Pause. Move. Pause. My pulse raced in my ears. The door was only six or eight feet behind me. If I could make it back to my phone…. My heel bumped the chair leg and the scraping sound it made dragging across the floor made us all jump.

Garrett spun back around.

I tried to run, knocking over the chair. Garrett kicked it at me. It slammed into the back of my ankles and I stumbled, falling to one knee and my hands.

"Where do you think you're going?" The gun swung uncomfortable close again as Garrett righted the chair.

"Bathroom?"

"Sit down."

"Sorry, I used all the rope." I shrugged. "Now there isn't anything for you to tie me up with." Sam made exasperated faces at me behind Garrett's back; no doubt she thought I was an idiot for choosing sarcasm to point out the obvious flaws in Garrett's plan right now.

"I'll still tie you up. Hold still." Garrett began fumbling with his belt.

Chewing on my bottom lip, forcing myself to sit still and act defeated, I waited for any chance, any opening to take advantage of his divided attention.

Garrett cursed as the buckle stuck. Frustrated, his one-handed attempts useless, Garrett put the gun down on the table and focused entirely on his belt.

This might be the last shot we had. Praying it worked, and hoping that either Sam or Deidra had gotten their ropes loose, I sprung up from my chair. With all the force I could manage, I rammed my elbow into Garrett's side, grabbing for the gun.

Garrett shoved me from behind, arm reaching around me. We grappled for the gun. I couldn't get a good grip. Not willing to risk Garrett getting it, I used the back of my hand to slide the gun away from us both.

Pain erupted along my jaw as Garrett grabbed a fistful of hair and shoved my head into the table. I slid to the ground. Garrett raised a booted foot above me and I curled inward, wrapping my arms around my head, bracing for the blow.

"Garrett, stop!"

The pain didn't come. I risked a peek out one eye. Garrett wasn't looking at me anymore. From below the table, I could see Sam's legs. She was standing. Her ropes lay coiled on the floor. *Praise God!* I scrambled to my feet, grimacing against my aching jaw. Warm liquid ran down my chin. Wiping my hand across my mouth, I found my lower lip bleeding.

"Piper, tie him up." Sam had the gun trained on Garrett.

Deidra stood, her ropes also removed, and tried to walk past me as I made my way around the table.

"Mother, where are you going?"

Deidra rubbed her wrists. "To get dressed, of course. We have a dinner to get to. You did bring the clothes, right?" She studied her hands again. "I'll have to change jewelry to cover these hideous marks."

"Mother!" Sam's voice startled me. She kept her eyes on Garrett, sparing a cutting glance for Deidra. "You aren't leaving yet. We are going to get to the bottom of this."

"I will not waste any more time in this room with this lunatic."

Garrett growled. "I should have shot you. I should have killed you just like you killed my father."

Deidra pushed past me.

"Do not leave this room, Mother."

"Or what? You aren't going to shoot me, dear." She fluffed her hair and took another step.

I raised my eyes at Sam. She gave me a nod of permission. Grabbing Deidra by the wrist, I held her in place. "Sam said stay. Not to mention, the police will surely be here soon. I have a feeling they would also prefer we are all still here not galivanting off to sip martini's and stuff yourself with shrimp."

Deidra's eyes flashed. "How dare you!"

I didn't see the slap coming. My already hurt jaw was set on fire when Deidra slapped the same side of my face. Thinking didn't come into play. I reacted. And I punched her in the stomach.

CHAPTER 22

"Oomph." She doubled over and I pulled her back into a chair.

"Well, hell."

My head snapped up as a new voice exclaimed in the room. *Landon!* Landon stood in the doorway, just behind one of the best sights of my life: a uniformed police officer with his gun trained on Garrett.

"Ma'am," the officer sent Sam a hard look. "You need to put the weapon down."

Sam shakily sat the gun down and leaned forward, palms on the table, breathing deeply.

My sense of relief turned into dread as I looked around. *Had Griff seen me punch his mother?*

Landon must have seen the look of guilt. "Griff is outside helping get that security guard guy into the golf cart."

I sighed. *Thank goodness.*

"Jerry." Sam supplied the name as she straightened. "The guard is Jerry. So, he's okay?"

Landon shrugged.

"I want these people arrested." Deidra pointed to Garrett and me. "Both of them. He broke into my house and she assaulted me."

The cop radioed outside for assistance. Cuffing Garrett, he looked at me. "Is this true?"

Sam spoke before I could explain. "Piper merely detained my mother as she tried to flee before giving a statement."

"Tell you what. We are all going downtown and everyone will give a statement." He tugged at his collar, clearly uncomfortable with the look of outrage Deidra shot his way. "This one is above my paygrade to sort out."

Griff appeared in the doorway and hurried inside. "What in the world?" He gave each of us an incredulous stare.

"It is a long, long story." I sagged, feeling energy drain out of me.

Sam nodded. "And I don't think we've heard the whole thing yet."

~

At the station, it didn't take long to sort out Deidra's accusations and see to it that she stopped trying to press charges. Sam confirmed my story that Deidra actually slapped me first. Given that dried blood covered part of my face and multiple colors of bruising had started, the police were inclined to agree that we were both at fault. I didn't correct their assumption that Deidra's slap had done most of the damage; it had definitely added to the array of colors dotting my face.

Mayor Lowe, called in from a late game of golf, showed up blustering about the nerve of the police department to detain his wife. They ignored him, insisting Deidra and Mayor Lowe stay to sort out the accusations of Garrett.

At Griff's request, they allowed us to listen to the interview.

"I didn't know these things were real." Sam ran her fingers around the glass, window on our side, mirror on the other.

I wrinkled my nose. "It smells like sweat and fish in here."

"Shh. They're starting."

I joined Sam to stand at the window. Griff chose a chair, leaning forward, resting his elbows on his knees.

"Please state your name, for the record."

"Wade Dunkin."

"Well, now we know Garrett's actual name." That confirmed my thoughts that he was the man who ran away from the older man's body at the church.

"Yeah. Now it's time to find out who he is." Sam shivered.

Placing a hand on her back, I nodded. "Whoever he is, we'll deal with it." I knew the accusations against her mother, supposedly his mother, hit her hard. Griff, I glanced back at him, well, Griff kept his thoughts hidden right now.

The crackling voice through the intercom snared my attention.

"You were heard accusing Deidra Lowe of killing your father. Your father," the detective consulted a notepad, "James Dunkin passed away this week of a heart attack. His body was found at the Sandy Shores Evangelical Church. No evidence of foul play turned up. You were the last person seen by the body."

"She killed him." Wade banged his fists on the table. I had trouble thinking of him as Wade and not as Garrett. "He may have had a heart attack but she may as well have shot him. My dad's heart broke when that witch tried to give me up for adoption without even consulting him. His heart broke when she made him buy me from her, threatening him if he even thought about taking her to court and creating a scandal. Said if she couldn't give me up for adoption that he had to pay to adopt me himself or she would sell me to someone else."

Sam's jaw clenched. I kept rubbing small circles between her shoulder blades. For her sake, I really hoped this Wade guy was delusional. Somewhere, deep in my gut, I feared everything he said about Deidra would turn out to be true.

"Mr. Dunkin, you weren't even born at the time. How is it that you came to this knowledge? Do you have proof?"

"I've got proof. My freshman year of school, I went looking for some money or some beer. Figured Dad probably kept it stashed in his room since there wasn't any in the fridge; he always smelt like beer, my old man. I knew there had to be some around. Instead, I found a box of photos and papers in my dad's closet." Wade stared into the corner of the room. His eyes grew distant. "The lid barely fit on the box. Stuff stuck out all the sides. I bumped it looking for some cash. Everything spilled in the floor and I thought 'oh shit, I better clean this up.' But the pictures were of my dad and this girl.

Everywhere, the park, the ocean, in bed. She looked wild and they both seemed crazy happy."

"Did you ask your dad about the box?" The detective looked up from taking notes.

"Yeah. I thought she must be my mom because there were pictures of her pregnant. Then I found the picture from the adoption agency and I got confused. I took it all out that night, spread it across the dining table and demanded he tell me about her."

Wade shook his head. "I thought he'd be angry. I was angry. Ready to fight. But he wasn't. He got scared, so, so scared, man." Tears welled at the corners of Wade's eyes. "He told me that nobody could find out. That he'd promised her. Turns out, the pretty lady in the photos decided she could do better than dear old dad when she caught the eye of a well-to-do politician. She erased all traces of her old life. Couldn't have the scandal, she told dad, couldn't let anything threaten the career of the man who would one day sit in the White House."

Sam balked. Her mother had abandoned a man and child for a greedy dream of power.

"Dad told me to let it go." Wade continued, getting angrier. His face turned red. "He started drinking even more. I started getting into trouble. Finally, I left and decided to find her. I couldn't get close as Wade Dunkin. I knew that. So, I became Garrett Hopsinger. A few fake stories about success. Shiny gold watches and a nice car, stolen or rented, and it worked like a charm. All Deidra Lowe saw were dollar signs, same as before." A harsh laugh burst from Wade's throat. "She played right into my hand, trying to foist her barbie-doll daughter off on me. I would have ruined her, too, caused a great incest scandal just to see Deidra's face when she found out who I was. Little sister wasn't interested in money like Mommy-Dearest; lucky for her, I guess. She wasn't interested but I could still let the whole world see what kind of scum the perfect mayor's wife really was."

"So, you leaked stories and photos to the paper and media?"

"That's right. There's more than enough proof of what kind of person Deidra is. I just dug it up and let people see it."

"Why go to her home? Why break in, tie her up? Why not release the story about your birth and let it run its course?"

"It wasn't enough. I heard the paper might not print any more stuff with her threatening to sue. She had to know money didn't make her better; it didn't make her untouchable."

CHAPTER 23

By the time we left, Sam shook from head to toe. Griff agreed to let me take her to my place. I doubted she wanted to see the duplex gifted to them by her parents on their ascent to greater things; I doubted she wanted to think of them much at all. Thankfully, my truck was in the lot in front of the police station. I didn't know or care how it got there, only grateful that someone had brought it from Deidra's home.

Nothing else major came from the interview. The detective gathered additional details, details that could be confirmed later. Wade demanded a DNA test and requested that it be released to the public. I doubted anyone would be accommodating that demand, though the DNA test was ordered and I wouldn't be surprised if news "accidentally" spread.

Deidra and Gregory showed up to dinner at the country club that night where Gregory Lowe, pale-faced and rigid, announced his resignation as mayor.

The rest of us avoided the dinner and as much social media coverage of it as possible. It fleetingly occurred to me that Vinny would be disappointed that all of his hard work on outfits had gone to waste.

Speculation was spinning by the time the late-night news came on as to whether or not the mayor's marriage would survive any better than his political career after one photo caught Gregory giving Deidra a rather distasteful look before the speech. I turned off the television, disgusted with the parasitic nature of people to latch onto scandal like a tic on a dog.

Sam didn't argue when I gave her Ibuprofen and Benadryl and sent her to bed early. She hadn't spoken much on the way home. It was tempting to blabber, keeping up a stream of conversation to try to make her feel better but I knew she would be okay. She just needed time for the shock to wear off.

CHAPTER 24

Friday morning, I woke before the alarm and turned it off, sneaking out while Sam slept. She needed the rest and the Ooey Gooey would be fine without her for the morning.

She disagreed. By ten I had a dozen texts from her asking why I let her oversleep. I smiled. She might still be hurting, no doubt, but her take charge attitude asserted itself again; she was coping. I silenced my phone and got back to work. Sam would undoubtedly be here in no time.

Sam: Don't you know it is party day!!!

Sam: We have so much to do.

Sam: I'll be there soon. Have to find clothes.

Sam: Your closet is pathetic.

The last message made me laugh out loud. Victoria waited for me to share the joke but I shook my head. Back to business. "Are all the special desserts ready for tonight?"

Victoria gave me a flour-coated thumbs-up. "You bet."

"Great. I'm going to run to Flo's and make sure they have the balloons and bouquet ready."

I knocked on the back door. Flo opened it wide. "Come in. Is it true?"

"Is what true?" The question caught me off guard.

"The mayor resigned after he had to get his wife out of jail yesterday?"

My jaw dropped. Boy, rumors in a small town were like chicken pox at a sleepover, popping up overnight, all big and crazy. "No. Well, he resigned but Deidra wasn't in jail. I mean, she was at the jail but not arrested. We all were. Not arrested." Words stammered out of me, none making sense. I rubbed both hands down my face. Really, I was too tired for this.

"Maybe you should come sit down and start over." Flo led me to a row of stools.

BeeBee popped in from the store as I sat down. "Hey!" She looked happier each day.

It cheered me to see her thriving after all that she had been through. I wanted desperately to tell her Landon might find someone who knew Eva soon but I bit my lip. "Hey yourself," I said lamely. "I came to see if the party flowers would be ready tonight or if y'all needed any help?"

"Everything is ready." Flo nodded for BeeBee to open up one of the cabinets near her.

I clapped my hands. The arrangement for Millie begged to be photographed. In a gorgeous pewter vase, they had arranged flowers into bold sections of color: yellow, orange, red, violet, blue, white. Behind the flowers, an oversized painter's palette stood making each group of flowers look like the colors of paint dabbed on it. Breathtaking. "Millie is going to love this." I laughed. "She'll probably start sketching it immediately."

"Thanks." Flo blushed. "I'll admit, it took a lot of thinking to come up with the idea. BeeBee actually suggested adding art supplies to the arrangement. It was the perfect suggestion but I didn't have any. When I went shopping and saw this giant palette, I just knew."

I understood. Sometimes cookies were like that for me. Most likely anyone who created had experienced the struggle, the angst and banging your head against the wall on some days whereas on others ideas sprang to life on their own and begged you to bring them to life.

BeeBee took me to the store of the shop to show me several new flowers. I left out the front and strolled slowly down the sidewalk back to the Ooey Gooey. Millie, I noticed, had cleaned all of the windows, removing all traces of the paint used to attract customers during the blackout. The café hummed with energy when I went in the door. Many customers looked up and greeted me. I stopped to chat with several, whispering an invite to tonight's party to a few, explaining the need for secrecy.

Most were excited to be invited. Grandpa Rex, looking very disappointed, said that he wouldn't be able to make it and left.

"Sam's here." Gladys pointed back to the kitchen when I made my way to the counter at last.

"How is she?"

"You mean, besides mad at you for not waking her up?" Gladys chuckled. "She seemed fine."

Last night, after Sam went to bed, I had called and updated Gladys, thanking her for calling the police.

"You want those recipes now?"

My blank stare clued Gladys in that I had no idea what she was talking about.

"Girl, your memory is getting worse than mine. You need to get one of those reminder apps; they're great." Gladys handed me two index cards. "The recipes for savory French desserts that you wanted from Frédéric. Here., I got them."

"Ohhh! Oh. Yes." I took the cards. "Thanks, Gladys." Now I had to come up with a day to make savory French desserts or else tell Gladys that I hadn't needed them, only time to distract her. Nope. French desserts sounded way better. Looking at the cards, I read the recipe titles. Pistachio Profiterole and Chocolate Chili Éclair. *Definitely sound interesting, though I don't understand the trend to mix chilis into chocolate.*

Too busy to stay mad long, Sam forgave me for letting her sleep. She did look tons better today, her color bright, her smile in place didn't look forced. It still drooped occasionally but then she'd be laughing with Millie or Victoria again in no time. Business stayed busy and Sam stayed in the kitchen. A good decision, since several of the new faces out front probably only came to find out from Sam if the rumors about Deidra were true. They didn't have to wait long. The six o-clock news ran an extra feature all about the skeletons in the Lowe family closet. The news app on my phone sent me an alert when the story broke. Before turning it off, I learned that Wade Dunkin had been sentenced to fifteen years in prison.

When the customers in the bakery thinned to only those invited to the party, I returned to the kitchen and sent Millie out front under the guise of helping Gladys. Sam texted Flo to tell her we were ready. Victoria and I carried trays of goodies while Sam held the swinging door open for us. Flo and BeeBee came through the street-side entrance in the front.

"What's all this?" Gladys wanted to know.

Millie looked up from wiping down a table. Her eyes found the Artist's Love Bouquet, as Flo called it, and gasped. Putting a hand to her throat, Millie stood transfixed as Victoria took the bouquet from Flo and presented it to her.

"You didn't think you could sneak out of town without a party, did you?" Victoria teased.

Another handful of guests crowded through the front door, including a particularly snazzy looking off-duty fireman. Millie blushed.

"Surprise!" Sam smiled.

"Happy going away party." I hugged Millie.

"I really don't know what to say." Millie shook her head, stunned. "This, all of it," she gestured to the food and balloons all around, "this is so incredible. I can't believe it."

One more jingle of the bell announced the arrival of Frédéric. Looking to Millie, I said, "Hope you don't mind sharing the spotlight but we're also having a Wedding Reception for Gladys."

"What?" Gladys's look of shock made the crowd laugh.

"Double surprise!" Sam laughed.

"You two girls." Tears rolled down Gladys's nose from the corners of her eyes. "Thank you, very much."

The bakery bash lasted half the night. Millie agreed to go out with the cute fireman before she left town, exchanging phone numbers. Victoria's creations, some regular dessert favorites and others new recipes, were a hit. Not a crumb remained.

"I'm going to miss you girls." Gladys sniffed as the last of the guests were leaving. Frédéric held the door, waiting on her.

Sam hugged her. "You aren't leaving on your cruise for several more weeks."

"That's right. You aren't rid of us yet." I winked. "Goodnight Frédéric."

"Thank you for coming." Sam shook his hand. "And congratulations again."

"Bonne nuit." The French accent rang crisply through the room. "Good night. Thank you to you girls."

We waved then turned and looked at the mess that was the café of the Ooey Gooey Goodness Bakery.

"Goodness, that's a lot of cleaning to do." Sam looked at her watch.

"And you're sure it would be wrong to call the guests of honor, who happen to be employees, back to help with the cleaning."

"Yep."

"Okay." I sighed. "Guess we better get started if we plan to get home before morning."

"Guess so." Sam kicked her heels off, sliding them into a corner.

BeeBee tackled the hardest task, already in the kitchen cleaning dishes. She had insisted that Victoria leave and continue to celebrate with Millie.

The kitchen door swung open. My insides melted and I grinned wide enough to hurt my sore jaw. Griff walked out wearing my apron. Landon, two steps behind him, matched wearing Sam's.

"Did someone call for a cleaning crew?" Griff spread his arms wide.

I felt luckier than a chocoholic left alone in the candy factory. "What would I do without you?" I placed a quick kiss on Griff's cheek.

"I don't plan for you to find out." He cupped the back of my head and pulled me in for a much longer kiss.

Raucous whistles from Landon and gagging noises from Sam eventually brought my feet back down to earth as I floated away from Griff to scrub at an already clean spot on the counter.

Epilogue

"Really? Cool. Really? Wow! Great. Yes," Sam nodded. "See you then."

"Who was that?" I pointed to the phone in her hand as she hung up.

"Landon." Her eyes sparkled. We were at the Ooey Gooey Goodness Bakery early this Sunday morning, getting everything prepped before it was time to go to church.

"Did he decide on a place to live?"

"Yes, he found a dilapidated beach house. Damaged during the storm, the owners are high-tailing it to somewhere without hurricanes and tropical storms so they are selling it at a steep discount."

"Oh? That's awesome."

"But that isn't the best part!" Sam clapped her hands together.

Tilting my head to the side, I studied her. "Wait – did her…?" I didn't want to say it out loud and jinx it.

"He found her." Sam nodded, her smile stretching to her ears.

"Incredible. Praise God!"

"He's going to tell BeeBee after church today."

I couldn't wait for her to find out that Eva had been found. My hands itched to text her even now and share the amazing news.

The sermon seemed to last infinitely longer than normal, no doubt due to my giddiness for BeeBee and desire to be there when she found out. I hadn't seen Landon before church started but assumed that he was around somewhere. Gregory and Deidra Lowe were also noticeably absent, though that didn't surprise me at all.

Now, as Pastor Dan finally began the closing prayer, I could barely sit still.

"Amen." The congregation echoed Pastor Dan as he gave thanks for the town's protection during the crazy storms of the past week.

I practically leapt to my feet, craning my neck to peer through the crowd of exiting members.

"Piper, are you okay?" BeeBee flashed concerned eyes my direction.

"Never better!"

"I think she's just ready for lunch." Sam raised her eyebrows at me. "Landon is meeting us at the bakery with Shrimp Baskets from Momma's Diner."

"He is? I mean, yes, that's it. I'm famished, let's go."

"Famished?" Sam whispered to me as I led the way through the throng of people toward the double doors at the rear of the church. "You are really terrible at secrets.

"Hush. I use big words all of the time; it doesn't mean something is up."

"Whatever you say."

I stuck my tongue out at Sam and walked to the passenger side of her car. She, BeeBee, and I climbed inside. Griff would meet us at the Ooey Gooey.

~

As Sam passed the parking spots on the street in front of the store, driving around to the back as always, I noticed not only Landon's car but also Gladys's and an unfamiliar third vehicle parked by the curb.

I unlocked the back door and led the way into the empty kitchen. Muffled voices sounded through the door from the café.

"We aren't eating in the kitchen?" BeeBee wondered aloud. It was where we typically gathered to snack or eat before we worked.

"Sounds like Landon and Gladys have the food set up in the café." Sam smiled. "Let's go and see."

My grin by this point probably looked crazy enough to scare children. I had a sneaking suspicion that Landon was planning to do more than just break the news of Eva's location to BeeBee. Griff's truck rumbled up and I went to hold the door open for him. Taking his hand, I drug him inside and hurried to catch up to Sam and BeeBee who were going through the swinging door.

BeeBee stood rooted to the spot right behind the counter. Landon stood, helping an older woman to her feet. A young pre-teen girl peered around them both, shiny black hair framing her face and extending below her elbows.

"BeeBee, I have someone here who would like to see you." He clasped the elderly woman by the elbow, bringing a steadying presence to her shaky legs. "I've found Mrs. Clark and she was kind enough to bring Eva to Seashell Bay this afternoon."

"Eva." BeeBee whispered the word, cupping both hands over her mouth. Her head shook from side to side as if she were afraid to believe it.

Eva looked up to Mrs. Clark who nodded, laugh lines creasing at her eyes as she smiled widely at the girl. Blessing received, Eva dashed forward and crashed into BeeBee's torso. Wrapping her arms around her big sister, Eva said softly, "You're real. I thought maybe I only imagined you but you're real. My big sister."

BeeBee sobbed, grabbing hold of Eva and picking her up off the floor even though they were nearly the same height.

Sam and I dabbed our own eyes, gladly accepting napkins that Gladys passed us before blowing her own nose. Mrs. Clark looked as joyful as the girls as Landon helped her to sit back down.

"There isn't really any shrimp, is there?" Griff's voice cut into the sniffling and crying.

I laughed out loud, swatting at him. "No. There is no shrimp but you can go get us some if you want to."

"On it." He winked and left, going back through the kitchen.

BeeBee held tight to Eva's hand as she hurried over to hug Landon. "Thank you!" She turned to Mrs. Clark. "And thank you, Mrs. Clark, for taking care of Eva all this time. I'm so sorry that I didn't talk to you or find a better way…."

"Don't apologize." Mrs. Clark frowned. "You were only a child. Eva has been my greatest blessing. She kept me company and brought me great joy every day; I'm only sorry that I'm a daft old lady who didn't realize you needed help." Mrs. Clark sighed. "The first night at my house, Eva tried to sleep in the cat kennel."

My stomach lurched at the thought of the terrible things these girls and so many others like them had endured.

Mrs. Clark continued. "After several days of not being able to get her to talk and not finding anyone at that massage place again, I finally decided I would have to take her to the police station. That's when she told me everything. At least, everything she could. She told me about the men that beat you and that you told her the only way to stay safe from the bad men was to stay with me. She told me about sleeping in big boxes. I probably shouldn't have kept her, not without telling someone, but it scared me to death to think that if I turned her in, she might have to go back to a life like that again."

"So, nobody ever asked questions about where she came from?" Sam looked shocked.

"I didn't have a big social calendar. Being a reclusive old lady has its benefits. Intimately familiar with our tiny library, I checked out books and homeschooled Eva as best I could. Eventually, I asked about how to use the computers and a nice boy working there for the summer showed me how to take free classes. As Eva got older, she used the computers at the library to study." Mrs. Clark smiled. "She even made a few friends over the years, the type she could chat with and laugh with in the library though they never got closer than that."

"How did you find them?" BeeBee looked up at Landon and asked, awe in her expression. He would be her hero forever.

After explaining to BeeBee about narrowing the search down to the two addresses in Fairfield, Landon said, "The first Clark residence that I called had three children, triplets, and didn't know anything about a missing child. When I spoke to Agnes," he placed a hand on Mrs. Clark's shoulder, indicating her, "she was hesitant to answer my questions. Instead, she kept turning them back on me. I got the sense that she definitely knew something but wanted to protect her information."

BeeBee glanced at Mrs. Clark who nodded, a sad smile. "I always feared someone would come to take Eva from me. I felt guilty for not reporting her even though I felt like it was the best situation for her."

"I called her again. Three days in a row and each day I asked my questions but I explained a little more about myself and my goal as well. On that third day, she agreed to bring Eva here to meet you."

Mrs. Clark patted BeeBee's arm. "God gave me peace about it. I knew you girls needed each other."

"Thank you!" BeeBee hugged Mrs. Clark and Landon and her sister all again.

I had a feeling she would be hugging everyone in sight for quite some time. Griff strolled in bearing plastic bags full of cartons of shrimp, crawfish, and red potatoes. I stole into the kitchen and hunted up enough leftover cookies to fill a platter. Returning to the café, I nodded my head to Sam and the door.

Following my silent request, she locked the front door and returned the sign to the closed side. Mina the mini-palm gave a little happy dance as Sam walked past. Today wasn't a day for business. Today was for family, new and old; our wonderful, eclectic little Ooey Gooey family.

Keep reading for a sneak peek at book one of the upcoming Adventures of Gladys series!

BONBON VOYAGE

Adventures of Gladys Book 1 Sneak Preview

"Sheesh. I thought Sam was bad." Piper stared in disbelief at the luggage in front of her.

"Hey!" Sam smacked Piper in the arm.

"How long did you say this cruise will be?" Piper hefted one of Gladys's three large suitcases onto the portable luggage cart.

"Nine days." Gladys twirled a bright purple umbrella above her head, flinging light drops of rain at everyone around her.

"Gladys, how could you need three full suitcases for a nine-day trip?"

"I'm sure some of it is Frédéric's." Sam defended.

"No. He didn't bring much." Gladys shrugged. "Says he plans to buy some new things during the trip."

"Then what all is in here?"

"You know, just the essentials"

Sam and Piper shared a look. Sam raised her eyebrows at Gladys while Piper crossed her arms. "No, I'm afraid we don't know what could fill three suitcases for nine days of travel; that would be like only three days of clothes per bag."

"And these are big bags." Sam tapped a high-heel clad foot on the pavement.

"I did think they would hold more." Gladys frowned. "It seemed every time I turned around the clothes I packed had grown and I was out of room. That's mostly all I packed." She met the skeptical looks of her friends and sighed. "Well, plus a few supplies: pepper spray, gloves, extra shoes and swimwear, wigs."

"Wigs?!" Piper gaped.

Sam snickered. "Please, tell me, why do you need wigs?"

"To try out new hair colors of course." Gladys fluffed one side of her short silver-gray hair. "Your trips to the salon inspired me to try some new colors, too. Of course, I'll try them on fake first before committing to an actual color job."

Sam smiled. "So, what colors did you bring?" Sam spent more time getting her hair colored than some people spent eating breakfast. Somehow, no matter the color, it always turned out beautifully. This month alone it had been a deep lavender and now she was adding teal highlights soon to get the "mermaid hair" look that was so hot right now.

Gladys listed off several wig colors from blonde to black.

"Does your new hubby know you brought all of those?" Piper tilted her head, studying Gladys.

"No. I figured it would be a little surprise. Imagine his face when he goes to bed with an old lady and wakes up with a blonde!"

"Where is Frédéric anyway? I haven't seen him this morning." Griff turned in a circle, shading his eyes and making a big deal of scanning the parking lot. In reality, he was probably trying to avoid the image of Gladys in bed, blonde or not. Griff Lowe was Sam's brother and Piper's boyfriend – but that is a story for another day.

"You barely missed him." Gladys pointed to the gangway leading onto the gigantic cruise ship across the street from the parking lot where they all stood. "He went ahead to print our boarding passes and make sure we would be departing on time."

"As long as the storm holds off, I'm sure everything will be fine." Piper spoke, stepping aside for Griff to lug the last suitcase into place on the cart.

Thunder rumbled loudly overhead.

"Uh-oh."

"Good job, Piper. You spoke too soon."

Piper stuck her tongue out at Sam. A big fat raindrop plopped right on it.

"Come on, let's move." Griff steered the luggage cart between cars and to the sidewalk.

Sam whisked a pocket umbrella from her Burberry raincoat as they walked and clicked it open. Piper huddled underneath with her as they made their way to the cruise terminal.

Gladys strolled along between Griff and the girls, humming and merrily spinning her umbrella, unfazed by the downpour.

"Why didn't y'all park in one of those covered lots?" Griff shouted to be heard.

"Frederic says he wasn't worried about that old car getting beat up or stolen."

"You think Chef Fabio is loaded?" Piper whispered to Sam. Chef Fabio was Frederic's chef persona cooking name. The girls and Gladys originally met him at the O Heavenly Day Spa when they signed up for his cooking class.

"Why do you ask?"

"Doesn't pack luggage, doesn't care about what happens to his car while they're gone. It just seems a bit cavalier to me."

"But they live in Gladys's house. I've never even heard her mention Frederic's home, have you?"

"No." Piper admitted.

They arrived in the departures line a wet, haggard bunch. Griff offered to help Gladys check her luggage while Sam and Piper waited.

Gladys returned with Frederic in tow and Griff bringing up the rear. "Look who we found."

Frederic shook hands with the girls and greeted them in his polite, if formal, manner. They had given up on any warmth from him weeks ago, wondering if all French people were aloof.

Gladys beamed, unaware of any awkwardness. "Frederic says we've been upgraded to a room with a balcony."

"That's fantastic!" Piper clapped her hands together.

"I bet it will be gorgeous." Sam agreed. "Take lots of pictures."

"I will."

A crackling voice over the intercom announced that boarding for groups one to three was open.

"We should go. Thank you all for seeing us off." Frederic inclined his head to Piper, Sam, and Griff, wrapping Gladys's elbow in his hand.

"One moment, please." Sam smiled. She unzipped the giant beach bag flung over her arm and held it open for Piper to reach inside.

"Surprise!" Piper handed a pastry box to Gladys. Visible beneath the clear window in the lid were assorted chocolate and white chocolate bonbons, all decorated to look like beach balls or sunshine wearing sunglasses.

"What better way to wish you Bon Voyage than to wish you Bonbon Voyage?" Sam grinned, kissing Gladys on the cheek.

"Bonbon Voyage – I love it!" Gladys laughed so hard her whole body shook.

"Piper came up with it."

"Sam did the decorating though."

"Thank you! These look better than ice in a desert." Gladys looked up at her husband. "Aren't these wonderful?"

"Oui, you have very special friends."

After a few more hugs, Gladys waved goodbye to her friends as they exited the terminal. A small pang of sadness hit her at the thought of not seeing them or the bakery for a week. She felt a squeeze on her arm.

"You are ready, ma chaton?" Frederic looked down at her, question written in his dark brown eyes.

Note from the Author

 Hey there! Thank you again, wonderful readers, for coming back for book 3. Piper and Sam would be so sad without you.

Also, did you know you can sign up for my newsletter to receive updates and deals before anyone else? **My newsletter subscribers even took a survey and helped me choose the title of book #4.** Does that sound like something you want to get in on? If so, go to the following link in your web browser and sign up for my newsletter now!

https://mailchi.mp/3ed2f71e303c/kbbnewsletterbookishinfo

If you have enjoyed the books, I would really appreciate you leaving a review on Amazon, Goodreads, or BookBub as well.

Reviews are a great way to help my book reach other readers like yourself.

Thanks again!

Sincerely,

Katherine

Other Books by Katherine Brown

Ooey Gooey Bakery Mystery Series:

Rest, Relax, Run for Your Life

Pastries, Pies, & Poison

School is Scary Series (Children)

Kindergarten Teachers are Witches

Fingernails of First Grade

Second Grade Stinks

Third Grade's Terrible Trip

Fourth Grade's Fossil Find

Fairy Tale Retellings

Marigold and the Bear Necessities

Cloaked

Other Children's Books

Princess Bethani's First Garden Party

Made in the USA
Columbia, SC
22 July 2019

MW00772944

VOICE FOR THE VOICE

VOICE FOR THE VOICELESS

OVER SEVEN DECADES OF STRUGGLE WITH CHINA FOR MY LAND AND MY PEOPLE

HIS HOLINESS THE DALAI LAMA

WILLIAM MORROW

An Imprint of HarperCollins*Publishers*

FIRST EDITION

Designed by Nancy Singer
Map by Alexis Seabrook
Title page illustration @ 心灵艺坊/stock.adobe.com
All photographs in the photo insert are courtesy of Tibet Museum, Dharamsala

Library of Congress Cataloging-in-Publication Data has been applied for.

ISBN 978-0-06-339139-0

25 26 27 28 29 LBC 5 4 3 2 1

Contents

*

Contents

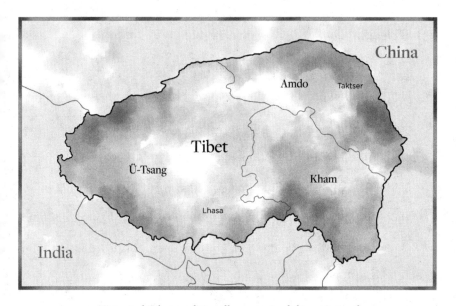

Historical Tibet traditionally comprised the regions of
Ü-Tsang, Kham, and Amdo.

Disclaimer: This map is not to scale and is for illustrative purposes only. The boundaries shown are neither authenticated nor intended to reflect the official position of any government. For official boundaries, please refer to the Survey of India or the relevant authoritative sources.

Preface

✳

On March 17, 1959, in the darkness and frozen air of the night, I slipped out of the main gate of the Norbulingka Palace disguised and wearing a *chuba*, an everyday layman's form of clothing. That began what turned out to be more than six decades of life in exile away from my homeland of Tibet. Although the seed that grew into my need to flee was sown by the Communist Chinese invasion of my country in 1950, the immediate trigger was the tension that had been building up in the Tibetan capital city of Lhasa, exploding into a people's uprising on March 10, 1959. For nearly nine years, after the invasion, I had tried to come to some kind of accommodation with the Communist Chinese for the sake of my people's well-being, but it was an impossible task. A few days after my departure, China's People's Liberation Army bombarded the city. In this way, the tragic tale of my homeland and people over the second half of the twentieth century and into the twenty-first unfolded.

Ever since first being forced into exile in India in 1959, my primary task has been the cause of Tibet and its people. I am now approaching my ninth decade. The issue of Tibet remains unresolved, while my homeland is still in the grip of repressive Communist Chinese rule. Tibetans inside Tibet continue to be deprived of their dignity as a people and their freedom to live their lives according to their own wishes and their culture, as they did for more than a millennium before 1950. Since any expression of Tibetan identity is seen today as a threat by Tibet's new rulers, there is the danger that in the name of "stability" and "territorial integrity" attempts might be made to erase our civilization.

This book is, primarily, an account of more than seven decades of my dealing with successive leaders of Communist China on behalf of Tibet and its people. It is also an appeal to the conscience of the Chinese people—many of whom share with us a spiritual heritage in Mahayana Buddhism (which I refer to as the Sanskrit tradition)—as well as the broader international community, to care for the plight of the Tibetan people. Ours is an existential crisis: the very survival of an ancient people and their culture, language, and religion is at stake. Drawing on the lessons learned from my long period of engagement with Beijing, the book also aims to offer some suggestions on what might be the path forward. Given that ours is the struggle of a people with a long history of distinct civilization, it will, if necessary, continue beyond my lifetime. The right of the Tibetan people to be the custodians of their own homeland cannot be indefinitely denied, nor can their aspiration for freedom be crushed forever through oppression. One clear lesson we know from history is this: if you keep people permanently unhappy, you cannot have a stable society.

Introduction

✳

Unlike all my other missions, which I have chosen for myself, the responsibility for the nation and people of Tibet was placed upon me the moment I was recognized as the Dalai Lama at the age of two. It was formalized in 1950, when I became Tibet's temporal leader at the age of sixteen.* Since that time, I have carried the duty of protecting Tibet and its people as well as our culture at the center of my heart and will do so as long as I am alive.

This principal commitment is in addition to the other commitments that I have taken on as part of my life's mission, including promoting fundamental human values based on a universal or secular approach to ethics, fostering interreligious understanding and harmony, and encouraging a deeper appreciation of India's ancient wisdom and knowledge. In these other domains, I feel happy that I have been able to make some tangible contributions, through

---

* This is according to the Tibetan system of counting; according to the non-Tibetan system, the Dalai Lama's age at the time was fifteen. All annotations, as well as the Selected Bibliography, were prepared by the editor, the Dalai Lama's longtime English translator Thupten Jinpa, to help offer the reader key sources and necessary further explanations.

wide-ranging conversations, the writing of books, and extensive international visits.

In the case of Tibet, my first and most intimate charge, it has been much more difficult. I have tried my best, ceaselessly, to make openings for a negotiated settlement with the Chinese Communists, who invaded my country in 1950. There have been three periods of intense dialogue: in the 1950s, when I was resident in Tibet as a young leader; in the 1980s, when the Chinese leader Deng Xiaoping opened up China; and in the first decade of this century. In all other aspects of my life and in all other domains of my work, I have engaged with people who have shown a commitment to shared vision, an openness to trust, the honesty to express one's thoughts even in disagreement, and the willingness to truly engage and learn. With the Chinese Communist leadership, from Chairman Mao Zedong to President Xi Jinping in the current era, sadly, the situation has been very different. I have often complained that the Chinese Communist leaders have only a mouth to speak but no ear to listen.

Take, for example, the white paper on Tibet issued by the Chinese government in May 2021. The document began with the statement that, after the Chinese invasion of 1950, the people of Tibet "broke free from the fetters of invading imperialism for good, embarking on a bright road of unity," and today Tibetans enjoy "a stable social environment, economic and cultural prosperity." According to this narrative, ever since Communist China's "peaceful liberation" of Tibet, the Tibetan nation and people have been on a continuous upward trajectory to freedom, prosperity, and contentment within the family of the People's Republic of China (PRC). Had this been true, at any period since the invasion, how does one explain more than seven decades of continued resistance and resentment of China's presence on the part of the Tibetans? It seems that Communist China has a simple answer: it's because of "the splittist activity of the Dalai clique." What they are referring to here is our long nonviolent campaign for the freedom of our people, and our efforts to save our unique language, culture, ecology, and religion. We Tibetans are the people who have traditionally inhabited the Tibetan plateau for millennia, and have every right to continue to be the custodians in our own homeland. The issue of Tibet is not about the matter of economic development, which we acknowledge as having improved significantly since the economic liberalization of the People's Republic of China. The issue is about a people's need and right to exist with their distinct language, culture, and religious heritage. Since the people inside Tibet have no freedom to speak out, it has fallen to me especially, since I came into exile in 1959, to be the voice of the voiceless.

While our goal remains to find a mutually agreeable negotiated solution, that aim would require in the end that the Tibetans and the Chinese sit down together and talk. Until such a negotiated solution is found, we Tibetans who are in the free world have the moral responsibility to continue to speak on behalf of our brothers and sisters inside Tibet. Doing so is neither anti-China nor "splittist." Indeed, far from splitting, being honest and open is the only way to create the basis on which each side can understand and accommodate the needs of the other. Only when we have created an atmosphere where both sides can speak and negotiate freely can there be a lasting settlement.

We have been fortunate to have so many friends around the world who have stood in solidarity with us and our cause. Governments, especially at the parliamentary level, and international organizations across the free world have strongly supported our approach, which seeks genuine autonomy for Tibet—a middle way between the independence cherished by the Tibetans, on the one hand, and, on the other, the current reality on the ground that denies agency or any meaningful self-rule for the Tibetan people in their own homeland. A series of resolutions has been passed by the United Nations, by the European Parliament, and in many countries, including especially the United States, where, in addition to resolutions, important acts have been adopted.

We have been particularly fortunate in having received such a generous welcome and such continuing support from India and its people, including successive governments since I arrived in India as a refugee. From India's first prime minister, Pandit Jawaharlal Nehru, to the present prime minister, Narendra Modi, India has never wavered in its hospitality, generosity, and support to me, the Tibetan refugees, and our efforts at educating our youth and the rebuilding of our culture and institutions in exile. For me personally, this has been deeply heartwarming.

Ever since the seventh century, when the Buddhist texts were first translated from Sanskrit into Tibetan, we Tibetans have looked up to India as "the land of the noble ones" (Aryavarta). Our Buddhist tradition, which we cherish so deeply, came from India. Our written script was invented in the seventh century, taking the Indian Devanagari as its model. Our philosophies, psychology, logic, and cosmology are the gifts of the Indian Nalanda school. Our astro-sciences and calendar system are deeply enriched by the Indian Kalachakra tantra. Our medical science and practice have been influenced by Indian Ayurveda. So, to have found India as my second home has offered me a powerful anchor.

I have spent the greater part of my life in India. And I sometimes describe myself as a son of India. My mind has been nourished by India's rich philosophical tradition, while my body has been fed by Indian rice and dal. When I used to travel internationally, I often stated that I am a messenger of two great gifts from India to humanity—religious pluralism and the teaching of ahimsa, the principle of nonviolence.

I have had more than seven decades of engagement with the People's Republic of China since 1950. During this long period, we have seen at least five different eras within the leadership of the country. First, under Chairman Mao, ideology was prominent amid vast and constant social upheaval, culminating in the disastrous Cultural Revolution. Millions died and many more suffered tremendously. Then, in the era of Deng Xiaoping, ideology became less important and the stress was on wealth creation. Deng, in fact, became famous for his slogan "To get rich is glorious." This was followed by the age of Jiang Zemin, during which Communist Party membership expanded to embrace other sectors of Chinese society, under the slogan "Three Represents."* Next came the period of Hu Jintao and his slogan "socialist harmonious society," where, at least on the surface, there was a focus on closing the growing wealth gap that had developed since the era of Deng. Today, China is under the leadership of Xi Jinping, who proclaimed the slogan of "New Era of Socialism with Chinese Characteristics." Judging by Xi's last decade in office, when it comes to individual freedom and everyday life, China seems to be reverting to the oppressive policies of Mao's time, but now enforced through state-of-the-art digital technologies of surveillance and control. What we have in China is, in essence, market capitalism tied to a Leninist obsession with state control. This is a fundamental paradox—profoundly unstable because essential to capitalism is the opening up of the economy, which ultimately requires the opening up of society, while the fixation on control at every level by the Party requires the closing of society. These two polar forces are pulling in opposite directions. The question is, how long can this last?

Even within a history of approximately seventy-five years, there has been tremendous change hidden beneath the apparent continuity of a single governing Communist Party. Specifically, between the eras of Mao and Deng, change was fundamental and astonishingly swift. Those who are old enough to remember the Cold War might recall how the Soviet Union seemed so stable and enduring. But when change came, it did so with extraordinary speed and in ways very few Kremlinologists had predicted. One thing is for sure: no totalitarian regime, whether headed by an individual or a party, can last forever, because

---

* Jiang articulated this theory to define a new relationship between the Chinese Communist Party and the people, with the need for the Party to represent what he called: (1) the development trend of China's advance productive forces; (2) the orientation of China's advance culture; and (3) the fundamental interests of the majority of the Chinese people.

they abuse the very people they claim to speak for, and also yearning for freedom is a powerful force within human nature. Furthermore, the very nature of their rule—paranoid, suspicious, and afraid of ordinary citizens—makes totalitarian regimes inherently unstable, even if the gun may prevail in the short term. In the case of Communist China, the popular movement of students in 1989 in Tiananmen Square demonstrated the deep aspiration of the people for individual freedom and a real opening. Regardless of how China might look today from the outside, the simple fact remains that this aspiration for greater freedom has not gone away.

Thanks to Deng's turn to capitalism and his opening up of China to the outside world, it is undeniable that today China is a major economic power. And of course, with economic power comes military might and international political influence. How the country exercises these newfound powers over the next decade or two will define its course for the foreseeable future. Will it choose the path of dominance and aggression, both internally and externally? Or will it choose the path of responsibility and embrace a constructive leading role on the world stage in meeting the collective challenges of humanity, such as peace, climate change, and the alleviation of poverty? Today, China stands at a crossroads. That it chooses the latter path is in the interest not only of the whole world but of the Chinese people themselves. In essence, this is a matter of the very heart of China as a country and its people. Here, I believe that resolving the long-standing problem of Tibet through dialogue would be a powerful signal, both to its own people and to the world, that China is choosing the second of these two paths. What is required on the part of their leadership are long-term vision, courage, and magnanimity.

CHAPTER 1

The Invasion and Our New Master

On October 7, 1950, some forty thousand soldiers of the People's Liberation Army crossed the Drichu (Yangtze) River in Kham (eastern Tibet). By the nineteenth of the month, they had taken Chamdo as well as the governor of eastern Tibet, Ngabö Ngawang Jigme, who had been recently appointed to the post. Thus began Communist China's invasion of my country. The newly independent India protested to the People's Republic of China, stating that the invasion was not in the interest of peace in the region. I was only sixteen years old at the time, according to the Tibetan system of counting age. By then, I already had a suspicion that something terrible was looming, for I had once, snooping, seen a sign of disbelief on the face of Regent Tadrak Rinpoche as he read a letter presented to him.* I later discovered that the letter was in fact a telegram from Ngabö, the governor of eastern Tibet, reporting a raid on a Tibetan post by Chinese soldiers.

---

* Tadrak Rinpoche was, at the time, both the regent for the young Dalai Lama as well as his senior tutor, responsible for overseeing the latter's formal education.

A few minutes later, the regent walked out of his room and gave orders to summon the Kashag (cabinet). On November 11, the Tibetan government appealed to the United Nations:

To the Secretary General of the United Nations,

The attention of the world is riveted on Korea where aggression is being resisted by an international force. Similar happenings in remote Tibet are passing without notice. It is in the belief that aggression will not go unchecked and freedom unprotected in any part of the world that we have assumed the responsibility of reporting through you recent happenings in the border area of Tibet. . . .

. . . The conquest of Tibet by China will only enlarge the area of conflict and increase the threat to the independence and stability of other Asian countries.

Only El Salvador attempted to place Tibet on the agenda of the General Assembly of the United Nations. Sadly, none of the great powers supported the move. One would have hoped, given Great Britain's historical involvement in Tibet, including the signing of bilateral agreements, such as the Lhasa and the Simla Conventions (respectively of 1904 and 1914), that it would have had greater sympathy and might have stood by us, especially at this crucial moment in Tibet's history. The world seemed to have abandoned us.

Great Britain and the other powers asserted there was a lack of clarity about Tibet's exact status. Yet they knew very well that in 1950 Tibet was an independent nation. The status of Tibet's independence according to international law was confirmed later by the International Commission of Jurists in 1959, following my escape into exile. The tragic irony is that it was, in fact, Great Britain and Russia, the two empires competing for power in Central Asia in what came to be called the Great Game, who were among those responsible for muddying the waters of Tibet's international status. Great Britain, in particular, had dealt with Tibet directly as an independent nation capable of making decisions on its own. It had even supplied weapons so Tibet could protect its eastern border against the Chinese. Yet it had also conducted bi-party negotiations with Nationalist China as if the latter had some claim over Tibet, invoking the obscure concept of suzerainty* and distinguishing it from sovereignty. If you will allow me to provide some historical context, Britain chose not to appreciate the crucial difference between the Qing empire and the modern nation-state of China: The former was a Manchu empire that had, at various times, different nations under its protectorate. Modern China, on the other hand, was claiming to be an anti-imperialist multi-nation state, not an empire. So the basic logic behind China's claim over Tibet, even in terms of suzerainty rather than sovereignty, was flawed. The failure (or political unwillingness) to see through this flawed logic and the refusal to accept the actual facts on the ground that showed Tibet's independence, as well as the various moves already made in the Great Game, are what had created the fog obscuring Tibet's "legal status" from the international point of view.

Communist China's invasion impacted me personally in a profound way. I remember hearing from the sweepers at the Potala Palace that posters had been put up around the Tibetan capital city, Lhasa, asking that I be given full temporal power. I was told that street songs were being sung by people demanding that the Dalai Lama be given his majority. The opinion on what to do, however, was divided—with one side saying that the Dalai Lama was too young, while others asserted that the time had indeed come to empower me. In the end,

---

* *Cambridge Dictionary* defines "suzerainty" as "the right of a country to partly control another."

the Tibetan cabinet headed by the regent decided to consult the State Oracles.*

At a certain point in the ceremony, whose tense atmosphere was unmistakable given the stakes, one of the oracles, while in a trance, laid a *kata* (ceremonial white scarf) on my lap and shouted, "*Dü la bab*" (The time has come). So, on November 17, 1950, I was enthroned as Tibet's temporal leader, two years before the traditional age in normal circumstances. To mark the occasion, I granted a general amnesty across Tibet and asked that all prisoners be freed.

Communist China's forcible invasion thrust me into this leadership role. With a single stroke, it turned a carefree young boy into someone with the heavy responsibility of leading a nation under attack. This is why I often say that at age sixteen I lost my freedom. My country too suffered the same fate: by the end of November, about seven weeks after the invasion, Kham (eastern Tibet) had effectively fallen.

As the new leader of a people faced with the threat of full-scale war, toward the end of the year I decided in consultation with my cabinet to send delegations to India, the United States, Great Britain, and Nepal, hoping to persuade these countries to intervene on our behalf. I also sent a delegation to Chamdo in eastern Tibet with the hope that we could negotiate a withdrawal of China's army from our territory. With the Communist Chinese forces consolidating in eastern Tibet, it was decided that I should move with the cabinet from Lhasa to Yadong (Yatung) near the Indian border, in case we needed to flee the country. Strangely, one of my first major acts as Tibet's ruler turned out to be the escape toward the Indian border. My mother took this opportunity to go to India on a pilgrimage, and she left accompanied by my youngest brother, Tenzin Choegyal.

---

* The practice of consulting oracles is common in Tibetan Buddhism, and the State Oracles here refer principally to Nechung and Gadong, who are associated especially with the lineage of the Dalai Lamas.

The People's Liberation Army meanwhile paused at Gyamda, near the western borders of Kham. The road to Lhasa was open, but they wanted to take the rest of the country without the use of force. We had no option but to authorize a delegation to go to Beijing to conduct a negotiation forced upon us. It was the same governor of eastern Tibet, Ngabö, who was chosen to lead this delegation. We told Ngabö that he could open negotiations with my authority on the condition that the Chinese advance no farther. In April 1951, my delegation arrived in Beijing and formal discussions began.

Although there was sporadic communication with the team by wire at the beginning, thereafter there was silence while I waited at the monastery in Yadong. Then, on May 23, 1951, while listening to my old Bush radio, I heard on the Tibetan-language broadcast from Radio Peking that a Seventeen-Point Agreement for the Peaceful Liberation of Tibet had been signed that day by the People's Republic of China and what was described as "the local government of Tibet." You can imagine my shock. The broadcast went on to say Tibet had been occupied for the last hundred years by aggressive imperial forces who had carried out all kinds of deceptions and provocations, plunging the people into the depths of enslavement and suffering. I felt physically sickened by this cocktail of lies and insults.

Only after my delegation returned to Lhasa did I discover what had actually happened during the negotiations. My representatives were coerced, insulted, abused, and threatened with personal violence against themselves as well as military action against the people of Tibet. As the delegation sat down to negotiate, they were presented with the already prepared text of a ten-point draft agreement. My delegation argued that Tibet is an independent country, and produced evidence to support the case. The Chinese side, of course, dismissed this. They then revised the original ten-point draft into a seventeen-point document and presented this as a final ultimatum. Under duress, the Tibetan delegation had no choice but to yield. In the absence of any communication with me or my government, Ngabö and his colleagues

5

had no authority to sign any agreement on behalf of Tibet. Still, the Chinese asked if Ngabö had brought the official seal of the Tibetan government, and although he had the seal of the governor of eastern Tibet with him, he denied possessing any seal. Undeterred, the Chinese then forged new seals for each delegate and had the document signed on May 23, 1951, effectively in the individual names of the five Tibetan delegates.

On July 14, I received a delegation from China bearing a letter to me from Chairman Mao. I told Chinese General Chang Ching-wu that I would reply to Mao on the issue of the Seventeen-Point Agreement after I'd returned to Lhasa from Yadong and was able to consult with other Tibetan officials. Understandably, there was an intense debate within the Tibetan National Assembly in Lhasa as to whether I should return to the capital. I decided against fleeing to India from Yadong then, and turned down also an offer from the United States to broker a place of refuge. In the end, I decided that it was best to return to Lhasa, and in September 1951, the Tibetan National Assembly held a special session. Ngabö made a formal presentation of the supposed agreement. After a long debate, it was felt that we had no choice given the massive numbers of Communist Chinese troops at our door. At the time, the entire Tibetan army consisted of approximately 8,500 soldiers, while more than 80,000 battle-hardened soldiers of the People's Liberation Army stood ready to march into Tibet. Tibet's small force was armed mostly with old British Enfield rifles, machine guns, and mortars.

The Seventeen-Point Agreement opens with a preamble that presents a fanciful revision of the history of Tibet in relation to China—"the Tibetan nationality is one of the nationalities with a long history within the boundaries of China, . . . our great Motherland." Let me quote the following key provisions:

- "The Tibetan people shall return to the big family of the Motherland—the People's Republic of China."

- "The local government of Tibet shall actively assist the People's Liberation Army to enter Tibet and consolidate the national defense."
- "The Tibetan people have the right of exercising national regional autonomy under the leadership of the Central People's Government."
- "The Central Government will make no change with regard to the existing political system in Tibet. The central authorities will not alter the established status, functions and powers of the Dalai Lama."
- "The religious beliefs, customs, and habits of the Tibetan people shall be respected, and lama monasteries shall be protected."
- "The spoken and written language and school education of the Tibetan nationality will be developed step by step in accordance with the actual conditions in Tibet."[*]

Although the agreement was forced upon us, the text of the document clearly commits the People's Republic of China to guaranteeing regional autonomy and self-government to Tibet, including freedom of religion, protection of language, custodianship of our land and its ecology, and our right to exist as a distinct people with its unique culture and heritage. This agreement became the basis of my government's relationship with China until 1959, when I escaped. It also appeared to have become the basis for the position of some in the international community on the status of Tibet. There seems to be a strange contradiction here. Regardless of the geopolitical situation at the time, the fact remains that consideration of Tibet as having become part of the People's Republic of China after 1950 accepts the justification

---

[*] The full text of the Seventeen-Point Agreement can be found in International Commission of Jurists, *Question of Tibet*, 139–42; Tsering Shakya, *Dragon in the Land of Snows*, appendix 1.

of the rightness of conquest and the validity of an agreement signed under duress. On the part of Tibet, the Seventeen-Point Agreement was imposed on a coerced delegation and at the threat of a conqueror's massed army at the door.

Even though Beijing would later justify its forcible invasion on historical claims of ownership of Tibet, it seems clear that, for Mao at least, at the time of the invasion of Tibet it was a blatant land grab of an independent nation by force. His view of Tibet as independent is reflected in a statement I was told he once made to the American journalist and author Edgar Snow. Referring to the foraging for food committed by his Red Army in Tibetan areas during the Long March, Mao said that this was the Chinese Communists' only foreign debt, which would need to be repaid one day. Today we also know, from archival records, that in January 1950, Mao asked Joseph Stalin if the Soviet Union would lend China military transport planes to ferry Chinese troops in a plan to invade Tibet.

I am told that some geopolitical scholars and historians suggest two primary motives behind Mao's invasion of Tibet, in the immediate aftermath of establishing a Communist government in Beijing. One relates to what Mao and his Communist colleagues saw as the need to restore China's "national honor," especially in the wake of what they refer to as the "hundred years of national humiliation." An important part of this, according to their view, was the reclaiming of territories that had once been part of the Manchu Qing empire. In this regard, Mao may have felt that Tibet's independence represented a visible "loss" or contradiction, given Communist China's claim to all territories once portrayed as part of the Qing empire.

The second reason, the experts suggest, pertains to Tibet's strategic geography with its borders touching East Turkistan (Xinjiang), India, Nepal, and Bhutan, and, of course, China to the east. In 1954, the Panchen Lama, three years my junior in age, whose institution is one of the most prominent in Tibetan Buddhism and closely associated with the Dalai Lamas, joined me on a trip to Beijing. Mao told him the following: "Now that the Tibetans are cooperating with the Han, our national defense line is not the Upper Yangtse River but the Himalaya Mountains."* Regardless of their motivations, we found ourselves under Communist China's boot.

---

* What Mao said to the Panchen Lama then is cited (in English translation) in Melvyn C. Goldstein, *A History of Modern Tibet*, vol. 2, *The Calm Before the Storm: 1951–1955* (Berkeley: University of California, 2007), 22. "Han" refers to ethnic Chinese who constitute the overwhelming majority within the People's Republic of China.

CHAPTER 2

Meeting Chairman Mao

In my role as the Dalai Lama, I was trying to mitigate the disaster for my people. On October 26, 1951, approximately three thousand troops from the People's Liberation Army's Eighteenth Route Army entered Lhasa. Soon after, a further large detachment of soldiers arrived, and combined with a large influx of horses, this led to a serious food shortage. Lhasa in 1951 had a local population of just over thirty thousand, so one can imagine the impact of such a massive influx of Chinese troops in the city. This situation came to worsen further as thousands of Tibetans came as refugees from eastern Tibet.

The period between 1951 and 1959 proved to be one of the most challenging times of my life. In part, I was still studying intensively for my final Geshe Lharam degree. Geshe Lharam is the highest academic degree one can obtain within the formal scholarly training of the great monastic universities of the Geluk school, analogous to a doctorate in divinity, which would culminate in February 1959. In part, I was going through a massive learning curve as a young man in the complexities of politics, having received no formal training in any of these matters.

Of course, the rigorous education I was receiving in Buddhist philosophy and psychology did help me immensely in maintaining my sanity against the complex political challenges I had no choice but to face as the leader of the Tibetan people. And my on-the-job education meant dealing with the very real disagreements between my government and the Chinese generals who were stationed in Lhasa and had all the guns. I was often caught between the extremely reluctant and at times confrontational Tibetan officials, on the one hand, and the increasing heavy-handedness and haughty attitudes of the Chinese generals, on the other. Ultimately, in 1952, my two prime ministers (one lay and one monastic) were forced to resign by the Chinese. I made the decision not to appoint replacements to these posts since they would simply be scapegoats, and it was better that I accept the responsibilities myself. The situation in Lhasa was getting more tense by the day.

I also still had to govern, and one of my priorities was to improve our system and society. I set up a reform committee to help create a more equitable system with explicit attention paid to the needs of the ordinary people and the poor. As a child growing up, I learned a lot from sweepers at my residence, who were often my playmates, about the problem of injustice and abuse by the powerful. But I faced major obstacles from the Chinese since they wanted reforms according to their own system, along lines introduced in mainland China. They probably felt that if changes were initiated by the Tibetans themselves, it might hinder their own agenda.

So, when in 1954 the Chinese government invited me to Beijing, I felt it was the only option left to me to attempt to improve my people's deteriorating situation. In June, I received a telegram from Deng Xiaoping, then the senior figure responsible for Tibetan affairs in the Chinese leadership, inviting me to attend the inaugural National People's Congress in Beijing in September 1954. The same invitation was extended to the Panchen Lama. Although the Tibetans in Lhasa were deeply concerned about my trip to Beijing, I decided that it was best that I go for the sake of my people. To assuage their fear, during a large gathering of Tibetans at a religious ceremony at Norbulingka, my summer residence, I reassured them and promised to be back within a year.

To this day, I remember when I left Lhasa for Beijing, there were so many people crying. I heard some of the older women shouting, "Please don't go! It would be not good!" As there was no bridge over the Kyichu River at the time, we had to cross it in the traditional Tibetan coracles, made out of yak hide stretched over a willow frame. On the sides of the river there were so many people crying; some even seemed they might jump into the river. Later I heard that some fainted and even died.

On September 4, 1954, Panchen Lama and I, with our delegations, finally arrived in Beijing by train from Xi'an. We were received at the station by Prime Minister Zhou Enlai; Vice Chairman Zhu De, who was also the commander-in-chief of the People's Liberation Army and a member of the Standing Committee of the Politburo; and other Chinese officials. A few days later, I met Chairman Mao Zedong himself for the first time. He was sixty-one years old to my nineteen. He was warm and welcoming.

This meeting, joined by other top leaders, including Zhao Enlai and Liu Shaoqi, took place at the house of reception, a former imperial garden adjacent to the Forbidden City and later transformed into a compound that houses government offices as well as residences for senior leadership. The setting of this meeting was quite majestic with its opulent imperial legacy unmistakable. Here we were, myself only nineteen years old and the Panchen Lama sixteen years old, in a formal meeting with Chairman Mao himself, flanked by Communist China's most senior leaders. That we felt awed and somewhat nervous would be an understatement. At this first meeting, only Chairman Mao and I spoke. Mao said that he and the Central Government were very happy about my first visit to Beijing, and that the relationship between Chinese and Tibetans was very important. He also assured me that in the future the Central Government would make great efforts to help develop Tibet. On my part, I responded to Mao, saying I was very happy to have the opportunity to meet him and other leaders of the Chinese Communist Party.

The meeting lasted about an hour. As we left, Mao and other leaders accompanied us out of the house, and Mao himself opened the car door for me. As I was getting into the car, Mao shook my hand and said, "Your coming to Beijing is coming back to your own home. Whenever you come to Beijing, you can call on me. . . . Don't be shy; if you need anything, just tell me directly."

I came out of that meeting impressed with Mao and encouraged at the possibility that things could improve in Tibet. With me in the car was Phuntsok Wangyal, a rare Tibetan Communist, who was my official interpreter during my stay in Beijing. I was so relieved that this first meeting with Mao and other Chinese leaders went well—in fact, I hugged Phuntsok Wangyal and told him that Mao was truly unlike anyone I had met. The success of this first meeting also reassured my Tibetan entourage, including especially my senior tutor, Ling Rinpoche, who had been feeling quite worried about me. Phuntsok Wangyal was a true believer in Communism in its original Marxist internationalist sense. And at the time he believed, later to his disappointment, that the Chinese Communists also shared this internationalist vision of Marxism. (Decades later, when Phuntsok Wangyal was allowed to visit Europe, I was able to speak with him by phone. I asked him, "What happened to your dream of true socialism?" He just laughed.)

On September 16, I addressed the first National People's Congress, noting that the draft constitution of the People's Republic of China states, in particular, that all nationalities may draw up their rules governing the exercise of autonomy and separate regulations in accordance with the special features of the development so that they can exercise full autonomy. By then, I had been made a vice president of the steering committee of the People's Republic of China.

During my stay in Beijing, I had several meetings with Mao and other leaders, including Zhou Enlai and Deng Xiaoping. In Beijing, I was introduced to a number of senior international leaders as well, including the Indian Prime Minister Jawaharlal Nehru, the Soviet leader Nikita Khrushchev, and the Burmese Prime Minister U Nu. Whenever I had some free time, I also took classes from my senior tutor Ling Rinpoche on the philosophically dense "insight" section of Tsongkhapa's *Great Treatise on the Stages of the Path to Enlightenment*. Technically, I was still a student, studying for my Geshe Lharam exams. One memorable experience of my stay in Beijing included the conducting of a formal Buddhist teaching—in fact, an important initiation ceremony of a meditation practice known as Vajrabhairava—to an assembly of Chinese Buddhists who were followers of Tibetan Buddhism. My translator at this teaching was the Chinese monk Fa-Tsun, who informed me that he was working on a Tibetan translation of a major Buddhist philosophical text, *Great Treatise on Differentiation* (*Mahavibhasha*)—a second-century work extant only in Chinese translation. By then Fa-Tsun had already translated a major Tibetan work, entitled *The Great Treatise on the Stages of the Path to Enlightenment*, by the fourteenth-century master Tsongkhapa.

Then I went on an arranged tour of cities within China, such as Tianjin, to see the way in which the Communist government had industrially developed the country. Phuntsok Wangyal was assigned as my translator during this tour, and I was accompanied also by another Communist cadre by the name of Liu Geping, a member of the ethnic Hui (Muslim) minority. I met many party members of different ranks, some veterans of the revolution and many very sincere Communists. Incidentally, one of these was Xi Zhongxun, father of the current Chinese leader Xi Jinping. He had an affable personality and seemed quite broad-minded. I really liked him. (I was told that he treasured all his life a wristwatch I had given him at the time.)

I was impressed by the sense of purpose and dedication displayed by many of these first-generation revolutionaries, as well as their obvious successes in their attempt to create a more egalitarian society. I learned much about Marxism-Leninism, and was particularly struck by the emphasis in Marxist economic theory on equal distribution of resources rather than pure profit-making. The idea of taking care of the less privileged people, of the working class, is wonderful. To oppose all exploitation, and to strive for a society without national boundaries— these are excellent ideals. As I was exposed to all this in my youth, these aspects of socialist thinking left a strong impression such that I sometimes describe myself as half-Buddhist and half-Marxist. However, as I have thought about it over the years, what is lacking in Marxism is compassion. Its greatest flaw is the total neglect of basic human values, and the deliberate promotion of hate through class struggle. Furthermore, as time went on, in the case of Communist China, Marxism seemed to have given way to Leninism, with state control of the people by the Party as the primary objective.

During this tour around China, I had the rare opportunity to cross into Inner Mongolia for a brief visit.* It was a moving experience given the long and close association between Tibetans and Mongols spiritually. Although for me this tour of Chinese cities was educational and enjoyable, most of my officials, including my two tutors, were completely uninterested. So when it was announced that there was going to be no more sightseeing, there was a collective sigh of relief. My mother, in particular, did not enjoy her stay in China, especially the hectic sightseeing schedule. At one point she even got ill with a serious case of flu. Since my return to Beijing from the tour was close to Losar (Tibetan New Year), I decided to host a banquet and extend invitations to Chairman Mao and the other three senior Chinese leaders—Zhou Enlai, Zhu De, and Liu Shaoqi. They all accepted and we had a memorable celebration.

---

* "Inner Mongolia" refers to a historical part of Mongolia that is today the Inner Mongolia Autonomous Region within the People's Republic of China. Today's independent Mongolian People's Republic contains the bulk of the territory that was at one point known as Outer Mongolia.

One day Chairman Mao paid an unannounced visit to my lodgings. During this meeting, he unexpectedly asked if Tibet had a national flag. Somewhat nervously, I replied that we did, and he said that it would be fine for us to keep it. Mao's surprising response implied that, at that time at least, he had in mind a model of the diverse nations within the People's Republic along the lines of the republics within the Soviet Union. In fact, I know Mao gave orders to senior Chinese officials stationed in Tibet at the time—Zhan Jingwu, Zhang Guohua, and Fan Ming—to display the Tibetan flag alongside China's red star and also my photo alongside his own. So later, in exile, when Tibetans and international Tibetan supporters would display our national flag in public, especially when greeting me during international travels, I used to tell them that Mao himself had given permission to keep our flag. Today, sadly, the Tibetan flag is illegal in Tibet, and anyone caught in possession of it will go to prison.

Before I left Beijing, I had a final meeting with Mao. He looked very happy and told me to communicate directly with him through the telegraph, saying I should train some trusted Tibetans to do this. He then came close to me and said, "Your mind is scientific, and that is very good. I have watched your thinking and activities all these months. Your mind is a very revolutionary mind." He gave me excellent practical advice about government and I took notes.

As the meeting came to a close, Mao told me, "Your attitude is good, you know. Religion is poison. It reduces the population because the monks and nuns must stay celibate and it neglects material progress." I was shaken and attempted to hide my feelings by leaning forward as if to write something. It was then I knew despite all the hints of positive dialogue that he was the destroyer of Buddha Dharma.

As I prepared for my journey back home to Lhasa in March 1955, despite Mao's last disconcerting comment about religion, I still had hopes of saving my people from the worst consequences of the Chinese occupation. I thought my six-month visit to China had helped in two ways. It had shown me exactly what we were up against and had appeared to have persuaded the Chinese leaders not to go ahead with their original plan of governing Tibet directly from Beijing through a military and political committee: we seemed to have a firm promise of autonomy. In fact, on the way back to Tibet I met the Chinese General Zhang Guohua, who was stationed in Lhasa but was en route to Beijing. I told him that on my way to China I was full of anxiety, but now on my way back home I felt more hopeful and confident. So I had some faith that we could work with the Chinese. Tibet could be modernized and its people would live on some kind of equal terms with the Chinese majority within the People's Republic of China.

I worked earnestly to seek a lasting accommodation that would save my nation and people within the constraints of the Seventeen-Point Agreement. I tried to institute some reforms—notably to establish an independent judiciary, to encourage proposals for the development of a program of modern education, and to build modern roads. It proved to be a hopeless task, constantly undermined by the Chinese Communist military and civil officials stationed in Tibet, with rising resentment of repression and the risk of spontaneous revolt from the Tibetan people. My efforts were blocked at every stage by the Chinese officials and military. The Preparatory Committee for the Autonomous Region of Tibet (PCART), which was meant to give the Tibetans autonomy over the process of reform and of which I was the chair, turned out to be just a show, with all actual power in the hands of the Chinese.

The promises and assurances received in Beijing turned out to be empty; my messages to Mao elicited no response. During the many disasters and unspeakable acts against Tibetans that were to follow, I wrote three times to Chairman Mao, the third time ensuring that my letter was personally delivered. There was never an answer. Whatever little hope I had in Mao and the Communist leadership was shattered. The commitments that the Communist Party of China had made in the agreement it had forced upon us turned out to have no real meaning at all.

CHAPTER 3

✳

A Visit to India

In late 1955, I received a formal invitation from the crown prince of Sikkim in his capacity as the president of the Maha Bodhi Society of India to participate in the celebrations of the 2,500th anniversary of Buddha Jayanti (the birth of the Buddha). Initially, Fan Ming, a senior political officer in the People's Liberation Army stationed in Lhasa, urged me to refuse the invitation. He told me that the crown prince was not high enough in rank for me to be accepting such a formal invitation. So I quietly sent a message to the Indian Mission in Lhasa to explain the situation, which led to the arrival of a second invitation, this time from the vice president of India, Sarvepalli Radhakrishnan. After several months, I was told that Beijing had okayed my trip to India.

Before I left, General Chang Ching-wu warned me, "Be careful. There are many reactionary elements and spies in India. If you try to do anything with them, I want you to realize that what has happened in Hungary and Poland will happen in Tibet." He was referring to the suppression of the Poznan protests in Poland in June 1956, when tanks and troops fired on protesting civilians, and the brutal crushing of the people's uprising in Hungary by Soviet tanks and troops on November 4, 1956, a few weeks before my trip. Despite his warnings, I was thrilled at the chance to visit the holy land of India and the sites associated with the life of the Buddha.

At the same time, however, I was acutely aware of the worsening situation in Tibet, especially the growing arrogance and belligerence of the Chinese authorities in Lhasa. For example, by 1956, when Chinese interpreters came to see me, they would wear pistols under their coats, unlike before. One day, I clearly saw the mouth of the gun jutting out. The situation in Lhasa also continued to deteriorate, with tension rising due to the presence of the large number of People's Liberation Army soldiers as well as the growing number of refugees who escaped frightening conditions in eastern Tibet. In March 1956, for example, the People's Liberation Army attacked Lithang Monastery in eastern Tibet—an important foundation associated with the Third Dalai Lama—bombing the monastery, killing several hundred people, and capturing its abbot.

In November 1956, I was finally able to visit India. My Dharma brother, the Panchen Lama, had also been officially invited and joined me as well. My two elder brothers, Taktser Rinpoche and Gyalo Thondup, both of whom were then living outside Tibet, met me at the border of Sikkim. The first words they said, before any kind of greeting, were, "You must not go back." Their urgency really shook me, and I knew there was good reason based on what I described earlier. I found myself in profound doubt about whether I should return after the celebration. For now, though, we continued on, flying to Delhi on November 25, to be met by Prime Minister Jawaharlal Nehru, Vice President Radhakrishnan, and the speaker of the Indian Parliament, M. A. Ayyangar. We were then driven to the president's official residence to meet Rajendra Prasad. After this, the following morning, the first event in my program was to pay homage at Raj Ghat, the place where Mahatma Gandhi—perhaps the greatest being of our age, who applied India's ancient philosophy of ahimsa (nonviolence) into an effective political movement for the freedom of his people from British colonial rule—was cremated. At that site, I affirmed more strongly than ever that I could never involve myself with any acts of violence.

The formal celebrations of Buddha Jayanti took place in Bodh Gaya, the most sacred place for Buddhists everywhere. The Mahabodhi Stupa in Bodh Gaya marks the site where the Buddha attained enlightenment under a pipal tree, which later came to be known as the Bodhi tree. The tree that stands there today is a continuation of the very same tree—by way of a sapling brought from Sri Lanka in the nineteenth century that in turn was a sapling of the original tree—under which the Buddha sat, more than 2,600 years ago. How I felt when I came face-to-face for the first time with the sacred Bodhi tree, I described in my autobiography of 1962:

> Every devout Buddhist would always associate Bodh Gaya with all that is noblest and loftiest in his religious and cultural inheritance. From my very early youth, I had thought and dreamed about this visit. Now I stood in the presence of the holy spirit who had attained enlightenment in this sacred place and found for all mankind the path to salvation. As I stood there a feeling of religious fervor filled my heart, and left me awestruck with the knowledge and impact of the divine power which is in all of us.

In my address at the celebration, I touched upon the long history of Buddhism in India, how it came to Tibet from India, and the long historical and spiritual ties that lie at the heart of this transmission, as I highlighted earlier. I particularly emphasized the Buddha's teaching of nonviolence and how this teaching could contribute to ushering in a new era of peace in the world. I expressed my deep admiration of the adoption of Ashoka's Dharma Chakra (Wheel of Law) as the nation's symbol of India at independence, indicating the country's deep admiration of the universal values promoted by Buddhism. When the formal celebrations were over, I took the opportunity to go on a pilgrimage to other sacred sites around Bodh Gaya and Sarnath in Central India associated with the life of the Buddha: the ruins of Nalanda in Bihar, the greatest Indian Buddhist monastic university, as well as the ancient Buddhist monuments at Sanchi and Ajanta.

Prime Minister Nehru accompanying me on my visit to Rajgir, a site associated with the Buddha's life and especially sacred to Mahayana Buddhism because it was where the *Perfection of Wisdom* scriptures were delivered, was particularly unforgettable. A memorial for the seventh-century Chinese traveler Xuanzang was formally inaugurated at Rajgir, at which Premiere Zhou Enlai was supposed to represent the People's Republic of China. In the end, Zhou could not come so I was asked to present the check representing a gift from the Chinese government. These visits to the sacred Buddhist sites offered some of the most joyful and memorable moments—rare beams of sunlight amid the dark clouds surrounding me and my homeland.

During my time in India, a number of prominent Tibetans living there came to urge me not to go back home. They expressed very strong views against the signing of the Seventeen-Point Agreement. I also had important meetings with Prime Minister Nehru, who was then in his sixties and was the first prime minister since his country's independence. At my first meeting I took the opportunity to explain in detail the full story of the Chinese invasion, how unprepared we were and how hard I had tried to accommodate the Communists as soon as I became aware that no one in the outside world was prepared to acknowledge our rightful claim to independence. I then told him how desperate things had become by now in eastern Tibet, following the bombing of Lithang Monastery, and that I feared that the Chinese really meant to destroy our religion and customs forever. I explained that I wanted to stay in India until we could win back our freedom by peaceful means.

Nehru agreed with me that it was useless to fight against the Chinese. He was emphatic, however, that India could not support us, and said that I should go back to my country and try to work with the Chinese on the basis of the Seventeen-Point Agreement. When I protested that the Chinese authorities had broken my trust and that I did not believe that the agreement was workable any longer, he said he would speak personally to the Chinese Premier Zhou Enlai. At one of my meetings with Nehru, he actually brought a copy of the agreement in his hand. Going through it point by point, he demonstrated how it could be the basis for a genuine model of autonomy and self-rule. Nehru reported on his own conversations with Zhou Enlai and especially the unambiguous assurance Zhou had given him with respect to the autonomy of Tibet within the People's Republic of China.

The trip to India was also the occasion for several meetings with the Chinese premier. Zhou Enlai, in his late fifties then, was full of smiles and charm, a courteous man with a swift intellect—in brief, clever and smooth-talking. At my first meeting in November in Delhi, I told him straightforwardly of my concerns about eastern Tibet, how the Chinese authorities were behaving, and especially of the brutal repression and murder of innocent people following the Lithang bombing. I also asked Zhou what happened during their reforms there and in northeastern Tibet (Amdo) that had forced so many thousands to flee as refugees to central Tibet.

Zhou made a serious attempt to reassure me, admitting that major mistakes were made in eastern Tibet by the local cadres and that the leaders at the top too had to accept responsibility since they should have intervened sooner. He told me that reforms in Tibet would not occur until my government thought the conditions were appropriate. I also shared with him my observation of the contrast between the Indian Parliament and the Chinese Communist People's Congress. In India, the parliament members are free to express themselves as they really feel and criticize the government when they think necessary. In Beijing, I had observed that most of the members in the assembly barely dared to speak. Even if they did make a point, it was mostly about small corrections in wording, but nothing of substance. Zhou responded that I had only been at the first assembly in Beijing and that things had changed immeasurably for the better at the second assembly. Zhou also took the trouble to meet with my brothers and key cabinet ministers of my government, including Ngabö, who had been forced to sign the Seventeen-Point Agreement in Beijing on behalf of my government.

The last time I met with Zhou in Delhi was after his return from a trip to Pakistan. On December 30, 1956, I received a message from the Chinese Embassy that Zhou was back in India and wanted to see me. I rushed to Delhi by train to find the Chinese Ambassador Pan Zili waiting for me at the station. He insisted that I ride with him in his car. With the help of Indian protocol officials and security, we drove straight to the Chinese Embassy, where I met with the ambassador, Zhou Enlai, and Marshal He Long. By the time my staff reached the embassy I was already in the meeting, with my staff not knowing if I was inside or not, and some even wondering if I had been abducted! At some point someone brought a warm shawl for me, saying that my staff wanted to make sure that I was not cold. Later they told me that they were worried and wanted to let me know that they too had arrived at the Chinese Embassy.

I must admit I found that meeting intimidating: three seasoned Chinese political and military men—a premier, a marshal, and an ambassador—surrounding one inexperienced young Tibetan monk. The fact that we were in Delhi and not Beijing made me at least feel safe. I stood firm and expressed my fear that the Communist Party might force unacceptable reforms in Tibet. By this time, it appeared that Zhou Enlai had clearly consulted with Mao Zedong. So he repeated all the reassurances he had given me earlier, about dealing with the excesses of repression in eastern Tibet and about postponing reform. He conveyed to me Mao's pledge that the plan for Communist reform in Tibet would be delayed at least for six years, and, even after that, it would be up to me to decide whether or not to implement the reforms. He added that the Chinese government would not tolerate any outbreak of armed insurrection in Tibet, and stressed that I needed to return to Lhasa at the earliest possible moment. He concluded by telling me not to visit Kalimpong, an Indian town near the border of

Tibet where there was a community of Tibetans, some of whom had already fled into exile.

To this last point, I told Zhou that I would think about his suggestion. The morning after this meeting, Marshal He Long came to see me. He repeated Zhou's advice that I return to Lhasa. He then quoted the saying "The snow lion looks dignified if he stays in the snows, but if he descends to the plains he would be treated like a dog." He was, of course, issuing me a serious warning.

All of this added up to real pressure from many sides about whether I should go back to Tibet or remain in India. Certainly, among the Tibetan officials with me there were conflicting views. It also appears that Beijing was trying to influence matters behind the scenes. Zhou had even dangled before Nehru the possible offer of China abiding by the boundaries determined between India and Tibet known as the McMahon Line, if India would refuse asylum to me at the time. I realized in the end I myself would have to make the decision on whether to return to Tibet or not. There is a Tibetan saying, "Ask others for opinions, but make the decision yourself." So in my next meeting with Prime Minister Nehru, I told him that I had made up my mind to go back to Tibet for two reasons. "Because you have advised me to do so, and because Zhou Enlai has given definite promises to me and my brothers." As it would prove, Nehru was sincere but idealistic in his belief about the Chinese pledges; Zhou was simply lying.

In January 1957, ignoring Premier Zhou's advice, I left for Kalimpong from Calcutta. On my way back home, I stopped in Gangtok, where I was able to meet with many devout Buddhists and give formal religious teachings and blessing ceremonies, and also laid the foundation stone for the Namgyal Institute of Tibetology, at the invitation of the maharaja of Sikkim.

I had planned to stop in Gangtok for only a few days. However, due to a heavy snowstorm, the Nathu-la Pass had become impassable, which meant I was happily stuck in Gangtok for a few extra weeks. While there, I also extended a formal invitation to Nehru to visit Lhasa. I wanted to reciprocate his generous hospitality during my stay in India, and, more important, offer him an opportunity to acquire a firsthand impression of what was actually happening in Tibet. Although Nehru accepted my invitation and the Chinese initially did not object, later they pulled back by saying that they could not guarantee Nehru's personal safety in Tibet. This was sad, for I would have benefited immensely from his counsel if he had visited Lhasa.

Even though Nehru had not been able to come to the capital, he did end up putting a foot on Tibetan soil on his way to and back from Bhutan, which he visited in September 1958. He spent a night at Yadong, the very town where I had fled in 1950 when the Chinese Communist army invaded from eastern Tibet. A high-level Tibetan delegation was sent to formally welcome the prime minister and his daughter Indira Gandhi when they arrived. It was during this visit to Bhutan that Nehru gave a strong assurance that it was India's wish to see Bhutan remain an independent country, with its own people choosing their own way of life and taking a path of progress according to their own will. This contrast between how Bhutan's giant neighbor India was treating it and how Tibet was being treated at that very moment by our giant neighbor to the east was, of course, too painfully striking to miss.

Finally, as the weather improved and the way became open toward the end of February, we crossed the Nathu-la Pass and reached Tibetan soil. The farewell, especially to my immediately elder brother Lobsang Samten, before crossing the pass was a sad moment. Among all my siblings, he and I had been the closest since, as children, we shared the ten-week-long journey from Amdo to central Tibet, and immediately after my formal recognition as the Dalai Lama, we also went through early monastic tutorials at the same time. Lobsang Samten was not well at the time and was feeling quite weak. So I suggested we sit together quietly in the car for a while. He was crying and I was myself feeling sad, and all of this caused some delay, irritating the Chinese officials accompanying me back to Tibet.

*

CHAPTER 4

Fleeing Home

On my way back to Lhasa from Gangtok, I stopped in many places trying to reassure my countrymen only to receive increasingly disquieting reports. I arrived in the capital on April 1, 1957, knowing that the situation was slipping out of control—due to the Chinese government's actions and from my own inability to have any meaningful influence. By midsummer, it had become clear that virtually everything I had been told by Zhou himself and by him on behalf of Mao had been falsehoods and dissimulations. There continued to be open conflict in Kham and Amdo (eastern and northeastern Tibet). The People's Liberation Army showed no restraint—bombing more towns and committing such atrocities that I found difficult to believe for their levels of depravity but were later confirmed by the International Commission of Jurists in 1959: forced sterilization, crucifixion, vivisection, disemboweling, dismemberment, beheading, burning, beating to death, burying alive, dragging people behind galloping horses, hanging them upside down, and other horrors. Thousands more refugees from Kham and Amdo fled to Lhasa and camped outside the city.

Through 1958 and early 1959, the situation worsened further, with growing numbers joining an active Tibetan resistance that came to be based in southern Tibet, called the Volunteer Force for the Protection of the Faith (*tensung danglang magmi*), led by the energetic leader Adruk Gompo Tashi. To defuse tension, I had several meetings with the People's Liberation Army's senior-most generals in Lhasa, including especially General Tan Guansan, the head of the Chinese military in Tibet, known for his bad temper. Through these generals, the Chinese government insisted that the Tibetan government use our own Tibetan soldiers against the Tibetan guerrillas. It was unthinkable to send Tibetan troops against our own people, especially when they were fighting to safeguard our land and culture. At the same time, I received an intimation from the Americans that if I solicited assistance for the resistance movement, they would provide it. Of course, as a student of the Buddha and a deep admirer of Mahatma Gandhi's nonviolence philosophy, I could not imagine myself making such a request.

Part of me at the time, I must admit, admired the guerrilla fighters. They were brave Tibetans who were putting their lives at risk for the sake of our nation and Buddhist faith. I also knew that many of them saw themselves as fighting out of loyalty to me as the Dalai Lama. I wondered what advice Mahatma Gandhi would have given me in this charged situation. Would he have condoned violence here? I could not believe that he would. Practically speaking too, I was convinced that using force against the Chinese would be not only useless but actually suicidal. It would give the Chinese army the perfect excuse to crush Tibetans with maximum force.

In the midst of all this, I was preparing for my final Geshe Lharam exams, scheduled at the Great Prayer Festival of 1959. February 22, 1959, when I formally sat for my examination debates at the great Jokhang Temple in Lhasa, was a rare break from the incessant and challenging politics. The day I completed my formal Geshe debates was, perhaps, the happiest day of my life. It was the culmination of a series of debates I had participated in at the "three great seats of learning"—Sera, Drepung, and Ganden—the three largest monastic universities of the Geluk school in central Tibet, all established at the beginning of the fifteenth century. I was both excited and nervous about the debates at Tibet's great centers of learning. Later I found out that those who had been chosen to question me at these debates too were quite nervous, if not more so than me!

Following my final Geshe exams in Lhasa, over the next two weeks the crisis in the country reached a boiling point. The people's anxiety about my own safety and the presence of Chinese troops in Lhasa led to an explosive situation in the capital. With so many people gathered in one place—several thousand Tibetans from other parts of Tibet in addition to the local residents—and with such a large number of People's Liberation Army soldiers stationed in the city, there was a pervasive sense of nervousness and unease. Many felt something untoward was about to happen.

On March 10, I was supposed to attend a cultural show at the Chinese garrison in Lhasa, with the worrisome suggestion that my bodyguards should not accompany me. Word had gotten out, and thousands of people crowded the city to prevent me from leaving my residence at Norbulingka. The crowd grew through the day, with people shouting anti-Chinese slogans and saying that they would not allow the Dalai Lama to leave. It was soon out of control and became a massive popular uprising. Over the next few days, the situation became increasingly tense and chaotic with the crowd refusing to disperse. On the twelfth, thousands of Tibetan women took to the streets and assembled in front of the Potala Palace. They burned the Chinese flag, as well as photos and effigies of Mao, Zhou Enlai, and Zhu De, and shouted, "Tibet has always been free! Tibet for the Tibetans! Long live the Dalai Lama! Long live Gaden Phodrang," the last being the name of the Tibetan government under the Dalai Lamas. The leader of this women's protest, Gurteng Kunsang, and some of her colleagues would be later executed by firing squad. On March 14, I met with approximately seventy representatives chosen by the people in the hope that I could help defuse the situation. However, tension kept building, with the Tibetan crowds growing day by day.

From the tenth to the seventeenth of March, the Chinese army remained in its barracks while I exchanged messages with the short-tempered General Tan Guansan, which may have helped to buy time. My last letter to him was on March 16. It might also have been the case that the Chinese army was awaiting instructions from Beijing. We had information that they were planning to attack the crowd and shell the Norbulingka Palace. Within my own immediate circle, many were urging me to seriously consider leaving Lhasa for the time being. But I kept hoping that if we could find a way to reassure the mass of ordinary Tibetans gathered outside who were worried about my safety, we could somehow defuse the situation and avert an immediate explosion.

On the seventeenth, around 4 p.m., two heavy mortars landed just outside the north side of the Norbulingka, which, fortunately, did not cause any harm. Everyone thought that an attack was imminent. Earlier on that day, the State Oracle Nechung,* in a trance, had in fact urged me to leave, saying, "Leave! Leave! Go tonight!" This instruction was consistent with the outcome of a few divinations I had performed myself on the question of whether to stay or leave.† So the landing of those two mortars came as a reinforcement of what the State Oracle had instructed me to do—namely, to leave immediately. Not only was my own life in danger, but the lives of thousands of my people now seemed certain to be lost as well. With everyone around me urging the path of escape as well, I took the decision to flee Lhasa. I went to the

---

* Nechung (known also as Dorje Drakden) is an important oracle, historically connected with the Dalai Lamas, who communicates through a medium in a trance. The practice of consulting oracles is common in Tibetan Buddhism.
† "Divination" (*mo* in Tibetan), typically involving the throwing of dices and interpreting the result of the throw, refers to a method of examining the pros and cons of a particular course of action.

chapel of Mahakala, an important protector in Tibetan Buddhism, a chapel where I had always gone to say good-bye before embarking on a long journey. The monks there must have been a little surprised when I offered a long white scarf to the image, but they did not show it. Then, having changed my monastic robe into layman's clothing, I went to my prayer room to sit down for a quiet moment.

I opened the text that was lying on the small table in front of the throne, which turned out to be the *Eight Thousand Lines on the Perfection of Wisdom*, a scripture sacred to Mahayana Buddhism. I randomly picked up a page and read from the top, ending at the sentence "Have courage and confidence." Energized, I closed the book, blessed the room, and turned off the lights. One precious item I took with me was an old *thangka* (a traditional Tibetan painting on canvas framed with silk brocades that could be rolled into a scroll) that had belonged to the Second Dalai Lama.*

As I walked out of my room, a blanket of silence enveloped me, where I could feel every step I took and the ticking of the clock on the wall. I took the rifle of one of the bodyguards who was standing outside my room. And so, at 10 p.m. on March 17, I put my glasses into my pocket and stepped out of the Norbulingka Palace disguised as a layman with a rifle over my shoulder. This was a truly eerie experience. I was afraid, but also had a more immediate practical thing to worry about: how not to trip as I walked without my glasses. As I stepped out of the gate, I felt the presence of a great mass of people gathered outside the Norbulingka. Thinking of them, I prayed—worrying what fate lay in store for these thousands of innocent Tibetans.

After I left, the Tibetan government in Lhasa continued as if I were still in residence. Once we were away from the immediate threat

---

* The *thangka* is of Palden Lhamo, an important female protector deity connected with the Dalai Lamas since the period of the Second Dalai Lama, Gendun Gyatso, in the fifteenth century.

of being captured by the People's Liberation Army, personally, the most powerful thing I felt was a sense of relief. Alongside this was the acute awareness that I was now free to speak my mind and openly criticize the policies of the Communist Chinese government. This feeling of freedom was so vivid and strong. The nine years of working with the Communist Chinese in Tibet and Beijing, during which I had to carefully consider every phrase I uttered, had placed a heavy weight in my heart. And I was now able to breathe the air of freedom.

Early the next morning, as we were crossing the Chela Pass, one of the guides leading my horse told me that this was the last point from where we could still see the Potala Palace, with its striking white-and-red fortresslike structures covering the entire face of a rocky mountain overlooking Lhasa. He then helped turn my horse around so I could take a last glimpse. With a heavy heart, I said good-bye to Lhasa, Tibet's capital city, where I had grown up since age four. I prayed that I would be able to return there one day.

A few days later, on March 20, the Chinese army shelled the Norbulingka and the crowd, killing many. By that time, the People's Liberation Army had a well-integrated plan of attack. When I heard this news, from a messenger during my escape, I prayed for my people. Nobody knows exactly how many were killed in Lhasa—I was told that thousands of bodies were seen inside and outside the Norbulingka. What took place in Norbulingka, Lhasa, Chokpori (a hill opposite Lhasa and the site of the Tibetan medical school), and Sera Monastery over two days of relentless bombing was a massacre.

We made for Lhuntse Dzong in Lhoka (in the south), which is just on the Tibetan side of the border from India. Our original intention was not to go directly into exile to India. My idea was to negotiate with the Chinese from a place of safety to see if I could return to continue to lead the Tibetan government. However, as the news of what took place in the immediate aftermath of my flight and what was continuing to happen reached us, we became convinced that there was no point in talking with the People's Republic of China. Furthermore, the Chinese authorities in Lhasa had announced the dissolution of the Tibetan government.

I later heard that when Mao was informed of my escape, he reacted, "We have lost!"* Mao probably realized that with me gone out of Tibet, China would struggle with the question of legitimacy both of their authority and their presence in Tibet. He was right. This question of legitimacy still remains at the very heart of China's presence in Tibet, even after seven decades of occupation.

At Lhuntse Dzong we paused and took stock. Looking back at more than eight years since the Seventeen-Point Agreement was signed, and notably after my return from visiting China in 1954–1955 and India in 1956–1957, despite all the efforts I made to find an accommodation, it was clear to me that the task was simply impossible. There is an old Tibetan saying that captures the essence of the relationship between the Tibetans and the Chinese: "Tibetans are let down by their hopes; the Chinese are let down by their suspicions."

At Lhuntse Dzong, on March 26, 1959, I formally repudiated the Seventeen-Point Agreement and announced the reconstitution of our own government of Tibet as the only legally constituted authority for the country. More than a thousand people attended this ceremony, where Surkhang, one of the ministers in my cabinet, read the document aloud to the gathering. At the opening of this document, announcing the formation of Tibet's legitimate government, the text stated:

In the past, for several thousand years, this snow land of Tibet was widely known as an independent country that was ruled by

* Jung Chang and Jon Halliday, *Mao: The Unknown Story* (New York: Alfred A. Knopf, 2005), 447, reports that, according to a source, Mao is said to have sent a telegram to the Chinese General Tan Guansan ordering the Chinese army to let the Dalai Lama escape and not to kill him. He was concerned that killing the Dalai Lama could inflame world opinion, especially in India and the Buddhist countries in Asia, which Mao was courting at the time.

a system that combines the religious and the secular. . . . Except for the differences between a big and a small country, we have identical attributes, greatness, and qualifications for being an independent country in the world.

The concluding part of the text makes the call that "as soon as people see this edict, which contains the good news about setting up a new state called Gaden Phodrang, you should publicize it to all the monks and lay people in your area and make sure they have heard it." Copies of the proclamation of Tibet's independent government with my signature were dispatched across Tibet, with one sent to the Panchen Lama.

At this point, reports of Chinese troops nearby precipitated the decision to cross the border into India. I had the difficult task of bidding farewell to the Tibetan soldiers and resistance fighters who had so faithfully escorted me from Lhasa and who were now about to turn back to face the Chinese army. I knew that some were returning to certain death. They were going back to rejoin the Volunteer Force for the Protection of the Faith. As part of the US government's overall strategy to prevent the spread of Communism in Asia, as later I came to know, the Tibetan resistance movement led by Gompo Tashi did actually receive some support from the CIA, including a handful of them getting communication and combat training.

From Lhuntse Dzong we decided to head toward the Indian border. After two days of hard riding, we reached Mangmang, which is the last Tibetan village before the border of India. There, to my delight, was one of the officials I had sent earlier to inquire if India would receive me and my entourage. He brought the good news that the government of India was willing to grant asylum to me and my people. That night at Mangmang, I felt quite safe for the first time in many days. There was only one track leading to this place and that route was well guarded by several hundred Tibetan resistance fighters. So unless the Chinese army bombed us from the air, I knew we were safe.

But the weather wasn't so kind—it rained heavily and my tent was leaking pretty much everywhere. I was forced to sit up the entire night, with the result that I caught a cold the next day. With me being ill, we had to postpone our remaining trek to the border for two days. Still too sick to ride a horse, when we did move finally, I was placed on a *dzo* (a cross between a yak and cow). In this way, I left the last stretch of my own homeland. On March 31, 1959, my party entered India. I have not been able to go back to my homeland since.

CHAPTER 5

✳

A Geopolitical Reflection

Here I was at age twenty-five, a refugee in a new country. As the Tibetan saying goes, as a refugee, the only thing that was familiar to us was the earth and the sky. At that time, it was impossible to grasp the full significance of what had happened to my homeland in a global historical context. Predictably, the first and foremost experience for me and my fellow Tibetans was the shock of displacement. The immediate task, in the wake of my escape, was the very opposite of deep reflection—the urgent work of looking after the growing and desperate community of tens of thousands of refugees who managed to follow me over the course of several months into exile. Only later, with the benefit of time and hindsight, did it become possible for me to come to some more general reflections on the meaning of what has happened to Tibet.

Tibet, my homeland I had been forced to flee, is a landlocked country with the huge Himalayan mountain range to the south, beyond which are India, Nepal, and Bhutan; the deserts of Central Asia to the north, past which lie East Turkistan* (Xinjiang) and Mongolia; and to the east the lowlands and rice fields inhabited by the Chinese. We Tibetans, the inhabitants of the vast Tibetan plateau, are seminomadic eaters of *tsampa* (roasted barley flour), occupying a vast high-altitude plateau rimmed to the south by the mighty Himalayas beneath a deep blue sky. Ancient texts describe the land in terms of "high peaks and pure earth" and trace the origin of "the meat-eating red-faced race of Tibetans" to the union of a monkey and a rock-dwelling ogress to which were born six children. From these sprang the Tibetan people, according to this story of origin. I first heard this story as a child after my arrival in Lhasa. A monk told it to me, explaining a mural inside the Potala Palace showing the monkey. Tibetan histories identify Tibet's first king as Nyatri Tsenpo, whose reign began in 127 BCE. In fact, one traditional Tibetan calendar system, bö gyalo (Tibetan royal year), takes this to be year 1—making 1950, when Communist China invaded Tibet, year 2077 on the Tibetan calendar. An early chronicle says that this king descended from heaven and "went of his own accord to become the lord of all under heaven . . . to the center of the earth, in the heart of the continent, in the enclosure of snow mountains, at the head of all rivers, where the mountains were high, the earth pure, the country fine, . . . a place where swift horses flourished."

Given the Tibetan plateau's exceptional geography, which we often refer to as "the roof of the world" (*zamling sayi yangthok*), the Tibetans developed a lifestyle and culture over millennia that was uniquely adapted to the high-altitude environment and ecology. We Tibetans recognize the seventh-century Emperor Songtsen Gampo to be our greatest king, crediting his reign with a series of landmark achieve-

---

* Although Xinjiang (literally "New Frontier") is the name most recognizable in current international literature for East Turkistan, it is, in fact, a colonial name invented by China. The Uyghur people themselves refer to the geographic region that is their home as East Turkistan.

ments that enriched Tibetan civilization. It was during his rule that the current Tibetan writing system was invented and that the first Buddhist texts were brought from India to be translated from Sanskrit. The emperor established a universal legal system, standardized forms of measurements across the Tibetan plateau, and brought about many innovations to agriculture and craftsmanship. It was also during his reign that two of Tibet's oldest temples—the Jokhang and Ramoche—were built to house two sacred statues of the Buddha brought from Nepal and China by the two princesses whom Emperor Songtsen married. Even as a child, I knew the tale of the ancient marriage between Songtsen Gampo and the Chinese Princess Wencheng, given as a bride by the Tang Emperor Taizong. Every summer, I would look forward to the Shotön Festival in Lhasa, during which Tibetan operas were performed in the garden outside the Norbulingka Palace. One of the famous operas tells the story of Songtsen's marriage to this Chinese princess and also to a Nepalese princess called Bhrikuti. Like many ancient neighbors with a long history, there have been ups and downs in the engagement between Tibet and China, periods of friendship, periods of cool tolerance, periods of bickering, and times of outright conflict. However, Communist China's forcible invasion of Tibet marked an unprecedented tragedy for the Tibetan people.

Looking back, I have come to understand the ways Tibet and its people were the victims of tragic circumstances of history. The major powers that had historic connections with Tibet were all preoccupied in very particular ways during the crucial period. Great Britain, which had, after all, invaded Tibet in 1903–1904, had just given up India and had no stomach for the politics of South and Inner Asia. India had become independent on August 15, 1947, in the midst of a most traumatic partition, and almost immediately in October of that year was caught up in war with the newly partitioned Pakistan, lasting till January 1, 1949. There was no appetite for further conflict with another neighbor right next to the arena of the former war. The United States had become interested in Tibet as part of its concern to stop the spread of Communism after the end of the Second World War. The last thing it wanted to see was a repeat in Asia of what had happened in Eastern Europe in the immediate aftermath of that war. During the civil war in China from 1946–1949, for example, the United States gave significant support to the losing Nationalist government of Chiang Kai-shek. In the 1950–1953 Korean War, the United States committed troops on the ground to help defend South Korea from the Communist invasion from the north, the latter backed by the Soviet Union and Communist China. What little support the United States extended to the Tibetan resistance was largely motivated by the broader policy to stem the tide of Communism in Asia.

What happened to Mongolia around the same period is a profoundly interesting historical point of contrast. When the Manchu Qing dynasty fell in 1911, the political status enjoyed by Mongolia was exactly parallel to that of Tibet. Just as Nationalist China was claiming Tibet to be part of its territory, so too did it claim Mongolia. It is no coincidence that Mongolia and Tibet made a bilateral treaty reiterating each other's independence in 1913. Because the Soviet Union backed Mongolia's independence from China—following a referendum in 1945—the world powers persuaded Chiang Kai-shek to accept the result of that vote. As a consequence, although reduced in size, Mongolia is now an independent country and a member of the United Nations.

We Tibetans were not so lucky. To some extent, we have ourselves to blame. While the rest of the world was waking up to the significance of global understanding about the place of nations, especially in the wake of the First World War, we Tibetans had buried our heads in the sand. Significant mistakes were made during this period. For example, too few systematic initiatives were taken during this crucial period to express Tibet's status as an independent country at the international level. The Thirteenth Dalai Lama's measures for reform, especially in education and defense, were largely thwarted by various sectional interests and elites. After his death in 1933, efforts could have been made to join international forums, such as the League of Nations and later the United Nations. The crucial point that Tibet's ruling elite, with the exception of the Thirteenth Dalai Lama, simply did not grasp was that in the new political reality of the twentieth century it was not adequate for a country to enjoy independence. It had to make a series of international gestures to prove its presence on the world stage as one among many sovereign states. It was particularly unfortunate that, while the storm was gathering around Tibet, the ruling elite, including my two successive regents, were largely preoccupied with political infighting, which came to a climax in 1947 with the death of my first regent, Reting Rinpoche. So, by the time the People's Liberation Army was at the door in 1950, Tibet was completely unprepared, and it was too late.

When I think about the political life of my immediate predecessor, the Thirteenth Dalai Lama, there is a striking parallel with my own karma. Twice he was forced to flee into exile due to foreign invasion—first when the British forces under the command of Colonel Francis Younghusband invaded Tibet in 1903, returning only in 1909, and then again in 1910 when the armies of the Manchu Qing dynasty attacked Tibet from the east. The British certainly hadn't come to stay, but it is very likely that conquest was the intention of the imperial Manchu forces. However, the Qing itself collapsed in 1911, and with the last emperor's abdication in 1912, the Qing *amban* (the imperial representative) in Lhasa surrendered. It was after his return in 1913, as already stated, that the Thirteenth Dalai Lama tried to assert Tibet's independence internationally, with acts such as the signing of a treaty with Mongolia in 1913, in which both states mutually affirmed each other's independence. This independence was the status of Tibet when Communist China invaded in 1950. If we Tibetans had read the signs correctly in those years, we might have seen that another invasion was likely. This strongly suggests that we missed our opportunities during the crucial period between the death of the Thirteenth Dalai Lama in

1933 and the birth of Communist China in 1949, especially amid the chaos of an unstable government and civil war in China.

In fact, shortly before he died, the Thirteenth Dalai Lama left an extraordinary and prophetic final testament. I read this text when I was young. Let me quote from it at length since it shows both his foresight and the extent of the failure on the part of the Tibetan government to heed his very clear warnings. He wrote:

I am now almost fifty-eight years old, and soon it will be impossible for me to serve you any longer. Everyone should realize this fact, and begin to look to what you will do in the future when I am gone. Between me and the next incarnation there will be a period in which you will have to fend for yourselves.

Our two most powerful neighbors are India and China, both of whom have very powerful armies. Therefore, we must try to establish stable relations with both of them. There are also a number of small countries near our borders which maintain a strong military. Because of this, it is important that we too maintain an efficient army of young and well-trained soldiers that is able to establish the security of the country. . . . If we do not make preparations to defend ourselves from the overflow of violence, we will have very little hope of survival.

In particular, we must guard ourselves against the barbaric red communists who carry terror and destruction with them wherever they go. They are the worst of the worst. Already they have consumed much of Mongolia. . . . They have robbed and destroyed the monasteries, forcing the monks to join their armies, or else killing them outright. They have destroyed religion wherever they have encountered it. . . .

It will not be long before we find the red onslaught at our own front door. It is only a matter of time before we come into a direct confrontation with it. . . .

And when that happens, we must be ready to defend ourselves. Otherwise, our spiritual and cultural traditions will be completely eradicated. . . . The monasteries will be looted and destroyed, the monks and nuns will be killed or chased away, the great works of the noble Dharma kings of old will be undone, and all of our cultural and spiritual institutions persecuted, destroyed, and forgotten. The birth rights and the property of the people will be stolen; we will become like slaves to our conquerors, and will be made to wander helplessly like beggars. Everyone will be forced to live in misery, and the days and nights will pass slowly, and with great suffering and terror.

Therefore, when the strength of peace and happiness is with us, while the power to do something about the situation is still in our hands, we should make every effort to safeguard ourselves against this impending disaster. Use peaceful methods where they are appropriate; but where they are not appropriate, do not hesitate to resort to more forceful means. Work diligently now, while there is still time. Then there will be no regret.

Tragically, the regency and the Tibetan leadership, following the Thirteenth Dalai Lama's death, failed to grasp the urgency and seriousness of his warning. Pretty much every aspect has proven to be precisely correct.

When we think of the tragedy of Tibet in the wider global context, we see an extraordinary irony. Immediately after the Second World War, the imperial nations of the world were giving up their colonies everywhere—one thinks of the end of the British and French mandates in the Middle East in the late 1940s and, of course, above all, of Indian independence in 1947. When all other imperial powers were divesting themselves of former colonies, Communist China was acquiring its own. The new Communist China chose to invade an independent country, Tibet, and make a colony out of it. In any case, the forcible inclusion of Tibet into Mao's new People's Republic of China has been disastrous not only for us Tibetans. It has also been problematic, to say the least, for China itself. For the imposition of a single Chinese nationhood over multiple nationalities, including Tibetans—each with its distinct language, culture, history, and people who have never viewed themselves as Chinese—created an inherently unstable modern state with a chronic threat of ethnic tension that perpetually requires brutal colonialist subjugation from Beijing.

There is a second irony, which might be characterized as ethical and moral. In December 1948, the United Nations adopted the Universal Declaration of Human Rights, a fundamental document that lays the foundation upon which civilized societies in the modern world must treat their citizens and those of other countries. This declaration acquired a legal basis in 1976 as the International Covenant on Civil and Political Rights, reaffirmed again in 2022. Communist China, in contrast, moved in the opposite direction. Almost immediately after the Universal Declaration of Human Rights was adopted, China began what has been more than seventy years of systematic abuse of the human rights of the Tibetan people.

Around the fiftieth anniversary of the UN declaration, a few countries led by Communist China contended that the standards of human rights laid down in the Universal Declaration are not truly universal and do not apply to Asia because of the differences in culture, society, and economy. They argued that the concept of universal human rights needed to be revisited to accommodate what they referred to as "Asian values." I stated that I do not share this view and argued that if any aspects of a culture or traditional customs were to conflict with respect for basic human rights, it is the traditional customs that need to be modified, not the other way around. I said that the majority of people in Asia would agree with me on this point.

To be candid, I find the idea that somehow people in Asia do not value basic human rights, such as individual freedom and dignity, or that they do not need them, to be disrespectful toward the peoples of Asia. Anyway, worried by this attempt to dilute the spirit of what is a seminal document in human history, I repeatedly argued that basic human rights are truly universal, for they pertain to the inherent nature of all human beings to yearn for freedom, equality, and dignity, and their right to achieve them. There is nothing West or East, North or South about this. I deeply believe that the principles laid down in the Universal Declaration of Human Rights constitute something like a natural law that ought to be followed by all peoples and governments.

The cost of the conquest of Tibet for the Tibetan nation and its people is obvious. But it is worth thinking more broadly about the geopolitical effects in the region. To begin with, for the first time in history, the world's two most populated nations had a long border that had to be increasingly militarized. Up until this invasion of Tibet, there was only an Indo-Tibetan border, and no such thing as an Indo-Chinese border. In his letter to Prime Minister Nehru of November 7, 1950, shortly before his death, India's Deputy Prime Minister Sardar Vallabhbhai Patel lamented the "expansion of China almost up to our gates. Throughout history, we have seldom worried about our northeast frontier. The Himalayas have been regarded as an impenetrable barrier against any threat from the north. We had friendly Tibet which gave us no trouble."

Just as Patel worried, there was a Sino-Indian war in 1962, followed by another conflict in 1967. Patel was more of a realist and pragmatist; by contrast, Nehru was more of an idealist and a visionary. The latter was worried about the world becoming too polarized between the North Atlantic Treaty Organization (NATO) and the Warsaw Pact and, economically, between the north and the south. His dream of a nonaligned collaboration led to the signing of the Panchsheel Agreement (literally, "Five Principles Agreement") between India and China in 1954—which set out a plan for mutual respect for each other's territorial integrity, mutual nonaggression, noninterference in each other's internal affairs, equality and mutual benefit, and peaceful coexistence. In brief, the invasion and forcible occupation of Tibet has created long-term instability on the Tibetan plateau affecting a host of nations that traditionally relied on peace at their northern border—India, Nepal,

Bhutan, and Myanmar. It is with this concern for peace and security in Asia in mind that I later made the suggestion, in my Five Point Peace Plan of September 1987, that the Tibetan plateau be turned into a demilitarized buffer zone between Asia's two largest military powers.

Ecologically speaking, the Tibetan plateau houses the source of many of Asia's greatest rivers—including Yarlung Tsangpo (Brahmaputra) and Senge Khabab (Indus), which flow southward, and Dzachu (Mekong), Machu (Yellow River), and Drichu (Yangtze), which run east. The Communist Chinese occupation of Tibet has had a devasting effect on the health of these rivers, with significant environmental consequences to many countries in Asia. In the future too, unless responsible custodianship of the sources of these major rivers is ensured, there may be significant conflicts in connection with access to water, indispensable for the survival of hundreds of millions of people in India, Pakistan, Bangladesh, Myanmar, Laos, Thailand, Vietnam, and Cambodia. Some environmental specialists refer to the Tibetan plateau as "the Third Pole," to add to the North and South Poles, for reasons including it being the largest repository of fresh water. In addition, the ecosystem of the plateau plays a crucial role in the regulation of the monsoon across South Asia.

China's mass deforestation in the Tibetan plateau, aggressively carried out especially in the 1980s, is reported to have destroyed more than 50 percent of forests in Kham (eastern Tibet), for example. Environmentalists are deeply concerned about the long-term negative impact of such extensive deforestation in the plateau, especially in relation to temperature increase and flooding during the monsoon in the lower regions. With respect to climate change, many years ago, an environmental scientist told me that, given Tibet's high altitude and dry climate, any ecological damage done on the plateau will take much longer to recover. The same scientist also told me about how Tibet's vast northern plains, Jangthang, plays a crucial role in cooling the temperature through reflecting the sun's light instead of absorbing it.

One of the greatest sources of concern is the construction of megadams such as the one at Yamdrok Lake and the Zangmu Dam in the Lhoka region close to the border of Bhutan. Today, we know from environmental science that there is a connection between earthquakes and the construction of dams in the high-altitude Tibetan plateau, given that the region is one of the most seismically active areas in the world. The Tibetan plateau is also known for its vast mineral deposits. According to China's own Geological Survey bureau, the plateau is understood to have reserves of thirty to forty million tons of copper, more than forty million tons of zinc, and billions of tons of iron, including especially large deposits of rare minerals, such as lithium and uranium. In fact, the Chinese word for Tibet, Xizang, literally means "western treasure house." If mining is done at all in the Tibetan plateau, it has to be conducted in accord with the highest sensitivity to environmental impact. In the end, a careless, instrumental, or mercantile approach to extraction will lead to long-term consequences, which will be experienced way beyond the boundaries of the Tibetan plateau.

Lastly, there has been a large-scale forced migration of nomads from their traditional grasslands in different parts of the Tibetan plateau. Historically, Tibet's nomadic communities have lived in the vast open plains, including the grasslands, and have developed a symbiotic relationship with their environment such that their presence on the vast open space has served as the best form of caretaking for the ecology. Displacements of these traditional nomadic communities have not only been devastating for the nomads, but also they have created a new cycle of imbalance in the environment.

I had hoped, given that ecological health is a concern common to Tibetans as well as the Chinese, that the protection of Tibet's fragile environment would be one area where one could see systematic and sustained joint efforts. If the Chinese authorities were to allow environmental scientists, including especially Chinese scientists, to work hand in hand with local Tibetans who know their environment best, there is the possibility of creating an effective approach to reducing unnecessary ecological damage on the plateau. I was told that a noted

Chinese environmental scientist who had spent many years in Tibet has commented that where religious tradition is strongest, the environment is well protected, and this is something that should give us pause for thought.

Historically, with our cultural and religious practices that emphasize living in harmony with nature, Tibet's natural environment—including flora and fauna—had never suffered excessive abuse at the hands of the human inhabitants of the vast plateau. Very worryingly, there are many reports that Communist China has installed nuclear missiles in the high altitude of the Tibetan plateau. Setting aside the implications for regional and international stability, the risk of leaks or mistakes carries a devastating threat to the fragile ecology. Were the waters of the rivers to be polluted, the destructive impact on the lives of many millions dependent on these rivers cannot be calculated.

When you take all these issues together—the militarization of the Tibetan plateau, which includes the stationing of nuclear weapons; an increasing security face-off between two of Asia's largest armies across more than three thousand kilometers of border, of which some crucial parts remain disputed; and ecological destruction of the plateau through deforestation and extensive mining, as well as unpredictable management of the sources of some of Asia's greatest rivers, on whom the livelihoods of hundreds of millions depend—the invasion of Tibet has been truly tragic, not just for the Tibetans but for the whole of humanity too. It is a tragedy of historic proportions whose destructive fallout will continue to reverberate through the centuries.

Had Tibet been able to remain free, these geopolitical and ecological problems would not exist. This is the plain truth.

CHAPTER 6

Devastation at Home and Rebuilding in Exile

On March 31, 1959, around 3 p.m. Indian Standard Time, my party arrived in the Indian border village of Kenzamane, near Tawang. The moment I crossed into India I felt a tremendous sense of relief. It didn't matter that we might have been a pitiful sight to the handful of Indian soldiers guarding the border—approximately eighty of us physically exhausted by the ordeal of hard travel. Even my mother said we no longer had to be afraid of the Chinese and could say what we thought. Obviously, my mother too had been carrying a heavy burden of having to weigh every word she uttered and every action she engaged in.

We were met with an extraordinarily warm welcome from the local people and a cordial telegram from Prime Minister Nehru:

My colleagues and I welcome you and send you greetings on your safe arrival in India. We shall be happy to afford the necessary facilities for you, your family, and entourage to reside in India.

The people of India, who hold you in great veneration, will no doubt accord their traditional respect to your personage. Kind regards to you. Nehru

We were formally received on behalf of the government of India by a familiar face, P. N. Menon, an Indian foreign ministry official who had previously been stationed at the Indian Mission in Lhasa. Waiting there was also another familiar face, Kazi Sonam Topgyal, who had helped translate for me during my 1956–1957 visit to India. From the Indian border we traveled to the town of Tawang, in what was then known as the North East Frontier Agency (NEFA), today as Arunachal Pradesh. On April 18, I was taken by jeep to the town of Tezpur, where the international media were waiting. At the railway station I felt overwhelmed to find thousands of telegrams of good wishes waiting for me, and approximately a hundred journalists and photographers from across the world who had come to cover what they called "the story of the year." I took the opportunity to issue a statement to the world, giving a full account of the circumstances that led to my escape—the spontaneous people's uprising in Lhasa and our long, peaceful approach to seeking accommodation with the Chinese Communists—and announcing that I was in India to oppose Chinese Communist occupation of my country and to appeal to the free countries of the world. I concluded by saying that I hoped fervently that the crisis in Tibet would be over soon without any more bloodshed. Two days later, Beijing issued a statement asserting that the "so-called statement of the Dalai Lama . . . is a crude document, lame in reasoning, full of lies and loopholes." It then went on to claim that I had been abducted by rebels from Lhasa!

Understandably, there were heated debates in the Indian Parliament, the Lok Sabha, on what had just happened to Tibet, India's historic neighbor to the north. What the veteran politician and freedom fighter Jaya Prakash Narayan said captured the sense of frustration and moral dilemma felt by many Indian leaders at the time:

No one expects India to go to war with China for the sake of Tibet. But every upright person, every freedom loving individual should be ready to call a spade a spade. We are not serving the cause of peace by slurring over acts of aggression. We cannot physically prevent the Chinese from annexing Tibet and sub-duing that peaceful and brave people, but we at least can put on record our clear verdict that aggression has been committed and the freedom of a weak nation has been snuffed out by a powerful neighbour. Let us too not waver to tear the veil from the face of communism, which under the visage of the gentle Panchsheel hides the savage countenance of imperialism. For in Tibet we see at this moment the workings of a new imperialism, which is far more dangerous than the old because it marches under the banner of a so-called revolutionary ideology.

From Tezpur we traveled to Mussoorie, a beautiful British-era hill station in the foothills of the Himalayas north of Delhi. At every major train stop thousands of Indians came to welcome me, shouting, *"Dalai Lama ki Jai"* (Hail to the Dalai Lama) and *"Dalai Lama Zindabad"* (Long live the Dalai Lama). In Mussoorie, the government of India had established my first residence in exile. Here, on April 24, Nehru came to meet me and welcome me in person to India. We spoke for over four hours. Since Nehru was one of the powerful voices that had urged me to return to Lhasa in 1957, I reported how, despite all my best attempts to deal fairly and honestly with the Chinese according to the terms of the Seventeen-Point Agreement, they had been impossible to work with. On June 20, 1959, I gave my first formal press conference. I declared that Tibet had been independent, enjoying and exercising all rights of sovereignty, whether internal or external, and that by invading Tibet, Communist China's army had committed a flagrant act of ag-gression. This is something any objective person would agree with. In any case, I said at this press conference that since the Chinese side had violated key terms of the agreement, effectively it had become invalid.

49

If a treaty is violated by one of the parties to it, then it can legally be repudiated by the other party, at which point it is no longer in force. I also stated that, as far as Tibetans everywhere are concerned, where my cabinet and my person are present, there will exist the legitimate government of Tibet.

In the wake of my escape, many thousands of Tibetans managed to follow me into exile. At home in Tibet, the oppression had become intolerable. Listening to the accounts of the new arrivals, in the face of the destruction of my people and all that they live for, I devoted myself in exile to the only courses of action left to me—to remind the world of what happened and what was still happening in Tibet and to care for the Tibetans who escaped with me to freedom. All that we had heard from the accounts of refugees—and more—was confirmed by the report of the International Commission of Jurists' Legal Inquiry Committee on Tibet at Geneva in July 1959, entitled *The Question of Tibet and the Rule of Law*. What gives weight to this report is that it was commissioned and conducted by an independent judicial body beholden to no government or interested party. It was, in effect, totally impartial. The report concluded that "the evidence points at least to a prima facie case of Genocide against the People's Republic of China" and "Genocide is the gravest crime known to the law of nations." The Genocide Convention of 1948 condemns "acts committed with intent to destroy, in whole or in part, a national, ethnical, racial or religious group as such." In the second report from the International Commission of Jurists, *Tibet and the Chinese People's Republic*, published in 1960, "The Committee found that acts of genocide had been committed in Tibet in an attempt to destroy the Tibetans as a religious group, and that such acts are acts of genocide independent of any conventional obligation."

On September 4, 1959, I made an important trip to Delhi. There, in addition to crucial meetings with Prime Minister Nehru as well as other important leaders, including especially the president and the vice president of India, I also met with ambassadors from various countries.

Personally, the most moving part of this visit was the engagement I had with a gathering of several thousand Indians organized by Bharat Tibet Sangh (India Tibet Fraternity) and chaired by Acharya Kripalani, a noted Gandhian and social activist. (Acharya remained a staunch supporter of the Tibetan cause and a dear personal friend until his death in 1982.)

Now that I was in a free country, I also set about consulting with international experts about taking the case of Tibet to the General Assembly of the United Nations. So while in Delhi that September 1959, I wrote to the secretary-general of the United Nations, Dag Hammarskjöld: "In view of the inhumane treatment and crimes against humanity and religion to which the people of Tibet are being subjected, I solicit immediate intervention of the United Nations." On October 21, 1959, the General Assembly adopted a resolution sponsored by Ireland and Malaysia that called "for respect for the fundamental human rights of the Tibetan people and for their distinctive cultural and religious life," and acknowledged that "the fundamental human rights and freedoms to which the Tibetan people, like all others, are entitled include the right to civil and religious liberty for all without distinction." I continued in my appeals to the UN secretary-general and to many governments, updating them on the worsening situation inside Tibet. Notably, in 1960, the United States government announced its support for Tibet's self-determination. In fact, I received two letters from Secretary of State Christian A. Herter—one in February 1960 and the second in October of that same year—assuring me that the United States' position remained "that the principle of self-determination should apply to the people of Tibet and that they should have the determining voice in their own political destiny." In 1961, at the sixteenth session of the UN General Assembly, a further resolution was adopted, sponsored by Malaya, Ireland, El Salvador, and Thailand. This resolution solemnly renewed the UN's "call for the cessation of practices which deprive the Tibetan people of their fundamental human rights and freedoms, including their right to self-determination." One more resolution on

Tibet was passed at the UN, on December 18, 1965, at its plenary session, reaffirming the earlier resolutions and the UN General Assembly's grave concerns "at the continued violation of the fundamental rights and freedoms of the people."

In January 1960, I took the opportunity to visit Bodh Gaya and Sarnath, to pay homage, respectively, to Mahabodhi Stupa with the sacred Bodhi tree and the site of the Buddha's First Turning of the Wheel of Dharma—this time with my mind in a more settled state. (The last time I visited the sacred Buddhist site of Bodh Gaya in 1956, my mind had been racing with the question of whether to return to Tibet or seek asylum in India.) In Sarnath, near Varanasi, I officiated for the first time at a ceremony for the full ordination of monks. Tradition demands that the monk officiating at a full ordination ceremony be someone who has himself received full ordination vows for ten years, or at least five years earlier in the case of someone with exceptional qualifications. My two tutors insisted that I met the required qualifications and should conduct my first ordination ceremony for others at the site of the Buddha's first public discourse. I was then twenty-six years old. As someone to whom the identity of monkhood is close to his heart, this was both a profound honor and joy. I reflected on how fortunate I was to be able to perform such an ordination ceremony at the very place where the Buddha gave his first public sermon following his enlightenment, known as the First Turning of the Wheel of Dharma. Among those who took ordination in Sarnath was Dagyab Rinpoche, a high-ranking reincarnate lama in the Geluk tradition.

In Bodh Gaya too, I conducted an ordination ceremony, and among those who took full ordination there was Samdhong Rinpoche, who would later become the first directly elected political leader of our exiled Tibetan community. There in Bodh Gaya, in January 1960, we also had what was effectively the first formal gathering of the Tibetan people in the free world. Key constituencies—including representatives from the three Tibetan provinces of Ü-Tsang, Kham, and Amdo; senior members of Tibet's major Buddhist traditions; abbots of the great monasteries; and delegations from various parts of India—came together to host a long-life ceremony for my good health. At this ceremony, representing the Tibetan people in exile, they all took what was called the "Great Oath of Unity" (*Na-gan Thunmoche*). Those present pledged that from now on, they would strive for the unity of Tibetans from all three provinces and shoulder the responsibility to work for the common welfare of Tibet, under the Dalai Lama's leadership. It was in Bodh Gaya, also, where we decided that we would strive to establish a representative form of government for future Tibet and, of course, for our exile community.

Returning to Mussoorie, we commemorated the first anniversary of the Tibetan People's National Uprising of March 10, 1959. In this way, we began the tradition of a major address to the Tibetan people on March 10 every year, marking this tragic anniversary. On that first anniversary, I stressed the need on our part to adopt a long-term view of the situation of Tibet. I said that for those of us in exile in a free country, our priority must be ensuring the survival of our civilization, especially through the protection of our distinct language and cultural traditions. I assured my people that truth, justice, and courage would be our weapons and that we would eventually prevail in our struggle for freedom. While in Mussoorie, we began our plans to educate our younger generation. To this end, we set up the first Tibetan school in India with an initial number of fifty mature students. Within a year, we were able to send some from this first batch to various parts of India, as well as remote areas in Nepalese border regions like Khumbu Valley, to teach Tibetan refugee children, including the teaching of English language as well.

On April 30, 1960, I arrived in Dharamsala, which was to become my permanent residence in exile. There, we reconstituted what was, in effect, a Tibetan government in exile, called at the time the Central Tibetan Secretariat, later renamed the Central Tibetan Administration (CTA). With the help of my colleagues, I initiated a two-pronged strategy. There was first and foremost, after caring for the immediate necessities of more than eighty thousand Tibetan refugees, the need to establish resettlements for the Tibetans in a way that would enable us to preserve our culture and identity while in exile. The second was to reach out to the governments around the world, the United Nations, and the international community to help resolve the Tibetan issue. An important part of this strategy was to draw international attention to the plight of the Tibetan people and China's unjust occupation of our country. At that time, my hope and efforts in this regard were directed toward the ultimate goal of restoring Tibet's independence.

In my March 10 address of 1961 at my new residence in Dharamsala, I undertook to prepare a draft of the constitutional and economic structure to which I aspired for our country and said that I would place it shortly before the representatives of the Tibetan people in India and neighboring countries for their consideration. Ever since my first visit to India in 1956, especially witnessing democracy in action by contrast with what I saw in Beijing, I have been a deep believer that democracy really is the most appropriate form of government. So, once I was resident in a free country, I strove to initiate a process of democratizing the Tibetan political system. It took me and my officials two years, following consultations with various experts, studying a number of constitutions around the free world, as well as many internal debates, to finalize a draft, which we proclaimed on March 10, 1963. This constitution envisions a future Tibet as "a unitary democratic State founded upon the principles laid down by the Lord Buddha." Key provisions included an independent judiciary, an elected national assembly, prohibition of "discrimination on any ground such as sex, race, language, religion, social origin, property, birth or other status," as well as "the right to freedom of thought, conscience and religion." The document also includes, as Article 36, section (e), a clause for the possible abolition of the Dalai Lama's authority by two-thirds of the majority of the National Assembly. Over the course of years, this document has been revised into a fully democratic model governing the norms of the Tibetan people, at least in the exile community.

In November 1963, at my residence in Dharamsala, most memorably, we held the first summit representing all Tibetan Buddhist schools attended by, in addition to the heads of the lineages, senior lamas, reincarnate *tulku*s, *geshe*s (equivalent to holders of a doctorate in divinity), and scholars, as well as senior members of the Tibetan administration. This four-day meeting offered an excellent opportunity to create the basis for a strong sense of unity across the diverse traditions of Tibetan Buddhism as well as to encourage a united effort to preserve Tibet's rich religious traditions.

One of the important topics that Prime Minister Nehru and I discussed in the early days of my exile was the education of the refugee children. Nehru emphasized that in order to preserve Tibetan culture and identity it would be necessary to have separate schools for the Tibetans. He thus undertook to establish an autonomous body within the Indian Ministry of Education, with the government of India bearing the costs. Furthermore, Nehru advised that while it was very important for our children to have a thorough knowledge of their history and culture, it was vital that they be conversant with the modern world, and hence that we use English as our medium of education. From this emerged a network of Central Schools for Tibetans (CST), producing generations of modern-educated young Tibetans.

During the sixties, we reestablished in exile many of the historically important cultural and religious institutions of Tibet, including especially the monasteries and monastic universities belonging to the major schools of Tibetan Buddhism. New establishments founded in Dharamsala included the Thekchen Choeling Temple, the Tibetan Children's Village (TCV), the Tibetan Medical and Astro. Institute, the Tibetan Institute of Performing Arts (TIPA), and the Library of Tibetan Works and Archives. During this crucial decade, many of the refugees found work in the great effort of building roads at high altitude. I personally visited some of these road construction sites to encourage and give comfort to those many Tibetans who were engaged in such hard labor. A most unusual but memorable experience at one road construction camp took place when I visited Chamba, in northern India. There was a substantial number of monks among the road workers, and since my visit coincided with the day of a required bimonthly confession ceremony, I led the monks through the confession ceremony. Since the monks only had trousers and shirts, they had no choice but to participate in the ceremony in lay clothes. Recognizing that employment such as road construction would only be temporary, efforts were made to seek more long-term forms of livelihood for the refugees. Thanks to the generosity of several Indian states, we were able to establish more than twenty Tibetan settlements during the 1960s and early 1970s, especially in southern India. In this way, we ensured that, even in exile, we could live as a distinct community so that we could preserve our language and culture. We were also the beneficiaries of the generous support of many international aid agencies and nongovernmental organizations (NGOs). Two countries—Switzerland in the early 1960s and Canada in the 1970s—offered asylum to several hundred Tibetan refugees. We were also able to send many Tibetan children and young adults for education to the United Kingdom, France, Germany, Switzerland, Sweden, Denmark, Norway, and Iran, as well as Japan, many of whom were later able to serve in various capacities in our offices in exile. Throughout this period, there was no contact with the People's Republic of China, principally because Tibet was, just as China proper, engulfed in the chaotic period of the Cultural Revolution.

On May 27, 1964, sadly, Prime Minister Nehru passed away. He had been the constant face in all my international political dealings since I'd met him in Beijing in 1954, during my first trip to India, and then in my exile. And, of course, he had been so supportive and generous to our initiatives for the Tibetan refugees. His successor, Prime Minister Lal Bahadur Shastri, continued Nehru's policy of supporting the exile community, thus establishing an enduring position on the part of the Indian government in its support of the Tibetans in India. Shastri adopted a more robust position in relation to China, which was reflected in India's support of the UN resolution on Tibet of 1965.

Sadly, Prime Minister Shastri died in 1966, while visiting Tashkent in Uzbekistan. He was succeeded as the prime minister by Nehru's daughter, Indira Gandhi, whom I had known because of my long friendship with her father. Indira was familiar with the Tibetan situation and the Tibetan refugees in India; in fact, she once sat on the board of trustees of the Tibetan Homes Foundation in Mussoorie.

Meanwhile, inside Tibet, things were disastrous and grim. The response to my flight had been brutal, and the repression terrible, as if people were being punished for my escape. The most powerful account of what happened in this period is given in the seventy-thousand-character petition written in Chinese by the Panchen Lama in 1962, which Mao Zedong described as "a poisoned arrow shot at the heart of the Party." The petition, submitted to the Chinese Premier Zhou Enlai but seen by the outside world only years later, was entitled "A Report on the Sufferings of the Masses in Tibet and Other Tibetan Regions and Suggestions for Future Work to the Central Authorities Through the Respected Premier Zhou." Unlike me, the Panchen Lama had stayed behind in occupied Tibet, at his monastic base Tashi Lhunpo in Shigatse. Following a tour of parts of Tibet, he wrote:

> Because of many errors of mistakes . . . serious harm was done to agriculture and animal herding production. . . . Because the anguish of such severe hunger had never before been experienced in Tibetan history, and was such that people could not imagine it even in their dreams, the masses could not resist this kind of cruel torment, and their condition declined daily. Therefore, in some places, colds and other such minor infectious diseases caused a percentage of people to die easily. In some places many people directly starved to death because the food ran out; in some places, there was a phenomenon of whole families dying out. . . .
>
> No matter whether they were men or women, old or young, as soon as they saw me, people thought of the bitterness of that

57

period and were unable to prevent tears flowing from their eyes. A few brave people among them said through their tears, "Do not let all living creatures starve! Do not destroy Buddhism! Do not extinguish the people of our snowy land! These are our wishes and our prayers!" These are the hopes, concise but comprehensive and profound, more urgent than wanting water when you are thirsty, of the broad masses of the monastic and secular people, produced by bitterness resulting from what has happened and from the existing situation in Tibetan areas.

One of the key concerns raised by the Panchen Lama in his petition relates to the issue of protecting Tibetan nationality and cultural identity within the People's Republic of China. Clearly, this concern came from the fear of Han chauvinism.* He writes:

Once a nationality's language, costumes, customs, and other important characteristics have disappeared, then the nationality itself has disappeared too.

In relation to the destruction of religion, the Panchen Lama declares:

Before democratic reform, there were more than 2500 large, medium, and small monasteries in Tibet. After democratic reform, only 70 or so monasteries were kept in existence by the government. This was a reduction of more than 97%. . . . In the whole of Tibet in the past, there was a total of about 110,000 monks and nuns. . . . After democratic reform was concluded,

---

* By "Han chauvinism," the Panchen Lama is referring here to the ideology that the Han race is superior compared to the other ethnic members within the People's Republic of China and that other cultures need to be assimilated into the Han culture, an ideology that Mao explicitly attacked.

the number of monks and nuns living in the monasteries was about 7,000 people, which is a reduction of 93%.

The Panchen Lama's courage in writing in the above manner in the midst of the cruelest totalitarian oppression deserves the deepest admiration. It was written on the basis of his visiting many Tibetan areas, including Amdo, as well as East Turkistan (Xinjiang). In personal terms, he paid a terrible price. The petition confirmed my worst nightmare of what might have happened in the wake of the Tibetan People's Uprising of March 1959 and my own escape. In 1964, the Panchen Lama was declared an enemy of the Tibetan people and publicly humiliated through the ritual of what came to be called "struggle sessions,"* which would later become a hallmark of the Cultural Revolution. He was arrested and remained in prison until 1977, and then kept under house arrest until 1979.

After his release, the Panchen Lama spoke out forcefully on behalf of the Tibetan people and criticized Chinese policies in Tibet. Particularly, in March 1987, he spoke candidly at the Tibet Autonomous Region's Standing Committee meeting in Beijing, during the National People's Congress, criticizing Communist Chinese policies inside Tibet, including especially the language policies, as well as Han chauvinism. My heart goes out to the memory of this heroic figure who did so much to protect the Tibetan people in their darkest hour, especially after his release in 1979 and until his sudden death under suspicious circumstances in January 1989.

Five days before his death, I understood that he made the following statement:

---

* "Struggle session" (*thamzing* in Tibetan) was a public humiliation ritual where the target is made to wear a dunce hat and, with their head bowed, subjected to insults, shouts, and spitting from the "ordinary" public.

Since liberation, there has certainly been development, but the price paid for this development has been greater than the gains.

I was fortunate to have phone conversations with him during his trips outside the People's Republic of China. This gave me a chance to express my thanks and admiration personally. The Panchen Lama was three years younger than me and had been my companion on the trips to China in 1954–1955 and to India in 1956–1957. Not a man of patience for diplomatic niceties—for the Panchen Lama what mattered was honesty and integrity. Over the years, the Chinese Communists tried to create and exploit conflict between us on the old colonial principle of divide and conquer. Yet even though we were unable to have contact for a long time, I advocated awareness of the fate of Tibet to the outside world, while, with immense courage, he presented the truth to the leaders of the oppressors themselves.

The Panchen Lama's petition describes the situation before the Cultural Revolution, which Mao unleashed in May 1966 and which lasted until his death in 1976. Recognizing that China as a whole suffered immensely during this decade of turbulence, it was a terrible time, especially for Tibet. It began in Lhasa with Red Guards invading the Jokhang Temple—destroying ancient frescoes and images and burning scriptures in the courtyard in the name of abolishing "the four olds," which were old ideology, old culture, old habits, and old customs. As I noted in my March 10 Statement of 1967, among the countless images destroyed was one of Avalokiteshvara made in the seventh century and considered one of the most sacred icons of Tibet. The destruction spread to the Norbulingka and across the city, and ultimately there would be street battles in Lhasa and other cities between rival factions.

In this chaotic period, not only did many thousands die, but numerous historic monuments were destroyed, such as Ganden Monastery, founded by Tibet's great philosopher-saint Tsongkhapa in 1409. In essence, everything Tibetan was attacked: the practice of the Buddhist faith was outlawed; incense burning, ceremonies, and festivals were banned; traditional songs and dances were prohibited. Struggle sessions and public humiliations were meted out to monks and "class enemies." In brief, Tibet experienced a large-scale and systematic attempt to erase its cultural identity and collective memory.

If any of my colleagues who fled with me into exile in 1959 ever had any doubts about the correctness of our course of action, then the Cultural Revolution utterly dispelled them. Had I stayed in Tibet, I wouldn't have been able to do anything meaningful in the face of this insane and systematic onslaught.

In January 1976, the Chinese Premier Zhou Enlai died, followed by Marshal Zhu De in July and Chairman Mao himself on September 9. Mao's legacy includes the deaths of more than forty million people, especially during the famine of his Great Leap Forward in 1958–1962. On the geopolitical side, instead of decolonizing as the great empires were doing at the time, Mao's China chose a policy of colonialist imperialism in relation to Tibet, Mongolia, and East Turkistan, couched ironically in strident anticolonial rhetoric. What this has created for Mao's successors is a legacy of perpetual instability, paranoia, and repression, especially against the non-Chinese nationalities. As a result, today, even after more than seven decades of occupation, any expression of Tibetan identity is seen as a threat questioning Chinese legitimacy in Tibet.

The death of Mao was the beginning of an intense power struggle in which Mao's wife Jiang Qing, who had been one of the instigators of the Cultural Revolution and the Gang of Four, lost power to the faction headed by Hua Guofeng. While this was happening, I was watching events from India with interest and some hope.

Among the noticeable changes was the visit of the former American Defense Secretary James Schlesinger for a three-day tour of Tibet soon after Mao's death. Schlesinger's visit was the beginning of a chance to obtain a clearer picture of the conditions inside Tibet. I was told that he described the Communist Chinese presence there as oppressive, even by colonial standards, since it aimed at total domination.

Until then, the People's Republic of China had only allowed foreign visits to Tibet from among their close allies. Shortly after, Beijing began to allow sympathetic Western journalists and writers into Tibet. For nearly two decades since my flight into exile in 1959, the entire Tibetan plateau had been run like one giant prison. No one was allowed to communicate with the outside world, which meant that, except for a few messages received through secret channels, the Tibetans living in exile were totally cut off from their compatriots and families back in our homeland. Back home, Tibetans had been told that those in exile were living in abject poverty, since it was only the socialist countries that had successfully achieved economic prosperity.

When the dust settled from the power struggle in the Chinese Communist Party in the aftermath of Chairman Mao's death, it was my old acquaintance Deng Xiaoping who emerged as the paramount leader of China in 1978.

CHAPTER 7

Overtures Toward a Dialogue

I had met Deng Xiaoping, now the paramount leader of China, several times during my visit to Beijing in 1954–1955 and knew that he was one of the senior Chinese figures who had been most involved in matters related to Tibet. In an overture to this new regime in China, in my official March 10 Statement of 1978, I said:

> If the six million Tibetans in Tibet are really happy and prosperous as never before there is no reason for us to argue otherwise. If the Tibetans are really happy the Chinese should allow every interested foreigner to visit Tibet without restricting their movements or meetings with the Tibetan people. This would enable the visitors to really know the true conditions in Tibet. Furthermore, the Chinese should allow the Tibetans in Tibet to visit their parents and relatives now in exile. These Tibetans can then study the conditions of those of us in exile living in free countries. Similar opportunity should be given to the Tibetans in exile.

Quite unexpectedly, at the end of 1978, my brother Gyalo Thondup, who was then living in Hong Kong, received an invitation to meet with Deng Xiaoping in Beijing. This was clearly an overture and Gyalo Thondup consulted me about what to do. In November of that year, thirty-four members of my former government in Tibet were released from prison with great public ceremony: clearly a hopeful message was being sent. On February 1, 1979, the Panchen Lama made his first public appearance after fourteen years and called for my return to Tibet. At the same time, the United States established formal diplomatic relations with the People's Republic of China, signaling the possibility for a fundamental shift taking place in China vis-à-vis the international community.

I told my brother that he should accept the invitation but at this stage to do so in a personal capacity, rather than as my formal representative. On March 12, 1979, he met Deng Xiaoping in the Great Hall of the People. Deng opened the meeting by asking how my health was, and he asked how long it had been since my brother was last in Beijing. He answered that it was in 1949, thirty years ago. As their conversation progressed, Deng told my brother that complete independence of Tibet was nonnegotiable. "But except for independence, everything is negotiable. Everything can be discussed," he said. Deng was extraordinarily open and indeed positive about a series of questions Gyalo Thondup raised, even though my brother had made it clear that he was speaking in a personal capacity. Deng agreed to open up the border between Tibet and India so family members who had been cut off for two decades could see each other. He accepted that we send from our exile community Tibetan language teachers into Tibetan areas, and even agreed to the opening of a liaison office in Beijing to begin the process of a conversation. Deng assured him that China's new leadership was committed to fundamental and lasting change, and if the Dalai Lama had doubts, then we should send people to investigate the situation inside Tibet. He said that it is better to see things with one's own eyes than hear something a hundred times from other people.

By the early 1970s, after careful and deep contemplation, I had come to some important realizations on the nature of our struggle and what might be the best means to move forward. One thing I realized was that if our side insisted on our goal of restoring Tibet's independence, this would mean the Tibetans might even have to consider the possibility of a prolonged armed struggle against Communist China, which would be not just impractical but, in fact, suicidal. I vividly remember what Prime Minister Nehru said about the unrealistic nature of our quest for restoring Tibet's independence—that the United States is not going to go to war with China for the sake of Tibet.

Of course, as someone categorically opposed to violence, I could no longer lead the freedom movement if the Tibetan struggle were to choose violence as its path. Furthermore, I came to recognize that what mattered most to us Tibetans was the protection of a people with a unique language, culture, and religion, who are historically connected with the unique geography that is the Tibetan plateau. Finally, there was the crucial understanding that to resolve the Tibetan issue we would have to eventually sit down and talk with the Chinese. And for that, despite the historical truth of our independence and the Tibetan people's deep attachment to this ideal as well as their right, we recognized that to call for Tibet's independence would be a nonstarter for the Chinese side. Now, if our problem was to be solved through a peaceful process of negotiation, this required us to take into account seriously the perspective of the Chinese side. I understood that what mattered most to the People's Republic of China was stability and territorial integrity, while on our part, what mattered most for us Tibetans was the ability to survive and thrive as a distinct people with our own unique language and cultural heritage. The seed was sown for what later came to be known as the Middle Way Approach—seeking not independence but genuine autonomy within the framework of the People's Republic of China.

So, even before we received the overture from Deng, by 1974 I had shared my thoughts with a small circle of key leaders within our

Tibetan community in exile. We discussed in a candid manner the pros and cons of continuing to seek the restoration of Tibet's independence versus the new perspective I had come to formulate. We also discussed and debated how and when we might bring this new approach to the broader Tibetan exile community as well as to our international supporters. After a series of serious discussions, the key members of our exile administration, including the cabinet, were all on the same page as me. So when Gyalo Thondup brought the message from Deng that except for independence everything could be discussed, I was convinced that there was indeed a scope for a meaningful conversation within a framework acceptable to both sides.

Deng was as good as his word, at least with respect to sending delegations to Tibet. Between August 1979 and June 1985, we were able to send four fact-finding missions to Tibet. Remarkably, the Chinese government agreed that they could visit all Tibetan areas, not just what the Chinese call the "Tibet Autonomous Region."* I don't know what impression the Chinese leadership expected from our delegation, or how they supposed the Tibetans inside Tibet would react to their presence. In fact, fearing that our delegates might be attacked physically by "right-thinking" local people, the Chinese authorities actually briefed the locals to show courtesy to the visiting delegates.

When the five members of our first delegation, led by Juchen Thupten Namgyal (then a senior minister in my cabinet in Dharam-

---

* "Tibet Autonomous Region" (TAR) is a modern construct created by the People's Republic of China, following its invasion of Tibetan in 1950 and formally established in 1965. The region, containing the historical Tibetan province of Ü-Tsang and western Kham, roughly corresponds to the territory under the rule of the Dalai Lama government of Lhasa at the time of the Communist Chinese invasion of Tibet in 1950. Historically, Tibet consists of Chol-kha-gsum, the three provinces of Ü-Tsang (central, southern, and western Tibet), Kham (eastern Tibet), and Amdo (northeastern Tibet).

sala), arrived in Amdo, my birthplace, they were mobbed in adulation by thousands of people, especially the young. This alarmed their Chinese minders, who signaled ahead to warn the authorities in Lhasa. The reply came back saying that people in Amdo and Kham were simple nomads without class consciousness, but thanks to the standard of Marxist training in the capital, there was no possibility of embarrassment there. Yet in Lhasa, the crowds were immense and ecstatic. One of the delegates overheard a senior Chinese cadre's remark: "The efforts of the last twenty years have been wasted in a single day!" In fact, everywhere the delegates were mobbed by people crying and recounting the terrible tragedies they had suffered. There was a horrific litany of human rights abuses, and cultural destruction was graphically illustrated by many photographs of monasteries and nunneries reduced to rubble.

Despite the Chinese leadership's evident surprise and embarrassment at the Tibetan reaction to our first delegation, I should acknowledge that it was magnanimous of Deng to allow the planned second, third, and fourth delegations to go ahead, although in the end the second delegation, led by Tenzin Namgyal Tethong (at the time my representative at the Office of Tibet, New York) and consisting of young Tibetan leaders, was sent back early. (The third delegation was led by Jetsun Pema, my younger sister, and the fourth led by the former senior Tibetan official Kundeling Woeser Gyaltsen.) Perhaps Beijing interpreted the outpouring of grief on the part of the Tibetans as an immediate expression of anguish at the excesses of the Cultural Revolution rather than reflecting deeper feelings against Communist Chinese occupation. What these visits demonstrated to us was the massive support within Tibet for the struggles we were undertaking for them in exile and my own leadership.

One of the immediate results of our delegation visits was the unprecedented fact-finding mission of the new Party Secretary Hu Yaobang and Vice Premier Wan Li, who went to Lhasa in May 1980. They were dismayed by what they saw and subjected the local Chinese leadership to a severe dressing-down. Hu declared:

> We feel that our party has let the Tibetan people down. We feel
> very bad! The sole purpose of our Communist Party is to work for
> the happiness of the people, to do good things for them. We have
> worked for nearly thirty years, but the life of the Tibetan people
> has not notably improved. Are we not to blame?[*]

Hu is said to have compared the situation in Tibet to colonialism. He announced a six-point policy, including full rights for Tibetans to exercise regional autonomy, the development of Tibetan culture, language, and education in accord with socialist orientation, and an increase in the number of Tibetan officials. This new, more liberal policy led to the reappearance of individual religious practices, the reopening and rebuilding of monasteries, permission for new young monks, and reprinting of classical Tibetan texts in modern book format. The Communist Party made good on Deng's promise to my brother Gyalo Thondup, allowing both exiled Tibetans to return for visits and resident Tibetans to go abroad, especially to India to meet their relatives.

Among those able to leave Tibet in the early 1980s was Lopon-la, a senior monk at Namgyal Monastery in the Potala Palace complex, whose monks are traditionally responsible for assisting the Dalai Lama in rituals and official ceremonies. Following my departure from Lhasa in 1959, Lopon-la had spent eighteen years in Chinese prisons. After

---

[*] Hu Yaobang's critical statement to the local Chinese leadership in Tibet is cited in Wang Yao's "Hu Yaobang's Visit to Tibet, May 22–31, 1980: An Important Development in the Chinese Government Tibet Policy," in Robert Barnett and Shirin Akiner, eds., *Resistance and Reform in Tibet* (London: Hurst & Company, 1994). Wang Yao was a member of the delegation accompanying the Chinese leader Hu Yaobang on the latter's visit to Tibet.

he rejoined his old monastery, now reestablished in Dharamsala, his tall and somewhat stooped posture became a recognizable presence.

Since I had known Lopon-la in Tibet and liked him a lot, I met with him on many occasions. During one such meeting, when we were having tea together, he casually remarked that during his prison time there were two or three occasions when he felt real danger. Thinking that he was speaking of some kind of threat to his life, I asked, "What kind of danger?" He replied, "The danger of losing my compassion toward the Chinese." When I heard what he said, I just bowed to him. Later I learned of similar stories from other Tibetans, especially monks and nuns, who took extreme care not to lose sight of the humanity of the Chinese, even those who were inflicting such harm and hardship on them.

In my efforts to deal directly with the Chinese leadership in the spirit of what Deng Xiaoping had said to my brother in 1979, I wrote a letter to Deng in March 1981. I expressed my appreciation of Hu Yaobang's trip to Tibet and his efforts to right the wrongs and for frankly admitting past mistakes. I acknowledged the invitation through my brother that Deng and I should keep in contact with each other, and I thanked him for allowing us to send delegations to the Tibetan areas. I wrote:

> If the Tibetan people's identity is preserved and if they are genuinely happy, there is no reason to complain. However, in reality, over 90 percent of the Tibetans are suffering both mentally and physically, and are living in deep sorrow. These sad conditions have not been brought about by natural disasters, but by human action. Therefore, genuine efforts must be made to resolve the problems in accordance with the existing realities in a reasonable way.
>
> In order to do this, we must improve the relationship between China and Tibet as well as between Tibetans in and outside Tibet. With truth and equality as our foundation, we must try to develop friendship between Tibetans and Chinese through better

understanding in the future. The time has come to apply our common wisdom in a spirit of tolerance and broadmindedness to achieve genuine happiness for the Tibetan people with a sense of urgency.

The Chinese response came swiftly, through a private meeting between my brother Gyalo Thondup and Hu Yaobang in July 1981. Hu articulated a five-point basis according to which a rapprochement would be possible from the Chinese point of view.* This was disappointing because the focus in that proposal was entirely on my personal position and my return to Tibet, rather than on the much bigger question of the well-being of the six million Tibetan people. Effectively, nothing of substance was on offer, and whatever Deng Xiaoping had said to my brother in 1979, it was clear, at least from this proposal, it was not true that except for independence everything was negotiable.

In any case, following the opening of direct conversations with China, both formal and informal, and the opening up of China itself, as

---

* Hu Yaobang's five points were, as later published in the *Beijing Review*, December 3, 1984: (1) The Dalai Lama should be confident that China has entered a new stage of long-term political stability, steady economic growth, and mutual help among nationalities; (2) the Dalai Lama and his representatives should be frank and sincere with the Central Government, not beat around the bush. There should be no more quibbling over the events in 1959; (3) the central authorities sincerely welcome the Dalai Lama and his followers to come back to live. This is based on the hope that they will contribute to upholding China's unity and promoting solidarity between the Han and Tibetan nationalities, among all nationalities, and modernization program; (4) the Dalai Lama will enjoy the same political status and living conditions as he had before 1959. It is suggested that he not go to live in Tibet or hold local posts there. His followers need not worry about their jobs and living conditions. These will only be better than before; and (5) when the Dalai Lama wishes to come back, he can issue a brief statement to the press. It is up to him to decide what he would like to say in the statement.

well as some opening in Tibet, it became clear that we were in a much more complex phase with respect to our advocacy for Tibet compared to before. Previously, our role was to bring attention to the crimes and destruction taking place and to make the case for freedom and human rights. Now we needed to bring substantive proposals from our side that might lead to a mutually acceptable agreement. So, in my official March 10 Statement of 1981, I noted that past history had disappeared into the past, and what was more relevant was that in the future there actually must be real peace and happiness through developing friendly and meaningful relations between China and Tibet. For this to be realized, I said, it was important for both sides to work hard to have tolerant understanding and be open-minded.

I decided to send a high-level delegation to Beijing, and in April 1982 my three-member exploratory delegation, consisting of two of my *kalons* (cabinet ministers)—Juchen Thupten and Phuntsok Tashi Takla—and the speaker of our Assembly of Tibetan People's Deputies, Lodi Gyari, left for Beijing. They were briefed on my thoughts and ideas for a possible resolution. We were eager to find out if there had been a real shift in the Chinese Communist position, and what Deng Xiaoping's statement "except for independence, everything is negotiable" meant in concrete terms. For example, one of our negotiators asked whether Tibetans, in view of our different race and history, should not have the same rights as the ones being offered by the People's Republic of China to Taiwan. He was told that Tibetans could not expect to get what they were willing to give to Taiwan, because Taiwan was, unlike Tibet, not yet liberated.

When my exploratory delegation arrived in Beijing, however, the Chinese side was expecting a reply to the five-point proposal Hu Yaobang had given to my brother during his visit. This led to some initial confusion. The members of my delegation and their Chinese counterparts were talking at cross-purposes. The Chinese side then provided a copy of the proposal and shared the official transcript of my brother's meeting with Deng Xiaoping in 1979. In the end, the Chinese simply reiterated their position. Clearly, there was no space yet for a substantive conversation.

That said, I was feeling quite positive about the changes taking place on the ground in Tibet. For example, at a formal Buddhist teaching in Bodh Gaya in 1983, hundreds of monks and laypeople from Tibet itself were able to come on a pilgrimage. As such, I publicly expressed my wish to visit Tibet, possibly in two years' time. I proposed to send an advance party to prepare for it, but unfortunately, they did not respond positively.

In May 1984, we held a special meeting in Dharamsala, attended by my cabinet and representatives from the Assembly of Tibetan People's Deputies and other key constituencies, such as the Tibetan Women's Association and the Tibetan Youth Congress, to discuss my ongoing engagement with Beijing. And in October of that year, I sent the same exploratory delegation for further talks in Beijing. There, our delegation pointed out that the five points proposed by the Chinese government concerned only the status and return of the Dalai Lama. We reminded the Chinese that the issue was Tibet and its people, and the delegation again conveyed my wish to visit my home country.

One substantive suggestion we made was the idea of a demilitarized Tibet (including Kham and Amdo) that would have internal autonomy within the People's Republic of China. The Chinese rejected any discussion of these proposals, denying that there was such a thing as "the Tibetan issue," and claimed that the only matter to be discussed was the position of the Dalai Lama. They reiterated Hu Yaobang's five points of 1981, making them public for the first time soon after my representatives returned to India from Beijing.* After what seemed to be progress, we were again at an impasse.

---

* As noted earlier, these five points were made public by the Chinese government through the *Beijing Review*, December 3, 1984.

CHAPTER 8

Reaching Out to Our Fourth Refuge

While no substantive progress was made with China, the facts on the ground in Tibet were now beginning to change in a worrying direction. On the one hand, it is true that Tibet had opened up to some extent, and that things were better compared to the period of the Cultural Revolution. On the other, contrary to Hu Yaobang's pledge to reduce the number of Chinese officials and cadres, a massive Chinese migration into Tibet had begun in the name of "development." This was profoundly concerning because, if left unchecked, it would fundamentally alter the demographics of the region, turning the Tibetan plateau into just another Chinese province with Tibetans marginalized in their own homeland.

The historical evidence of what China had done in the regions of other nationalities was clearly a source of deep anxiety. From a sociocultural point of view, this influx of Chinese in Tibet could signal the beginning of a process that had the potential to change the very character of places dear to us Tibetans, including especially the holy city of Lhasa. At the same time, politically speaking, the picture coming out of Tibet was getting confusing, to say the least. Under the Party leadership of

Wu Jinghua in Tibet, there seemed to be a newly liberal policy toward religious practice, exemplified, for example, by the permission given for the revival of the Great Prayer Festival in Lhasa in February 1986, for the first time since 1967. Yet from the senior Beijing leadership side, there seemed to be nothing but intransigence.

We needed to reassess our strategy. We made the decision to make our proposals more systematic and present them at international forums. Our discussions with Beijing left us no choice but to use some international stage to make our proposals. This strategy also allowed us to offer our supporters across the world, who had been patiently waiting to hear the results of our discussions, an opportunity to learn about what our deeper aspirations were. I often describe the international community as our "Fourth Refuge," in addition to the traditional Buddhist refuge of the Three Jewels—the Buddha, dharma, and *sangha* (community).

Some of our efforts had an effect. In July 1985, ninety-one members of the United States Congress signed a letter addressed to the president of the People's Republic of China. The letter expressed support for direct talks and urged the Chinese "to grant the very reasonable and justified aspirations of His Holiness the Dalai Lama and his people every consideration." The Chinese, concerned about the growing international attention to Tibet, invited the former US President Jimmy Carter to visit Lhasa in June 1987, followed by the German Chancellor Helmut Kohl in July of that same year.

In June 1987, the House of Representatives in the United States adopted a bill condemning human rights abuses in Tibet and urged China to establish a constructive dialogue. On September 21 of that year, the United States Congressional Human Rights Caucus invited me to address them. I opened with the following:

The world is increasingly interdependent, so that lasting peace—national, regional and global—can only be achieved if we think in terms of broader interest rather than parochial needs. At this time, it is crucial that all of us, the strong and the weak, contribute in our own way. I speak to you today as the leader of the Tibetan people and as a Buddhist monk devoted to the principles of a religion based on love and compassion.

Then I proceeded to lay out a five-point peace plan, as the basis for a potential negotiation with China. They were:

1. Transformation of the whole of Tibet into a zone of peace, demilitarized so that there could be a buffer between the armies of Asia's two most populous countries, India and China;
2. Abandonment of China's population transfer policy, which threatens the very existence of the Tibetans as a people;
3. Respect for the Tibetan people's fundamental human rights and democratic freedoms;
4. Restoration and protection of Tibet's natural environment and the abandonment of China's use of Tibet for the production of nuclear weapons and dumping of nuclear waste;
5. Commencement of earnest negotiations on the future status of Tibet and of relations between the Tibetan and Chinese peoples.

Shortly after, in October, the United States Senate passed the congressional bill that had previously been adopted by the House of Representatives. And in December of that year, President Reagan signed into law the Foreign Relations Authorization Act, which declared that the United States would take the treatment of the Tibetan people into account in its relations with the People's Republic of China—encouraging the Chinese government to respect human rights in Tibet, to reciprocate the Dalai Lama's efforts in establishing a constructive dialogue, and calling for the release of political prisoners.

The Chinese state media strongly criticized the Five Point Peace Plan. This criticism, especially of me personally, deeply hurt many Tibetans. Less than a week after my speech in Washington, on

September 27, monks from Drepung Monastery protested, carrying a Tibetan national flag and calling for independence. They were arrested. When I heard about the news, I was deeply concerned. Then, on October 1, monks from Sera Monastery staged a second demonstration, joined by large crowds demanding the prisoners' release, and a major disturbance began. The police station was burned down and Chinese police opened fire, killing several people. This was followed by a further protest on October 6. After a lull, on the last day of the Great Prayer Festival on March 5, 1988, another protest erupted by the monks from Ganden Monastery. This led to spontaneous protests across the country, and martial law was imposed on March 8, 1988, in Lhasa. All this amply demonstrated that the aspirations of the Tibetan people inside Tibet went way beyond mere economic improvement, not to mention a profound discontent.

In the meantime, as I had been invited to address the European Parliament in mid-June, I wanted to take this opportunity to formally elaborate on the Five Point Peace Plan. To prepare, I convened a special meeting in Dharamsala to discuss the key points of what I was planning to present in Strasbourg. For three days, June 6–9, presided by my Kashag (cabinet) and attended by the members of the Assembly of Tibetan People's Deputies, public servants, NGOs, selected newly arrived Tibetans, as well as special invitees and others representing Tibetan communities in diaspora, I discussed at length the key points of my proposal. Following this in-depth discussion as well as debates, the participants of this special meeting unanimously endorsed the proposal.

On June 15, 1988, I addressed the European Parliament in Strasbourg, including these key additional points:

The whole of Tibet known as Cholka-Sum (Ü-Tsang, Kham and Amdo) should become a self-governing democratic political entity founded on law by agreement of the people for the common good and the protection of themselves and their environment, in association with the People's Republic of China.

The Government of the People's Republic of China could remain responsible for Tibet's foreign policy. The Government of Tibet should, however, develop and maintain relations, through its own foreign affairs bureau, in the field of commerce, education, culture, religion, tourism, science, sports and other non-political activities. Tibet should join international organizations concerned with such activities.

The Government of Tibet should be founded on a constitution or basic law. The basic law should provide for a democratic system of government entrusted with the task of ensuring economic equality, social justice, and protection of the environment. This means that the Government of Tibet will have the rights to decide on all affairs relating to Tibet and the Tibetans.

We were effectively stating that we were not going to seek independence; we were expressing our willingness to remain part of the People's Republic of China but only with a guarantee of genuine autonomy. This position I later came to call the Middle Way Approach—a middle way between independence and the present reality that was threatening the survival of the Tibetan people and culture. In essence, what I was offering to Beijing leadership was this: since, with the invasion of 1950 and the subsequent signing of the Seventeen-Point Agreement, Communist China had chosen to force Tibet into a union with the People's Republic of China, I was proposing that we work together, with sincerity and dedication on both sides, to make this union truly viable. I was trying to find a way for both sides to make the Tibetans feel truly at home within the family of the People's Republic of China. I was not seeking to turn back the historical clock somehow. I was looking to the future, based on a hard-nosed awareness of the present reality of Tibet forcibly occupied by China. At the same time, I was seriously taking into account

Beijing's key concern, namely territorial integrity and stability. My proposal was aimed at mutual benefit and seeking a mutually agreeable solution. Sadly, Beijing chose not to appreciate the historic significance of what we were offering. I do not think this is due to their failure to grasp what was being offered; my own sense is that it is simply due to the lack of political will on the part of the Chinese leadership to seriously address the issue of Tibet. I still remain convinced that given political will and vision on the part of the Chinese leadership, it would not be that difficult for China to satisfy the needs of the Tibetans.

I admitted that, when I first presented it, many Tibetans, both inside Tibet and in exile, would be disappointed by the moderate stance the Strasbourg Proposal represented. But I insisted that the thoughts outlined in my Strasbourg speech represented the most realistic means by which to reestablish Tibet's separate identity and restore the fundamental rights of the Tibetan people while accommodating China's own interests. I also stated that it was my wish not to take any active part in any future government of Tibet, but would continue to work as much as needed for the well-being and happiness of the Tibetan people. In fact, the core of what was presented in the Strasbourg Proposal had already been shared with the Chinese leadership through my exploratory delegation who met their Chinese counterparts. In Strasbourg, we were bringing these ideas to wider international attention.

After my speech at Strasbourg, I visited Switzerland and met with a large gathering of Tibetans there, and I took the opportunity to share my thinking. I knew the moderate stance outlined in the Strasbourg Proposal entailed ceasing our advocacy for full independence, which could cause unhappiness among many Tibetans. I stressed at this gathering of Tibetans that the essence of what we aspired to—the ability to protect our language, culture, religion, and our identity as a people—could be achieved within the framework of the People's Republic of China. I also pointed out that, given Tibet's status as a landlocked country, from the economic development perspective, we Tibetans might actually stand to gain by such an arrangement. I also stated that, in the end, it is the Tibetan people who will have to decide their own destiny.

While I understand people's emotional attachment to ideas of sovereignty and independence, personally, I have always been more of a pragmatist. I am a huge admirer of the ideals behind the European Union. Today, nations like France and Germany, which traditionally saw each other as enemies, join together and cede part of their cherished sovereignty to a collective European body so that the citizens within the individual countries have a greater chance of flourishing. It is a historical fact that sometimes, due to geopolitical conditions, what were previously independent nations come together to form a composite entity. Yet at other times, again because of changed political situations, some nations newly obtain their freedom, such as Timor-Leste.* For me, at least, what matters is the presence of an adequate structure and framework that ensures the continued survival and thriving of a people with their unique language, culture, and identity.

In the immediate aftermath of my Strasbourg Proposal, not only was there disappointment among some Tibetans, there were, in fact, some sharp criticisms of this stance. For example, my own eldest brother, Taktser Rinpoche, sent a letter to prominent Tibetans in the diaspora criticizing the decision to relinquish the demand for Tibetan independence. He went so far as to characterize our proposal as a sellout. At the same time, the reaction from key Tibetan figures inside Tibet and China was encouraging. In the words of Phuntsok Wangyal, the Tibetan Communist who was my official translator during my visit to Beijing in 1954–1955, "the Dalai Lama's 'Middle Way Approach' of 'seeking only a meaningful autonomy for Tibet rather than

---

* Timor-Leste is a small Southeast Asian nation occupying one-half of the island of Timor, with the other half being part of Indonesia. Formerly a colony of Portugal and later under the occupation of Indonesia, Timor-Leste gained independence in 2002.

independence,' in the present historical context, is an expression of the great responsibility he takes in giving serious thought over the fundamental issues." Similarly, another prominent Tibetan scholar inside Tibet stated that because the Middle Way Approach was "mutually beneficial" to both Tibetans and Chinese, it was "the only way . . . to resolve the issue of Tibet once and for all."

Let me pause here to address an important question. Sometimes, Chinese authorities criticize me for "allowing" Tibetans inside as well as outside to speak about Tibetan independence. This criticism is premised on the strange idea that, somehow, I must or should have the power to ban any Tibetan from even mentioning the phrase "Tibetan independence." It's one thing for an authoritarian regime to ban free speech and use force when it deems someone has violated the ban. It is something else when it comes to a free and open society, such as the Tibetan community in exile. One of the defining marks of a democratic system is freedom of expression. Even though I disagree with those Tibetans who argue that advocating for Tibetan independence is the best way forward for our freedom struggle, I have the greatest respect for these people. The Tibetan Youth Congress, for example, has as part of its mission "to struggle for the total independence of Tibet."

My own aim, however, has been to ensure that the formal leadership of the Tibetan movement as well as the majority of Tibetans living in the free world are convinced of the correctness of our Middle Way Approach, seeking a genuine autonomy rather than separation from the People's Republic of China.

Despite my explicit public announcement that we were not seeking independence, when the Chinese Embassy in New Delhi issued a formal response on September 23, 1988, they stated, "The new proposal put forward by the Dalai Lama in Strasbourg cannot be considered as the basis for talks with the Central Government because it has not at all relinquished the concept of the 'independence of Tibet.'" Nonetheless, Beijing did accept our suggestion to engage in a series of talks to start in Geneva in January 1989. In the end, though, Chinese officials put forward a number of pretexts for not starting the talks; one of the reasons, it seemed, was they were upset that we had made public the composition of our team as well as the venue of the talks. We had even proposed that a pre-meeting be held in Hong Kong in April to resolve any issues and concerns they may have had in mind, but to no avail. It is possible that further demonstrations in Lhasa in December 1988, in commemoration of international Human Rights Day, might have been another reason why the meeting did not take place.

On January 28, 1989, the Panchen Lama died suddenly at his monastic base of Tashi Lhunpo. We mourned his death with a heavy heart, recognizing that we had lost a heroic Tibetan leader who had suffered much on behalf of his people. While he was alive, I felt that his efforts inside Tibet, especially on the front of the protection of Tibetan language, culture, and identity, and my own efforts to be a free spokesperson for the Tibetans in the outside world really complemented each other well. So his sudden death deeply saddened me, with the acute awareness that I had lost a truly powerful and courageous ally on the ground inside Tibet. We held memorial prayers for the Panchen Lama at the Thekchen Choeling Temple in Dharamsala, and similar religious ceremonies in many monasteries, including especially at Tashi Lhunpo, the Panchen Lama's traditional monastery reestablished in southern India. As is the custom, I composed a prayer for his quick return (*nyurjön söldeb*) consisting of nine verses, which contained the following lines:

Even under a canopy of dense clouds of constant threat,
with no control and freedom at all, you shouldered
the great burden of Buddha's doctrine and beings' welfare.
Alas! Sad indeed is your sudden departure into peace.
In accord with your aspiration cultivated for so long,
may the new moon of your unmistaken reincarnation
shine from the eastern snowy peaks, of the good fortune of the people of
*   the Land of Snows—*
May we soon find the joy to cherish this resplendent new moon.

The Buddhist Association of China, obviously acting with full knowledge of the government, invited me to participate in his memorial service. We took this invitation with great seriousness. However, Beijing had just canceled the planned Geneva talks, the relatively moderate Party leader in Tibet Wu Jinghua had been dismissed at the end of 1988, and the invitation was only to Beijing, rather than to Tibet. There was no clarity on whether I would be able to meet any of the senior Chinese leaders or any important Tibetan figures. With much uncertainty and no adequate time to evaluate carefully the implications, in the end we made the decision that I would not go. Afterward, events rapidly went out of control.

On March 5, 1989, in the run-up to the anniversary of March 10, the largest demonstration against the Communist Chinese rule since the Lhasa uprising of 1959 broke out. For three days, the Chinese police cracked down viciously on the Tibetan people, leaving several hundred dead. On March 8, the Chinese imposed martial law in Lhasa. The issue of Tibet was now being raised also in the parliaments of many European countries, with the first international hearing on human rights abuses in Tibet organized in Germany in that same year.

On April 15 of that year, Hu Yaobang, who had been dismissed from the Party leadership in 1987, died. A series of student-led protests began from that day continuing to June 4 in Tiananmen Square in Beijing. The students called for greater accountability, democracy, freedom of the press, and freedom of speech. At their height, more than a million people assembled, constituting the most significant challenge to the Chinese Communist Party since it rose to power. Like the rest of the world, I was transfixed by these events, following them with a mixture of admiration, anxiety, and hope. On May 14, I stated:

> I am watching with great interest the current movement in China for democracy and freedom. The Chinese people, particularly the youth and the intellectuals, are trying to convey their real feelings. . . . I support their movements and admire their courage.

These developments will benefit China. . . . It seems that at least a section of the leadership of China is trying to adopt a more positive approach to these developments [in spite of] tremendous pressure from within the system. I urge upon the Chinese leadership to have the courage to accept the reality and comprehend the aspirations of their people.

On May 20, martial law was declared in Beijing and some three hundred thousand troops mobilized in the city. As tension was building and the dramatic events were unfolding across the world's televisions, I felt that I must express my solidarity with the protesting students and their aspirations. Many within my circle advised me not to do so, for it could offend Beijing, with whom we were, after all, trying to negotiate. On June 3, 1989, as we all know, the Chinese leadership unleashed the People's Liberation Army on its own people, using live ammunition. On the fourth, they sent armored personnel carriers and tanks into Tiananmen Square. To this day, we do not know how many were killed. I was shocked—the sight of the Chinese army killing its own people simply because they were asking for more freedom and a better life was horrifying.

I called my secretary, Tenzin Geyche Tethong, and Lodi Gyari, then in charge of Information and International Relations, to come to see me at once. I asked them to work on a statement expressing strong opposition to the Chinese government's crackdown and my solidarity with the young Chinese people gathered in Tiananmen Square. They were understandably concerned that such a public statement from me would negatively impact our ongoing discussion with the Chinese leadership. But I said that if I did not speak out now, what moral right would I ever have to speak for freedom and democracy? I reminded them that those young Chinese in the square were asking for nothing more than greater freedom.

There are moments in time, especially in which fundamental issues of humanity are concerned, when one cannot remain silent out of expediency or self-interest. So I issued a statement, expressing my opposition in the strongest terms against the military actions of the Chinese leadership; I expressed my deep disappointment at the Chinese government's failure to appreciate the true feelings of its people. And mourning the loss of so many innocent lives, I said how I shared in the sorrow of those families, relatives, and friends who had lost their loved ones. I can say with confidence that on that day of June 4, 1989, Tibetans everywhere, both inside Tibet as well as outside it, stood in solidarity with the Chinese people.

Later, when I formally accepted the Nobel Peace Prize in Oslo, on December 10, 1989, I began by saying:

> I accept the prize with profound gratitude on behalf of the op-
> pressed everywhere and for all those who struggle for freedom
> and work for world peace. I accept it as a tribute to the man who
> founded the modern tradition of nonviolent action for change—
> Mahatma Gandhi—whose life taught and inspired me.

Since I felt it was essential to include a statement about the events of Tiananmen Square in my acceptance speech, I said:

> In China the popular movement for democracy was crushed by
> brutal force in June this year. But I do not believe the demonstra-
> tions were in vain, because the spirit of freedom was rekindled
> among the Chinese people and China cannot escape the impact
> of this spirit of freedom sweeping many parts of the world. The
> brave students and their supporters showed the Chinese leader-
> ship and the world the human face of that great nation.

While popular movements for freedom in the former Soviet Union and Eastern Europe succeeded, bringing down the Berlin Wall and freeing so many from Communist totalitarianism, the student-led freedom movement in Tiananmen did not succeed in bringing down

Communist China's bamboo curtain. Needless to say, historians and geopolitical experts will seek to understand fully what might explain this contrast. At the risk of sounding simplistic, two things come to mind. One is that Communist China's People's Liberation Army, despite its name, was willing to shoot its own people, which was not the case with Eastern Europe. Second, in Eastern Europe, when the challenge to power came in the form of popular movements for freedom, the momentum had the backing of pretty much the entire population. In the case of Tiananmen Square, even though protests supporting the student-led movement did spread to several hundred towns and cities in China, it did not seem to have reached a critical mass that could have made a real difference. But I do not believe, even for a second, that Tiananmen Square marks the end of the Chinese people's quest for greater freedom, dignity, and democracy.

It is not surprising that Tiananmen Square, though not related directly to Tibet, had a significant impact on our attempts to come to a negotiation with the Chinese. The process that had begun in 1979, with Deng Xiaoping's statement to my brother Gyalo Thondup that apart from independence everything could be discussed, had come to an end. Deng's leadership, which had promised so much, in the end proved capable of as much brutality as that of Mao's.

Martial law was imposed in Lhasa on March 8, 1989, and was only lifted on May 1 of the following year.

CHAPTER 9

In the Aftermath of Tiananmen

One immediate side effect of the tragedy of Tiananmen was that for the first time a large segment of the Chinese population—especially the many intellectuals and dissidents who had escaped China after the crackdown—began to have more empathy for the plight of the Tibetan people. In the years following 1989, I have had many meetings with Chinese involved in the pro-democracy movement who had fled to the outside world—Paris, London, Switzerland, Germany, the United States, Canada, Australia, and Japan as well.

Several key members of the Tiananmen Square protest movement formed an organization in Paris in September 1989 called the Federation for Democratic China (FDC). At their request, I had a moving meeting with their leadership in Paris in December 1989. Among the dissidents I met was Yan Jiaqi (once a political adviser to the Chinese Premier Zhao Ziyang and later a prominent advocate for a democratic China). I applauded them for their courage and commitment to bringing greater democracy in China. Given the size of China's population, the mission of a democratic China is truly a noble work, and they need perseverance and unflagging determination if they are to succeed. I shared with them our own struggle for Tibetan freedom and dignity and said that we would remain undaunted and totally committed to our cause, no matter how long it might take. I took the opportunity to stress to them that, with respect to our own struggle, we made the decision to pursue the Middle Way Approach to not seek independence; rather to seek genuine autonomy that would enable us to survive and thrive as a people with our own distinct language, culture, and religion. I reminded them that, in comparison to our struggle for freedom, their struggle for a democratic China had only just begun.

Later I also met other senior figures among Chinese dissidents, including especially Wei Jingsheng, the well-known human rights activist famed for his 1978 essay "The Fifth Modernization" posted on the Democracy Wall in Beijing, and Harry Wu, who was instrumental in exposing the horrors of China's gulag system. The latter, in fact, urged me on a few occasions to reconsider my stance and instead campaign for the full independence of Tibet.

In 1991, at a conference on human rights at Columbia University in New York, I had the honor to share the platform with the distinguished Chinese astrophysicist Fang Lizhi, who by then had also been living in exile. I met the remarkable Chinese writer Wang Ruowang as well, who famously wrote a letter to Deng Xiaoping supporting the student-led demonstrations at Tiananmen and helped lead a march to the Shanghai City Hall. What these great Chinese intellectuals as well as the hundreds of student leaders who fled China in the wake of Tiananmen were fighting for was greater freedom, dignity, and democracy in China. Regardless of how they were portrayed by the Communist Party, all of these individuals—who paid a heavy personal price for their conscience—were true patriots that cared deeply for the future of China and its place in the world.

I have always maintained that our struggle is not against the Chinese people but against an oppressive regime and for the rights of the Tibetan people. So logically, I have deep empathy for others oppressed by the Communist Chinese regime, which include the Chinese people themselves, the Mongols of Inner Mongolia, and the Uyghur people of East Turkistan (Xinjiang). I have met with a number of Uyghurs in exile, notably Isa Alptekin and his son Erkin Alptekin, and later Rebiya Kadeer and Dolkun Isa, respectively the former and current presidents of the World Uyghur Congress. I shared with them the importance of embracing strict nonviolence in one's just struggle for freedom and my enduring belief that only through nonviolence and consideration of the needs and concerns of both sides can there be a truly lasting solution to any conflict. And adopting an approach that is mutually beneficial is key to finding solutions through the nonviolence method. Speaking to them about our own Tibetan struggle, I repeated what I often tell our supporters in the international community: that I consider them neither anti-Chinese nor pro-Tibetan but pro-freedom and pro-truth.

The awarding of the Nobel Peace Prize to me in October 1989 and the subsequent ceremony in Oslo brought extensive international attention to the Tibetan cause. For Tibetans across the world, this prize was an important recognition of our steadfast commitment to a nonviolent struggle to regain our freedom and dignity. For me personally, one of the most moving aspects of the experience was to see the joyful and celebratory faces of so many Tibetans and our international supporters who have worked tirelessly over decades. To this day, I remember vividly the beautiful and joyful energy of the presence of so many who had come to Oslo to be part of the celebration. I took the opportunity to thank many of them in person. Back home in Tibet too, I learned that many Tibetans celebrated, despite the obvious dangers they faced for doing such a thing. If anything, the situation inside continued to worsen.

In July 1990, the Chinese Communist Party leader Jiang Zemin and the head of the People's Liberation Army General Staff Department Chi Haotian visited Tibet. By now, as in China, a much more hard-line faction was in control in Tibet. The Chinese authorities emphasized loyalty to "the motherland" and "the struggle against splittism"—that is, the struggle against me and the exile community. They greatly increased incentives for Chinese migration into Tibet, such that a newly arrived worker from China stood to gain a substantial increase in salary. This growing migration caused much resentment among the Tibetans, including Tibetan Communist Party cadres. This hardening inside Tibet was such a sad and strange development in comparison to what was happening in the wider world. For this was the period when the tide of freedom was sweeping across the world, including the ending of dictatorships in the Philippines in 1986 and in Chile in 1990 and, of course, the fall of the Berlin Wall in 1989. It was also a moment of genuine détente and significant nuclear disarmament between the Soviet Union and the United States. Yet in China, and in Tibet especially, this was the beginning of a new era of repression. My own efforts for seeking a solution through dialogue continually hit a wall of rejection.

On the international front, in May 1991, the US legislature passed a congressional concurrent resolution recognizing Tibet as an illegally occupied country and reaffirmed the United States' position on Tibet, as stated by the US ambassador to the United Nations in 1961, which is that the United States believes its objectives must include the restoration of human rights of the Tibetan people and their natural right of self-determination. The resolution concluded:

> [It] is the sense of the Congress that Tibet, including those areas incorporated into the Chinese provinces of Sichuan, Yunnan, Gansu, and Qinghai, is an occupied country under established principles of international law whose true representatives are the Dalai Lama and the Tibetan Government in Exile as recognized by the Tibetan people.

A few years later, in 1997, the US government established the Office of the US Special Coordinator for Tibetan Issues within the State Department. Today this office coordinates the US policies and programs related to Tibetan issues in accord with the Tibetan Policy Act of 2002, which was amended with the Tibetan Policy and Support

Act of 2020. I have had the pleasure to meet with every holder of the position since its inception.

Deeply concerned by the worsening situation inside Tibet in 1991 and, in particular, China's outlier status as an active agent of repression, that year I accepted an invitation to speak at Yale University. I began by recognizing the momentous era we were living through, and how the world had changed dramatically in the last few years. I reflected on how the fall of the Berlin Wall and the Soviet Union after seventy years of Communist control signaled the aspirations of people and nations for freedom and democracy. I spoke of how I felt deeply inspired during my recent visits to Mongolia and the Baltic states and Bulgaria, seeing millions of human beings enjoying the freedom they had been denied for so many decades. I particularly noted how this amazing transition took place without resorting to violence.

Emphasizing the need for the international community to continue to engage with China, I said that I was a firm believer that relations between people and between nations must be based on human understanding. The world should engage China whenever it is willing to take part in the international community in a constructive manner. But when it persists in violating fundamental norms of civilized behavior it should not be indulged like a spoiled child. China must be made accountable for its actions as a responsible member of the international community. With respect to our ongoing attempt to negotiate with China, I observed that the Chinese government's refusal to reciprocate my efforts to start negotiations had increased the impatience of many Tibetans inside Tibet, especially among the youth, with the nonviolent path we were following. Tension was increasing as China encouraged demographic aggression in Tibet, threatening to reduce Tibetans to a second-class minority in our own country. I was extremely anxious that, in this explosive situation, violence could break out. I said that I wanted to do what I could to help prevent this.

I then expressed my wish to be able to visit Tibet so I could communicate directly with my people and urge them not to abandon our path of nonviolence. My visit would offer the possibility for the senior Chinese leadership to understand the true feelings of the Tibetan people.

Since there had been no constructive response from Beijing to both my Five Point Peace Plan and the subsequent Strasbourg Proposal of 1988, in September 1991, I stated that I no longer considered myself bound by them. Yet I stressed that we remained fully committed to the path of negotiation. Of course, we continued with our efforts to keep lines of communication open with China. When, in December 1991, the Chinese Premier Li Peng visited Delhi, I sought unsuccessfully to meet with him. In June 1992, my brother Gyalo Thondup met Ding Guangen, a Politburo member, who carried a message from the Chinese government offering resumption of dialogue on the condition that I publicly renounce the idea of Tibetan independence. This was odd since we had already stated unequivocally and repeatedly that we were willing to cease our demand for independence as part of a negotiated settlement. Nonetheless, on September 11, 1992, I wrote formally to both the paramount leader Deng Xiaoping and General Secretary Jiang Zemin. I expressed my openness to talks and, by way of setting things in a broader context, included a supplemental note summarizing the history of our conversations thus far, since 1951. The letter was delivered to the Chinese ambassador in Delhi alongside a suggestion for regular monthly meetings at the Chinese Embassy to build confidence. However, it took until July 1993 before the Chinese government allowed my representatives to present this letter in person.

The letter, addressed to Jiang Zemin, conveyed my basic belief in the process of negotiation as the only viable means to solve the issue of Tibet. I wrote:

> I am pleased that direct contact has once again been established between us. I hope that this will lead to an improvement of relations and the development of mutual understanding and trust.
>
> I have been informed of the discussions Mr. Ding Guangen had with Gyalo Thondup on June 22, 1992, and the position of

the Government of China concerning negotiations for a solution to the Tibetan question. I am disappointed with the hard and inflexible position conveyed by Mr. Ding Guangen, particularly the emphasis on pre-conditions for negotiations.

However, I remain committed to the belief that our problems can be solved only through negotiations, held in an atmosphere of sincerity and openness, for the benefit of both the Tibetan and Chinese people. To make this possible, neither side should put up obstacles, and neither side should, therefore, state pre-conditions.

For meaningful negotiations to take place it is essential to have mutual trust. Therefore, in order to create trust, I believe it is important for the leaders and people of China to know of the endeavours I have made so far. My three representatives carry with them a letter from me, accompanied by a detailed note of my views and my efforts through the years to promote negotiations in the best interests of the Tibetan and Chinese people. They will answer and discuss any questions and points you wish to raise. It is my hope that through these renewed discussions we will find a way that will lead us to negotiations.

On my part, I have put forward many ideas to solve our problem. I believe that it is now time for the Chinese government to make a genuinely meaningful proposal if you wish to see Tibet and China live together in peace. I, therefore, sincerely hope that you will respond in a spirit of openness and friendship.

Accompanying this letter was a detailed note I prepared for the Chinese leadership outlining succinctly the history of my approach to the issue of Tibet and the thinking behind it, and my proposal for a discussion to move toward a substantive dialogue. In the conclusion of that note, I stated:

If China wants Tibet to stay with China, then China must create the necessary conditions for this. The time has come now for the

Chinese to show the way for Tibet and China to live together in friendship. A detailed step by step outline regarding Tibet's basic status should be spelt out. If such a clear outline is given, regardless of the possibility of an agreement or not, we Tibetans can then make a decision whether to live with China or not. If we Tibetans obtain our basic rights to our satisfaction then we are not incapable of seeing the possible advantages of living with the Chinese.

I concluded with an expression of hope, saying that I trusted in the farsightedness and wisdom of China's leaders and hoped that they would take into consideration the current global political changes and the need to resolve the Tibetan problem peacefully, promoting genuine lasting friendship between our two peoples.

In the meantime, the Chinese government published a white paper in September 1992 entitled *Tibet: Its Ownership and Human Rights Situation*. Misleadingly, the document dwells long on a history of Tibet presented as if it had always been part of China, indicating a defensiveness on the part of China's leadership on the legitimacy of China's presence in Tibet. The document presents a series of arguments against Tibetan independence, claiming that "the so-called Tibetan independence which the Dalai clique and overseas anti-China forces propagate is nothing but a fiction of the imperialists who committed aggression against China in modern history." Shockingly, the document further asserts, "Another lie is the claim that a large number of Hans have migrated to Tibet, turning the ethnic Tibetans into a minority," flatly denying a fact acknowledged by every independent observer and recognized as a major source of resentment for the Tibetan people.

Back home in Tibet, protests by more than a thousand laypeople erupted in Lhasa on May 23, 1993, initially over rising costs but swiftly becoming about independence. These demonstrations resulted in brutal suppression and mass arrests. One of the causes was clearly the increasing influx of Chinese migrants into Lhasa. In 1994, when the Third

Tibet Work Forum was convened by the Party Central Committee in Beijing, a set of new repressive policies was imposed. Among these was increased spending on security mechanisms of control, and a newly vitriolic attack on me personally. For example, one of their official statements contained the allegation that "although sometimes Dalai speaks softly and says nice things to deceive the masses, he has never ceased his splittist activities." It then went on to assert: "The focus-point in our region's fight to oppose splittism is to oppose the Dalai clique. As the saying goes, to kill a serpent, we must first cut off its head." This same document then urged the monastic community inside Tibet to renounce the Dalai Lama. It stated that "we must firmly stop the Dalai clique influencing lamas and nuns in Tibet in any way." The issuing of this statement was accompanied by a complete ban on any photographs or portraits of me, both in public spaces and private homes in Tibet. Effectively, a form of ideological indoctrination (especially in the area of education) that had not been seen since the Cultural Revolution was being imposed on Tibet. The Party leadership in Lhasa asserted:

> Ethnic education cannot be regarded successful if it successfully maintains the old culture and traditions. . . . The essence of educational work is to cultivate qualified constructors and successors for the socialist cause, and this is the sole basic mission in ethnic education.

Official statements such as this and the repressive policies on the ground targeting Tibetan identity, culture, and traditions, as well as the large-scale demographic change taking place on the Tibetan plateau caused me great alarm, compelling me to say that what was happening inside Tibet was either willingly or unwillingly, a form of cultural genocide.

CHAPTER 10

Practices I Find Helpful in
the Face of Suffering

Let me pause here and offer a reflection on how we can sustain our determination in the face of situations that seem daunting, even hopeless. It is human to feel discouraged when confronted with terrible suffering with no perceivable end in sight. This is the experience for those in Tibet, and for so many who have aspired for freedom under oppressive regimes. This must have been the overwhelming feeling for those many thousands of students in Beijing in 1989, in the wake of the cruel crackdown. Many a time, in the years since 1950, I too have been confronted with such feelings and have had to sustain my sense of hope.

Here are some practices I have found helpful in my own life. First and foremost, I remind myself that in any important journey we will face difficulties, so it is crucial to adopt a stance of being prepared right from the start. This way, when we meet adversities, they do not come as a shock out of the blue and catch us unaware. As a Tibetan saying goes, "Hope for the best, and prepare for the worst."

Suffering and problems are an inevitable part of human life; the question is how we respond. When we face suffering caused by natural disasters, despite the devastation and the loss of human life, generally, we are able to cope with the pain without giving in to defeatism or bitterness. These tragedies also bring out the best in humanity, and people respond spontaneously with compassion. There is, however, man-made suffering, for which we humans ourselves are the direct cause. It is this class of suffering that is harder to bear and requires more strength on our part to deal with. There is the risk of giving in to despair and hatred, or responding to violence with violence. Unfortunately, we humans tend to keep repeating this cycle. The key here is never to lose sight of our shared humanity, common to perpetrator, victim, and ourselves. It is exactly for this reason I have always urged my fellow Tibetans to guard against hatred toward the Chinese.

I once told my fellow Tibetans when marking the first anniversary of the uprising in 1959 that in spite of the fact that we have to oppose Communist China's actions, I can never bring myself to hate its people. I said that, especially from the perspective of our struggle for freedom, hatred of an entire people will be a weakness, not a strength. I also reminded them that when the Buddha spoke of hatred leading only to further hatred, he was not just giving a spiritual teaching; he was also giving practical advice. I truly believe that a movement rooted in hatred, however noble the cause, will destroy the basis for a lasting future resolution. In Buddhist teachings there is, in fact, a special emphasis on viewing one's adversaries—those who are creating trouble for you—as spiritual teachers. Regardless of their intention, they provide you with the opportunity to practice patience and compassion. Our adversaries are our most valuable teachers. This is a demonstrable fact of life. While our friends can help us in many ways, it is our adversaries who provide us the challenge to develop the virtues essential for cultivating peace of mind and bringing us true happiness.

Personally speaking, as a follower of Mahayana (a system of Buddhism that I personally refer to as the Sanskrit tradition, which we Tibetan Buddhists share with Chinese Buddhism), I have a deep appreciation for the ancient nation of China in preserving the Buddhist tradition. Buddhism came to China about four centuries before it arrived in Tibet. Many texts that are lost in their original Indian language today survive in Chinese translation, such as the famous fifth-century Buddhist logician Dignāga's work, *Hetumukha*. Within the two Tibetan canonical collections of *Kangyur* (translation of scriptures) and *Tengyur* (translation of treatises), there are several important texts translated from Chinese. The Chinese commentary on the famed Mahayana scripture *Samdhinirmocana Sutra* (*Unraveling the Intent*) by the Korean monk Woncheuk is highly admired in the Tibetan monasteries. Numerous schools of Mahayana Buddhism emerged, developed, and flourished in China—for example, Tiantai, Huayen, San-lun, Pure Land, and Chan. Admirably, it is only in the Chinese tradition that the lineage of full ordination for women as *bhikshuni* (fully ordained nuns) has survived, traceable all the way back to the time of the Buddha. The continued existence of this women's full ordination tradition gives me great joy. Among the numerous Chinese monastics I have met over the years—in Taiwan and in the West—two who inspired me most in the richness of the Chinese Buddhist tradition were the revered Chan master Sheng Yen and the great Chinese Vinaya master Dao-hai. I have had the opportunity to engage in formal dialogues with both, on our two Buddhist traditions—Tibetan and Chinese—with the latter once also in New York. I even had the aspiration to visit the sacred Buddhist site of Mount Wutai Shan with master Dao-hai so that we could conduct a reading in Chinese, Tibetan, and Sanskrit of Nagarjuna's famed *Treatise on the Middle Way*, which is dear to both Tibetan and Chinese Buddhism.

Needless to say, the courage and spirit of the indefatigable Chinese pilgrims who traveled to India in search of Buddhist texts and practice traditions has been a profound and continuing inspiration for me. From Faxian at the end of the fourth century to Xuanzang in the mid-seventh century, and Yijing in the later seventh century, these extraordinary monks risked everything for the sake of the dharma. One remarkable thing about these Chinese monks is the meticulous records they kept of their journeys. Of these pilgrims, Xuanzang's enduring contribution is universally recognized today. His story is the inspiration behind the famous fable of Monkey in the Chinese literary tradition. It was thanks largely to Xuanzang's *Records of the Western Regions*—a massive account of his travels formally prepared for the Tang emperor on his return—that many of the important sites associated with the life of the Buddha and with the history of Buddhism in India, such as Nalanda University, were later rediscovered. Today, millions of Buddhists from all over the world are able to make pilgrimages and honor these sites. So I have always been someone with a deep reverence and respect for the ancient nation of China and its people.

Second, I find it helpful to adopt a wider perspective, since our sense of being overwhelmed or powerless often arises from viewing a problem too closely. If you look at your palm up close, you can't see your hand properly. By looking too closely, we get fixated and our perspectives narrow. In contrast, if we can situate the given problem in a larger context, we are then able to appreciate its complexity—its causes, effects, and interconnections—allowing us to choose a course of action that is more in tune with reality and has greater likelihood of success. The wider perspective also allows us to see any issue within its right proportions, making what previously seemed insurmountable possible to manage, and to recognize any positive aspects there might be despite what has happened. The embracing of this kind of wider perspective also makes it possible for us to see the opportunities a specific adversity might bring. As I have often stated, becoming a stateless person brought me closer to reality. When you are a refugee, there is no room left for ceremony or pretension. Had I remained in Lhasa as the theocratic ruler of an independent Tibet, imprisoned in what might be called a "golden cage" as the holy Dalai Lama, today I might be quite a different person. Being outside my homeland as a refugee has allowed me to meet with people from so many diverse backgrounds and walks of life—from fellow spiritual seekers to scientists, from activists to political leaders, and from artists to engineers. I particularly cherish the privilege I have had to establish friendships and engage in deep conversations with scientists. I would argue that my own Tibetan Buddhist tradition too has gained a lot from my being in exile. Today, we have successfully instituted the Geshema degree (highest monastic academic accomplishment) for the nuns; introduced formal science education in the monasteries; and initiated ongoing dialogues and collaborations with scientists on the study of the mind and possible applications of mind-based tools for greater mental well-being. The point is that if, instead of adopting a wider perspective, we had chosen to remain fixated on our loss, we would have never had the will or inclination to explore the opportunities that opened up in the wake of our tragedy.

Third, it is essential to choose optimism as a basic standpoint, however bad things may seem. The problem with its opposite, pessimism, is that one has already chosen to give up, even before trying. Of course, optimism must be based on an appreciation of reality and a clear-eyed approach to seeking the best way forward. In the case of Tibet, for example, the issue is existential and we don't have the luxury of giving up. That is what pessimism is.

Fourth, it is important to recognize and appreciate past successes, no matter how small. This is vital for encouraging ourselves and recharging our motivation to keep on going. We must never lose hope and must always maintain it if we are to meet with success in the challenges we face. With hope, we have the courage to care and the courage to act.

Finally, regardless of whatever happens, we must never lose faith in humanity. Here the key is to remain in touch with our own natural capacity to care for others, and never become divorced from our shared humanity, even in relation to those who might have done us harm. Personally, I find this basic altruistic orientation of the heart to be the source of my greatest strength and courage. Every morning when I get up, I remind myself I am just another human being, one among the billions on this earth. We are all the same, each and every one of us wishing to be happy and not wanting suffering. As social beings, we seek connection with others and find joy through them. There is no such thing as my own independent interest separate from others', because our well-being is interconnected with the well-being of others. With this in mind, I chant these verses from the eighth-century master Shantideva:

All those who are happy in the world
Are so because they desire happiness for others;
All those unhappy in the world
Are so because they desire only their own happiness.
Therefore, if one does not switch the outlook
Of self-centeredness to other-centeredness,
Let alone the attainment of enlightenment,
Even in this life there can be no joy.
As long as space endures,
As long as sentient beings remain,
Until then, may I too remain,
And dispel the miseries of the world.

Chanting these verses gives me deep inspiration and reinforces my determination on a daily basis.

We are all the same human beings sharing this small planet. We all happen to have been born here at this time in the long history of humankind. At most, we have a life span of about a hundred years. This is but a blip in the great age of our planet. What matters most is what we do with our short life. If we live our life divorced from our shared humanity, embroiled in discord and division, and causing harm, what a waste of our precious life! If we choose to live our life caring for others—our human family and fragile planet—we will have made our life meaningful. So, when the final day comes, we will look back without regret and feel that our life on this earth has been worthwhile.

CHAPTER 11

As the Millennium Came to an End

One of the consequences of this hardening of Chinese policy inside Tibet—quite apart from its terrible effects on ordinary Tibetan people—was the tragedy that took place over the selection of the new Panchen Lama. I had genuinely hoped that I could help with the search for the Panchen Lama's reincarnation by working with the Tashi Lhunpo Monastery in Tibet and, through it, with the Chinese authorities. The recognition of the reincarnation of the Panchen Lama is, like in the case of important Tibetan lamas, a matter of great spiritual significance in Tibetan Buddhism, though the "official selection" of the Panchen Lama might have political significance from the perspective of Chinese authorities. In February 1991, on the third day of the Tibetan New Year, I conducted a divination on the question of whether the reincarnation had been born inside Tibet or outside, and the result indicated that he had been born within. So in March 1991, I conveyed a message to Beijing through the Chinese Embassy in New Delhi indicating that I would like to offer assistance in the process of the search for the new Panchen Lama. Ever since the Fourth Panchen Lama Lobsang Chökyi Gyaltsen's recognition of the Fifth Dalai Lama in the seventeenth century, the Dalai Lamas and the Panchen Lamas have played key roles in recognizing each other's reincarnations. Given this historical tradition, Tibetans everywhere, as well as the communities of Tibetan Buddhists in the Himalayan regions that have a historical connection with the Panchen Lama institution, reached out to me, asking that I recognize the new Panchen Lama. It was thus my responsibility, both historical and moral, to help in the search.

On July 17, 1993, Jadrel Rinpoche, the abbot of Tashi Lhunpo, in charge of the search process, met with my brother Gyalo Thondup in Beijing and handed him a scroll asking me to assist in the process. Naturally, I assumed that Jadrel Rinpoche was acting with full permission of the Chinese leadership, and consequently I invited him to Dharamsala for consultation. Although he could not come, at the end of 1994, I received a carefully selected list of more than twenty candidates from Jadrel Rinpoche. He also conveyed to me that he and his search team considered one of these candidates, Gendun Choekyi Nyima, to be the true incarnation. On the basis of this information, I performed a series of divinations and other traditional procedures, such as consultations with oracles, and was pleased to come to the same conclusion.

This information was passed confidentially to Jadrel Rinpoche in February 1995, with the text of a prayer for the long life of the young Eleventh Panchen Lama. I hoped he would be able to navigate the politics in Beijing. Given that the reincarnation of a lama is a religious matter in Tibetan Buddhism and since the chosen candidate would be within the territory under Chinese control, my hope was that Jadrel Rinpoche and his team's choice would be acceptable to the Chinese leadership. I also wrote confidentially to Geshe Yeshe Wangchuk, a senior monk at Sera Monastery at the time in Tibet, informing him that I was really happy with how my own observations confirmed the candidate the search committee had recommended. Sending a copy of the long-life prayer I had composed for the new Panchen Lama, I requested that Geshe use his influence to help assure the Chinese authorities that the parents of the new Panchen Lama had no contact with me whatsoever. I also informed him that, for the time being, I would keep the result of my observation confidential.

Unfortunately, in March 1995, the Chinese government insisted that three to five names be placed in a golden urn for selection by lot,* rather than approve the correct reincarnation. This put me in an impossible position. They were likely to choose a wrong candidate. So, after a series of divinations, I came to the conclusion that I needed to share with the Tibetan Buddhists around the world the result of my own divinations on the reincarnation of the Panchen Lama. Thus, on May 14, 1995 (the full-moon day of the fifteenth of the fourth month in the Tibetan calendar), having sent a day's advance notice to the Chinese government that was conveyed through my brother Gyalo Thondup, I formally announced that I had accepted Gendun Choekyi Nyima as the Eleventh Panchen Lama. I chose this day for this important announcement since it was an auspicious day connected with an important system of Buddhist teaching known as the Kalachakra tantra, a set of teachings and practice with special association with the Panchen Lamas. I also

---

* This use of a golden urn was probably an attempt on the part of Beijing leadership to invoke the "authority" of a custom first introduced by the Qing Emperor Qianlong toward the end of the eighteenth century. There are two important historical facts about the issue of the "Golden Urn" to keep in mind: First, it was introduced by Qianlong, a devout Tibetan Buddhist, to be used in the presence of sacred icons with the names of the candidates rolled inside dough balls and placed within the urn. The urn, on its own, has no meaning. An important part of Qianlong's motivation was to help prevent corruption or unnecessary factional disputes in the process of recognizing the new reincarnation of prominent Tibetan lamas. Second, even in instances when it was used in connection with the Panchen Lama and the Dalai Lama—that is, the selection of the eighth and ninth Panchen Lamas and the tenth to the twelfth Dalai Lamas—it was more ceremonial than actual. The real recognitions were made through traditional Tibetan systems of divination and other methods, especially consultations with oracles. In any case, it was illogical for Communist China, an avowedly atheistic state, to be invoking this custom for the recognition of the Panchen Lama.

made sure that a copy of my formal announcement was presented to the Chinese Embassy in New Delhi, with also a request to have a copy forwarded to Jadrel Rinpoche and his search team at the Panchen Lama's Tashi Lhunpo Monastery in Tibet. For me, this confirmation of the Panchen Lama's reincarnation was, first and foremost, a matter of integrity of Tibetan Buddhist tradition. Once I was convinced of the authenticity of the new Panchen Lama, the very person selected by the official search party set up by his own monastery, it was unthinkable that any other candidate could be endorsed.

Unfortunately, the fallout was terrible. Jadrel Rinpoche was imprisoned for six years, and Tashi Lhunpo Monastery was subjected to serious harassment, including the arrest of more than thirty monks. To this day, I have not heard any reliable news about Jadrel Rinpoche or his whereabouts, even though he is supposed to have been released from prison. Not only did he serve the previous Panchen Lama with dedication, but also he worked hard to ensure that the Panchen Lama's new reincarnation would be recognized in accordance with Tibetan Buddhist tradition. Furthermore, he tried his best to have the Beijing leadership approve the work of the search committee he was leading, and to that end, he kept Beijing abreast of all the stages in the search process. So to see him suffer so much for his sincere efforts was painful indeed. Gendun Choekyi Nyima, a boy of only six years old, and his family were detained, making the new Panchen Lama the youngest political prisoner in the world at the time. To this day, his whereabouts remain unknown, perhaps making this one of the best kept secrets in the history of the Chinese Communist Party. I have been told by some Chinese, one of them in fact quite a knowledgeable person, that Gendun Choekyi Nyima has been living under a form of house arrest within the compound of a military base somewhere in mainland China. The Chinese authorities proceeded to select a different candidate, Gyaltsen Norbu, whose parents were both members of the Communist Party, and thrust him upon Tashi Lhunpo Monastery as the new Panchen Lama. This act was accompanied by the stationing of a large number of Chinese soldiers in Shigatse, where the monastery is located. I feel deeply sad for the two boys caught up in this tragic situation. We know that the true Panchen Lama is missing, while the boy chosen by the Chinese Communist Leadership and enthroned at Tashi Lhunpo is referred to by Tibetans as well as some Chinese Buddhists as the "false Panchen Lama" or the "Chinese Panchen Lama." To this day, the photo of Gendun Choekyi Nyima remains banned.

In November 1996, the Chinese President Jiang Zemin came to India on an official visit for eight days. I recognized it was not possible to meet him, but I took the opportunity of this visit to appeal to him, through a statement, to reverse China's repressive policy inside Tibet. On February 19, 1997, China's paramount leader Deng Xiaoping died. In my statement on that day, I expressed my regret that serious negotiations on the issue of Tibet did not take place during Deng's lifetime and also my hope that there were now new opportunities to reset the clock. In my letter of condolence to Jiang Zemin, I wrote:

It is very regrettable that serious negotiations on the issue of Tibet could not take place during Mr. Deng's lifetime. However, I firmly believe that the absence of Mr. Deng provides new opportunities and challenges for both Tibetans and the Chinese. I very much hope that under your leadership the Government of China will realize the wisdom of resolving the issue of Tibet through negotiations in a spirit of reconciliation and compromise. For my part, I remain committed to the belief that our problem can be solved only through negotiations, held in an atmosphere of sincerity and openness.

Given Deng's initial overture with the statement to my brother that "except for independence, everything is negotiable," I had hoped that we could achieve some breakthrough during his leadership. Sadly, this was not to be.

Deng's death marked the end of an era—he was the last of the old

Communist revolutionaries to rule China and also the last of its senior leaders whom I knew personally. He had been responsible for the opening up of China, and, under his leadership, very significant headway was made in economic development, resulting in lifting millions of people out of poverty, especially the poverty caused by the famines of the Great Leap Forward and the suffering of the Cultural Revolution. At the same time, it was under Deng's watch that China's People's Liberation Army fired on its own people in Tiananmen Square.

In March 1997, I had the good fortune to visit Taiwan for the first time. My official host was the Buddhist Association of China (Taiwan), and the government, ruled by the Nationalist Party (known also as Kuomintang) originally founded by Chiang Kai-shek, who, following Mao's Communist takeover of mainland China in 1949, fled to this island. Given that Kuomintang (KMT) saw itself as a continuation of the government of the Republic of China, albeit away from the mainland, at the time it was still formally asserting sovereignty over all of mainland China, as well as Tibet. I was received officially by the Taiwanese President Lee Teng-hui, which indicated that there was a softening of Taiwan's "official" position on the status of Tibet. Needless to say, my visit to Taiwan, including especially my meeting with the Taiwanese president, angered Beijing, which accused me of colluding with Taiwan to undermine China. For me personally, the most memorable and valuable aspect of the visit was the chance to meet with so many Chinese Buddhists who were sincere in their devotion to Buddhism and were free to practice their faith without interference from the state. In 2001, I visited Taiwan for the second time at the official invitation from President Chen Shui-bian. At that time, I also had the opportunity to meet with Tsai Ing-wen, who would later become the president of Taiwan. This was the beginning of Taiwan's relinquishing of their claim to sovereignty over Tibet, resulting in the issuing of visas to stateless Tibetans from India on their Indian travel documents and the eventual closing of the United Front Office (known formally as the Mongolian and Tibetan Affairs Commission), originally established for dealing with the affairs of non-Chinese peoples like the Tibetans and the Mongols in Inner Mongolia.* Finally, in 2009, in response to an invitation, I visited the southern part of Taiwan to pray at the sites of a massive typhoon that had caused much suffering and loss of life.

As part of my usual approach of consulting the Tibetan people on an ongoing basis, an important gathering took place in September 1997, aimed at reviewing our position in relation to dialogue with the Chinese government. In the end, as I have often stated, it is the Tibetan people who must choose their destiny, not the Dalai Lama or the Communist Chinese government. At the conclusion of this meeting, the Assembly of Tibetan People's Deputies adopted a formal articulation of what I have described as the Middle Way Approach. The key points were:

- Without seeking independence for Tibet, the Central Tibetan Administration strives for the creation of a political entity comprising the three traditional provinces of Tibet;
- Such an entity should enjoy a status of genuine national regional autonomy;
- This autonomy should be governed by the popularly-elected legislature and executive through a democratic process and should have an independent judicial system;
- As soon as the above status is agreed upon by the Chinese government, Tibet would not seek separation from, and remain within, the People's Republic of China;
- The Central Government of the People's Republic of China has the responsibility for the political aspects of Tibet's international relations and defense, whereas the Tibetan people should manage

---

* The reference here is to the closing of the United Front Office in Taiwan, which was set up as a continuation of the same office in Beijing under the Nationalist government of Kuomintang (KMT) in China.

all other affairs pertaining to Tibet, such as religion and culture, education, economy, health, ecological and environmental protection;

- To resolve the issue of Tibet, His Holiness the Dalai Lama shall take the main responsibility of sincerely pursuing negotiations and reconciliation with the Chinese government.

On the Chinese side, one presumes in response, in February 1998, the State Council Information Office of the People's Republic of China issued a white paper entitled *New Progress in Human Rights in the Tibet Autonomous Region*, indicating an aggressive public strategy. The document concluded that "the exiled Dalai Lama has tried by every means to cover it up and vilify and attack the development of progress in new Tibet." It went on to say, "The Dalai Lama's wanton fabrication of lies and his violation and trampling of this commandment serve only to expose him in all his true colors: He is waving the banner of religion to conduct activities aimed at splitting the motherland."

In the meantime, on my part, I strove to encourage China's entry into the mainstream of the world community. My deep belief was then, as it is now, that the opening up of China was in the best interests of the Chinese people. So, when discussions and debates were taking place as to whether or not the United States should grant most-favored-nation trading status to China, I expressed my support for doing so. In fact, I wrote to the chair of the US Senate Foreign Relations Committee expressing my personal encouragement for granting this status. As far as our direct contact with the Beijing leadership was concerned, after 1989 nothing of substance happened for many years. That said, there were indeed a few meetings in Hong Kong and Chiang Mai, Thailand, confidential at the time, between my envoys Lodi Gyari and Kelsang Gyaltsen and an emissary from the Chinese President Jiang Zemin. Also, on September 28, 1997, when Senator Dianne Feinstein and her husband, the American businessman Richard Blum, met with the Chinese president, they were kind enough to deliver by hand a letter from me to Jiang Zemin. This was several months before the summit in Beijing between President Bill Clinton and Jiang.

At the press conference in Beijing, Clinton revealed that the question of Tibet had been discussed, and he urged the resumption of dialogue. Jiang commented:

> Actually, as long as the Dalai Lama can publicly make a statement and a commitment that Tibet is an inalienable part of China and that he must also recognize Taiwan as a province of China, then the door to dialogue and negotiation is open. Actually, we are having several channels of communications with the Dalai Lama. So I hope the Dalai Lama will make positive response in this regard.

This was the first time that the head of the People's Republic of China had publicly addressed the question of Tibet and spoken of the possibility for a genuine dialogue. Of course, as to Jiang's first condition, he knew that I had already made public statements relinquishing the call for independence, ever since my speech to the European Parliament in Strasbourg in 1988. With respect to the second condition, frankly, the question of Taiwan is totally unconnected to Tibet and our cause. Jiang may have been sincere in reaching out to my envoy, but it was unclear to what extent he had support within the Chinese Politburo.

As the eventful decade of the 1990s drew to an end, there was one pleasant surprise. The fourteen-year-old Karmapa, head of the Karma Kagyu lineage of Tibetan Buddhism, escaped into India from Tibet, arriving suddenly in Dharamsala on January 5, 2000. I knew his predecessor, the Sixteenth Karmapa, who had been an important lama among senior Tibetan spiritual leaders that came into exile in 1959. So, I was very happy to welcome the new Karmapa, Ogyen Trinley Dorje, and offered to assist him and his entourage in whatever ways I could, especially in relation to his education.

CHAPTER 12

*

The Final Series of Dialogues

In 2001, when I was sixty-six years of age, I took a major step within the political structure of the Tibetan exile community by choosing to go into semiretirement and devolve the executive aspect of Tibetan political leadership. For the first time, the executive in charge of the Tibetan exile administration would be directly elected by the people, and this leader would then nominate his or her own cabinet. Having already established an Assembly of Tibetan People's Deputies (equivalent of an elected parliament), I felt this was another milestone in moving toward full democracy of our own administration. To institutionalize these changes, we revised the Charter of Tibetans-in-Exile, and this amendment was adopted by the Assembly of Tibetan People's Deputies on June 14, 2001. Within this new structure, Professor Samdhong Rinpoche became the first directly elected leader of the administration, taking the title of Kalon Tripa (chief of the cabinet).

The thinking behind this was that were the issue of Tibet not to be resolved in my lifetime, we would need to institutionalize the movement for the freedom of our people so that it could remain vibrant for a long time to come. As long as I am alive, of course, I remain fully committed to doing all I can. However, I have always believed that overreliance on any single individual, especially in the case of the fate of an entire people, is unstable. To be honest, I feel that sometimes Tibetans rely on me too much.

On October 22, 2002, at the initiative of Beijing, my envoy Lodi Gyari met with an important official from the United Front Work Department (the body within the Chinese Communist Party charged with relations with, among others, peoples that the People's Republic of China considers "national minorities"), in Ottawa, Canada. This would open a new phase in our talks with Beijing, leading altogether to nine rounds of formal discussions, the last one ending in January 2010. Throughout this process, our representatives worked closely with me as well as with Samdhong Rinpoche, the Kalon Tripa.

We knew that the first few meetings would have to be devoted to establishing personal relationships and trust between my delegation, composed of four members and headed by my two envoys, Lodi Gyari and Kelsang Gyaltsen, and their Chinese counterparts from the United Front assigned with the task. Since by then the Summer Olympics of 2008 had already been awarded to Beijing, understandably a key concern on the part of the representatives of Beijing at our meetings seemed to be about ensuring a successful hosting of the Olympics. During the fourth meeting, which took place at the Chinese Embassy in Bern in 2005, my envoys made a serious effort to persuade their Chinese counterparts to consider a proposed visit to China by me on a pilgrimage, especially to the sacred site of Mount Wutai Shan, which I have always wanted to visit.

One important reason they shared was that, according to Tibetan tradition, I was soon approaching what is called a *kag* year (literally, "an obstacle year"), and the custom is to go on an important pilgrimage to ward off any potential obstacles.* They also made the request that permission be granted for a low-key visit by a small group of monks from the Tibetan exile community in India, who would make offerings at the presence of the sacred images in the Jokhang Temple in Lhasa, as well as various monasteries and sacred sites in Tibet, praying for my good health. The envoys also presented the idea that such a private visit from me might offer an opportunity to share with the Beijing leadership directly my aspirations for the Tibetan people. The Chinese delegation responded that this was a matter of national importance and that they themselves were not in a position to make any decision. They told my envoys that they would pass this suggestion on to the Beijing leadership. Sadly, nothing came of this suggestion.

While these dialogues did offer an opportunity for frank exchanges, including presenting a formal document that outlined what we meant by a genuine autonomy for the Tibetan people within the People's Republic of China, we were never able to engage substantively at a level higher than the leadership of the United Front. This meant that it was impossible to get to the point where we could negotiate with someone or a body empowered to make actual decisions. Between the seventh and the eighth meetings, the Beijing Olympics of 2008 took place. With the world's attention on China, especially that of the international media throughout the run-up, many Tibetans and sympathizers in various parts of the free world seized the opportunity to protest against what was happening inside Tibet and that no visible progress was being made from our dialogues with Beijing.

During that year's anniversary of the Lhasa uprising of March 10, 1959, spontaneous protests erupted in Lhasa as well, and rapidly spread across the Tibetan plateau. In fact, on March 10, 2008, when I first

---

* There is the belief in the Tibetan tradition that, depending on one's birth year, there are specific ages when one might be more susceptible to illness and other adversities.

The Dalai Lama was called upon to assume temporal leadership of Tibet and its people in November 1950, when he was barely sixteen.

The Fourteenth Dalai Lama with his family. *From left to right:* his mother, Dekyi Tsering; elder sister, Tsering Dolma; brothers, Gyalo Thondup, Taktser Rinpoche, and Lobsang Samten; His Holiness; his younger sister, Jetsun Pema; and youngest brother, Tenzin Choegyal.

Being greeted by Chairman Mao Zedong at the inaugural
National People's Congress in Beijing, September 1954.

With the Panchen Lama, accompanied by Vice Premier Deng
Xiaoping, walking past well-wishers at a railway station
in Beijing, 1954.

With the Panchen Lama (who was sixteen years of age to the
Dalai Lama's nineteen) in Beijing, 1954.

Hosting a banquet to celebrate Losar (Tibetan New Year) in Beijing. *From left to right:* Premier Zhou Enlai, the Panchen Lama, Mao Zedong, the Dalai Lama, and Lui Shaoqi (who would go on to succeed Mao as chairman).

With Indian Prime Minister Jawaharlal Nehru and Premier Zhou Enlai at an official function in India, 1956.

In February 1959, while tensions were building in Lhasa, Tibet's capital city—which would erupt in the Tibetan People's Uprising of March 10—the Dalai Lama, still a student, had to undertake his rigorous Geshe Lharam final exams.

The Dalai Lama being escorted by Tibetan soldiers and resistance
fighters as he escaped into exile in March 1959.

With his entourage after fleeing from the Tibetan capital city of
Lhasa, March 1959.

With his youngest brother, Tenzin Choegyal, walking down a
pass during the long journey to freedom, March 1959.

Large parts of Drepung Monastery (founded near Lhasa in 1416),
still in ruins in 1993, were completely destroyed by the People's
Liberation Army during the Cultural Revolution.

Spontaneous uprising of the Tibetan people in Lhasa on March 10, 1959.

Adruk Gompo Tashi, the leader of the Tibetan resistance, called the Volunteer Force for the Protection of the Faith (*tensung danglang magmi*).

Tibetan refugees arriving in India, following the Dalai Lama's escape into exile in March 1959. Altogether, up to 80,000 Tibetan refugees would manage to flee into exile from 1959 to the early 1960s.

Tibetan refugees working in road construction in northern India. The fall of Tibet to China meant that India now needed to militarily guard their more than 3,000 kilometers of border with Tibet.

Nehru visits the Dalai Lama in April 1959, in Mussoorie, where His Holiness was first hosted after his arrival in India.

Visiting the site of a new Tibetan settlement being established in southern India in the early 1960s.

Visiting another site of a new Tibetan settlement in southern India. The monk official on the far left was the Dalai Lama's senior secretary, Tara Tenzin Choenyi.

Greeting some of the Tibetan refugee children in
the early 1960s, at the Dalai Lama's first residence in
Dharamsala, Swarg Ashram.

With young Tibetan
students at a makeshift
school in northern India
in the early 1960s.

With young refugee children in the early 1960s.

With Indira Gandhi, Nehru's daughter, who would later become
India's third prime minister.

Conducting the Kalachakra Empowerment Ceremony (a major multi-day religious event connected with peace in Tibetan Buddhism) in Dharamsala, 1970.

Receiving the Nobel Peace Prize in 1989 in Oslo, Norway.

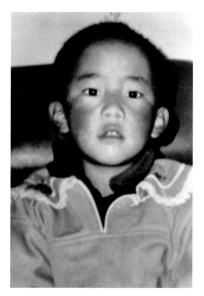

The Eleventh Panchen Lama, Gendun Choekyi Nyima, photographed at age six. To date, there is no reliable information on his whereabouts, and this photograph remains banned inside Tibet.

Receiving the Congressional Gold Medal from President Bush at
the United States Capitol, October 27, 2017.

heard through a message from Lhasa that a group of several hundred monks from Drepung Monastery were walking toward the city center demanding religious freedom, I was deeply worried and immediately prayed for their safety. The next day, several monks from Sera marched to protest, demanding the release of many monks detained the previous day. Then monks and nuns from other monasteries, including Ganden Monastery, began marching to Lhasa to join the protests. The police reacted brutally and arrested many. This cruel treatment of the monks and nuns was the spark that lit a fuse long laid by Chinese oppressive rule in Tibet. On March 14, there was a massive protest, demanding the release of the monks and nuns. When the police regrouped on that day, they were joined by the army, with tear gas, machine guns, and armored personnel carriers. From March 14, spontaneous protests spread to Amdo and Kham (the northeastern and eastern parts of Tibet) and lasted through much of April.

There were international demonstrations across many countries during the Olympic torch relays, expressing solidarity with the Tibetan people. This began with a disruption of the speech by the head of the Beijing organizing committee at the inaugural torch ceremony in Athens on March 24, 2008. A number of world leaders called on the Chinese authorities to exercise restraint and reiterated their support for the dialogue process we had begun. On the part of Beijing, however, instead of taking stock and reflecting on why the Tibetans should be reacting this way, the Chinese propaganda machine responded to the crisis by blaming me personally. They accused me of instigating these protests inside Tibet. On March 18, 2008, the leader of the Communist Party in Tibet said, "The Dalai is a wolf in monk's robes, a devil with a human face but the heart of a beast. . . . We are now engaged in a fierce blood-and-fire battle with the Dalai clique, a life-and-death battle between us and the enemy."

During his state visit to Laos, the Chinese Premier Wen Jiabao urged me (while speaking to international media) to calm the situation inside Tibet. In response, I offered to speak directly with the Chinese leader Hu Jintao. I did not hear back. Meanwhile, Communist China's state television broadcast across the mainland, portraying the Tibetan protests as an attack against the Chinese, with the propaganda having the tragic consequence of racism against Tibetans living in the Chinese mainland. I heard stories of discrimination against Tibetans, involving refusal by hotels to rent rooms, public transportation such as trains and airlines refusing to sell tickets, and Tibetans being spat upon in parks. Unwittingly, what the Chinese state media have succeeded in creating is a generation of deeply resentful Tibetans, who will never forget their experience of overt racism.

While the official Chinese government response to the spontaneous Tibetan protests was harsh, encouragingly, many Chinese, including intellectuals and writers in mainland China, showed unprecedented support and sympathy. More than a thousand articles appeared in the Chinese language from both within and outside the People's Republic of China expressing their support for the Tibetan cause, urging the government to engage in substantive dialogue with me. Liu Xiaobo, one of the architects of Charter 08 (a manifesto for human rights in China issued in December 2008) and who would later receive the Nobel Peace Prize in 2010 for his long and nonviolent struggle for fundamental human rights in China, was among those who wrote. A glimpse at the titles of some of these publications from Chinese authors—"Federalism Is the Best Way to Resolve the Issue of Tibet," "The Middle Way Approach Is the Panacea for Curing the Disease of Ethnic Animosity," "The Dalai Lama's Middle Way Approach Is the Right Way of Resolving the Issue of Tibet"—unmistakably demonstrates their support for our approach to resolve the issue of Tibet.

Meanwhile, I issued a series of appeals. I urged the Tibetans to practice nonviolence and not to waver from this path, however dire the situation might be. I also reminded them that, right from the beginning, I had supported the hosting of the Summer Olympics in Beijing, and I urged the Tibetans not to hinder the games, because I understood that the hosting of the Olympics was a matter of great pride to the world's most populous nation. (In fact, when I was invited to speak at the US Congressional Gold Medal Ceremony in October 2007, I spoke of how I have always encouraged world leaders to engage with China, and that I have supported China's entry into the World Trade Organization [WTO] as well as the awarding of the Summer Olympics to Beijing.) I emphasized again that our struggle is with the leadership of the People's Republic of China, and not with the Chinese people. We should never cause misunderstanding or do something that would hurt the Chinese people.

To the Chinese brothers and sisters across the world, I made appeals asking them to support my call for the end of the brutal crackdown inside Tibet, and to help dispel the misunderstandings between our two communities. I emphasized that the Chinese and Tibetan people share a common spiritual heritage in Mahayana Buddhism, that we worship the Buddha of compassion and cherish compassion for all suffering beings as one of the highest spiritual ideals. Concerned about the danger of rising enmity between Tibetans and Chinese, I also suggested to Tibetans living in different parts of the world to establish Sino-Tibetan Friendship Associations. Such associations could extend invitations to Chinese living in the same city to Tibetan festivals and celebrations and to share meals together.

Meanwhile, I instructed my envoys to yet again contact their Chinese counterparts and seek a meeting. It was a matter of urgency to defuse the situation inside Tibet, and to urge the Chinese leadership to investigate the real causes for these widespread protests and take seriously the genuine grievances of the Tibetan people. Our initiative led to an informal meeting between my two envoys and their Chinese counterparts in Shenzhen in May 2008. At that meeting, both sides agreed to hold the seventh round of formal dialogues in Beijing in July 2008. Soon after, on May 12, 2008, a massive earthquake struck the province of Sichuan, including the Tibetan area of Ngawa (Ngaba). When we heard the news, large-scale prayers were held for the victims of the earthquake across the Tibetan communities in the diaspora, including at the Thekchen Choeling Temple here in Dharamsala. I also made a personal donation to the relief fund through the International Federation of Red Cross and Red Crescent Societies. Later, in the same month, when I was visiting London, the Chinese Embassy there was gracious enough to permit my secretary to sign on my behalf the condolence book at the embassy, expressing my solidarity with the victims.

With respect to our dialogue, by the end of the sixth meeting, I was feeling frustrated that we had gone round in circles, having talks about talks. There is a Tibetan saying, "Your steps should contribute to your journey." So, after the sixth meeting, I asked my team to present me with an analysis of the conversation thus far. At that stage, they remained hopeful. They felt that, after all the hard work of listening to each side's complaints and concerns, perhaps a space had been created now to get into actual discussions.

Thus, the seventh round of meetings took place in Beijing in July 2008. At the start of this round, my envoys expressed to their counterparts that by now our discussions should touch upon substantive issues. They also shared my and the Tibetan community's rising frustration and impatience. We were asked for a formal statement of our views on the degree or form of autonomy we sought for our next meeting.

While our position had been clear for years, we prepared a formal document entitled "Memorandum on Genuine Autonomy for the Tibetan People," and presented this at the eighth round of talks on October 31, 2008. We reiterated our commitment not to pursue separation or independence but instead a solution to the Tibetan issue through seeking genuine autonomy compatible with the principles of autonomy in the Constitution of the People's Republic of China. Given that our foundational objective was (and remains) the protection of Tibetans as a people with our unique culture, language, and religion, a key point of our proposal was to seek a framework within which all Tibetan areas could enjoy the same form of protection and governance. We also stressed that if our autonomy was to be genuine, it needed to include the right, within the People's Republic of China, to self-government on the local level.

This document was in a format and language that carefully respected the Constitution of the People's Republic of China as well as the Law on Regional National Autonomy. We wanted to assure Beijing that we truly believed that our goals could be realized within the existing framework of the People's Republic of China and, to our understanding, fully compatible with its constitution.

Even though the Chinese knew the "Memorandum on Genuine Autonomy for the Tibetan People" represented our sincere attempt to present a formal basis for discussions, Beijing chose to react negatively, including making a public statement on November 10, less than a fortnight after our meeting. They accused us of "ethnic splitting" and "seeking a legal basis for so-called Tibetan independence or semi-independence or covert independence." They stated emphatically that "the doorway to Tibetan independence, semi-independence, or covert independence will never be open." (This same line of criticism was repeated later in China's white paper of 2009, issued to mark the fiftieth year since 1959, entitled *Fifty Years of Democratic Reform in Tibet*, in which it was declared that "There is no way for the Dalai clique to uphold 'Tibetan independence,' neither will it succeed in its attempt to seek semi-independence or covert independence under the banner of 'a high degree of autonomy.'") But the autonomy we were asking for was not, as claimed by the Chinese side, some kind of "high degree of autonomy" that is outside the Law of National Autonomy of the People's Republic of China.

In view of Beijing's initial negative response, and in accord with our Charter of Tibetans-in-Exile, a five-day special meeting was held November 17–22, 2008, to discuss our ongoing dialogue with Beijing. Nearly six hundred delegates representing Tibetan communities from different parts of the world as well as key sectors deliberated and, once again, overwhelmingly supported our Middle Way Approach.

A month later, addressing the European Parliament in Brussels on

December 4, 2008, I responded to the Chinese critique by underlining that our intention had never been to expel non-Tibetans from the Tibetan plateau, but rather to express our concern about the induced mass movement of primarily Han, but also some other nationalities, into many Tibetan areas, which in turn had marginalized the native Tibetan population and threatened Tibet's fragile environment. Confronted with such unreasonable and excessively negative responses to our proposal, I could not help sharing my frustration, saying that although my faith in the Chinese people remained unshaken, my faith in the Chinese government was becoming thinner by the day.

Beijing's official response to the memorandum was deeply disappointing. Throughout these rounds of negotiation, which began in 2002, at no point did the Chinese side present any substantive proposal. Despite their immediate and willful attack on our proposal, we nonetheless prepared a note on the memorandum responding to their reactions and claims, on the assumption that the issues may have been misunderstood. In this clarification note, we also addressed what the Chinese side referred to as "the three adherences," forming a kind of boundary line that could not be crossed. They are (1) the adherence to the leadership of the country by the Chinese Communist Party, (2) the adherence to socialism with Chinese characteristics, and (3) the adherence to the Law on Regional National Autonomy. Our clarification document was presented at the ninth round of discussions in January 2010. It turned out to be the end of the conversation. Formal dialogue has not resumed since.

ON MARCH 19, 2011, WHEN I was seventy-five years old, I made a public announcement that I had decided to go into full retirement, thereby completing the process of devolution of political authority that began in 2001, when we had our first directly elected full political leader within the exiled Tibetan community. I said that rule by kings and religious figures was outdated, and we had to follow the trend of the free world, which is toward democracy. Furthermore, it was most appropriate for me as the fourteenth in the line of the Dalai Lamas to voluntarily, happily, and proudly end the temporal authority of the Dalai Lama so that a democratically elected leadership could take on the role. On May 29 of that year, we were able to make the necessary preparations, including the amendment of the Charter of Tibetans-in-Exile, to institutionalize this fundamental change. This amendment of the charter was preceded by a special assembly of the Tibetan people, and my final executive act was formally signing this revised charter; with that, I went into full retirement, devolving all secular authority to the elected Tibetan leadership. In August 2011, having won the election, Lobsang Sangay assumed the office of Kalon Tripa (chief of the cabinet) and later took on the title of Sikyong (president of the Central Tibetan Administration), and after serving two five-year terms, in 2021, Penpa Tsering, the current Sikyong, was elected.

In announcing this full retirement from my political position in May 2011, I reassured the Tibetan people both within Tibet and in exile that my decision to devolve political authority did not in any way reflect a loss of interest or determination, or a giving up of my involvement in the Tibetan struggle for truth and freedom. As a Tibetan, and as someone karmically connected with the lineage of the Dalai Lamas, there is simply no way that I could abandon the cause of Tibet and its people. My motivation was solely that of what I believed to be best for the Tibetan people, especially with respect to ensuring the long-term sustainability of our struggle for freedom. If the Tibetan issue were to remain unresolved for several more decades, then we all knew that a time would come when I would be no longer able to lead the movement. If, instead, we instituted a system while I am alive whereby the Central Tibetan Administration took on the full responsibility of political leadership, our administration would have the time to acquire the necessary skills and experience to function without the need for my leadership. And, if during this period of transition, challenges were to arise, of course I would be there to assist in whatever way I was able. Also, this act of devolution would demonstrate to the world, and especially to Beijing, that our struggle pertains to the well-being of an entire people, not to that of the Dalai Lama or his institution. I was ending the Dalai Lama's political leadership of the Tibetan people not only voluntarily but also happily and proudly. This full devolution of power not only was a decision pertaining to my person, but it also marked the ending of the temporal authority of the Dalai Lamas, which had been established in the seventeenth century in the era of one of my predecessors, the Fifth Dalai Lama.

As it was becoming clear that our discussions with Beijing were not leading to any meaningful outcome, many Tibetan people grew desperate. One tragic expression of this was the wave of self-immolations that occurred inside Tibet, beginning on February 27, 2009, when a young monk, Tapey, from Kirti Monastery in the Ngawa county (in northeastern Tibet) set fire to himself in the marketplace. Since then, more than 160 monks, nuns, and laypeople—most of them young— have resorted to this form of protest, mainly in Tibet, but a few also in India and Nepal. One of the more recent instances took place on February 24, 2022. Tsewang Norbu, a famous singer with a large following both in Tibet as well as in mainland China, self-immolated in front of the Potala Palace. He was twenty-five years old. I am told that his songs were removed from music platforms in China, and all news relating to his death has been suppressed. In fact, his entire online presence, including any biographical information, has been erased such that no trace of his existence is to be found online in any resources available to people in China and Tibet. I am told that Norbu's father took his own life in May, after being repeatedly harassed by the Chinese police. This latest example powerfully demonstrates that the grievances of the Tibetan people transcend socioeconomic status and reside much deeper in their very psyche. These acts of self-immolation express the depth of desperation, hopelessness, and unhappiness Tibetan people fundamentally feel in the face of Communist China's rule in their homeland.

The first known instance of Tibetan self-immolation actually took place in New Delhi, in 1998. I personally went to see Thupten Ngodup as he lay dying in a burn unit in a hospital in the Indian capital. One of the first times I spoke publicly about my feelings on this very painful issue was at a press meeting during a visit to Tokyo in June 2010. It was about a year after that young monk at Kirti Monastery in northeastern Tibet had self-immolated. In response to a question from a journalist, I shared three things as part of my response: first, that I feel deep sadness and pain every time I hear about such an incident; second, that I cannot encourage such drastic acts because I do not believe it will have any real effect on the Chinese authorities; and third, that it is my hope that these tragic acts on the part of the Tibetans will make the Chinese authorities ask what is motivating these young Tibetans. To this day, I feel conflicted about this issue of self-immolation. On the one hand, I can empathize with the profound helplessness Tibetans feel about what is happening inside their homeland. On the other hand, the loss of every life is a loss too many. This act is undoubtedly extreme, but the fact remains that those who have committed it chose not to kill others, only to sacrifice their own lives.

⁜

CHAPTER 13

Taking Stock

As I've shared, since I came into exile in 1959, we have had only two substantial periods of discussions with Beijing. Neither of these have led to a stage where real substantive negotiation at the highest level could take place. Naturally, I have asked myself why these rounds of dialogue did not lead to a negotiated solution to the issue of Tibet.

Looking back, when we had our first series of conversations, spurred by Deng's overture to my brother in March 1979, and the latter's subsequent meeting with Hu Yaobang, we thought there was a real potential opening. On our part, we had placed much hope in the possibility of really getting to the specifics of how, within the framework of Deng Xiaoping's original statement—"except for independence, everything is negotiable"—a lasting solution could be found that was mutually acceptable. The aim was that these dialogues would culminate in an agreement formally signed by the Chinese leader and me. At least we knew that, at the very highest level of the Chinese leadership, there was an expressed willingness to talk. Moreover, it seemed clear that the Chinese government was genuinely open to serious discussions about unresolved international issues that remained at the heart of the

People's Republic of China's formation as a modern country. For in the same month, March 1979, Deng invited the governor of Hong Kong for discussions about the future of what was then a British colony, which was followed by a series of international negotiations, concluding in 1984 with the agreement to hand over the colony to China in 1997.

During one of the earlier rounds of meetings in 1982, the Chinese side shared with our delegation a copy of the text of the Special Administrative Region (SAR) being proposed that could be applied to the status of Hong Kong, which was later adopted as Article 31 of the Constitution of the People's Republic of China, and suggested that we study it, since the proposed Special Administrative Region could have relevance for Tibet. My delegation understood this to mean that crafting a solution along the lines of Article 31 could be possible, which would conform to the basic principle enunciated by Deng. In the end, though, as we've seen, the Chinese side showed no serious interest.

With regard to the second period of dialogues, 2002–2010, looking back with the benefit of hindsight, I wonder if there was ever a genuine intention on the part of the Chinese leadership for substantive discussion. Our conversations never went beyond the level of that wing of the United Front within the Chinese Communist Party charged with dealing with national minorities. One might ask why we persisted in this context. The answer is simple. In the end, the problem of Tibet should be and can only be solved by the Tibetan people and the Chinese people themselves sitting down and talking. There is no other viable option. By virtue of having become the Dalai Lama, it has been my responsibility and my role in life to speak and to keep on speaking on behalf of the Tibetan people.

One explicit response from Beijing to our "Memorandum on Genuine Autonomy for the Tibetan People" came in 2013 in the form of China's white paper on Tibet entitled *Development and Progress of Tibet*. It accused us of having "put forward the so-called concepts of 'Greater Tibet' and 'a high degree of autonomy,' which in fact go against China's actual conditions, and violate the Constitution and relevant laws." Perhaps the accusation about "Greater Tibet" was a reference to our proposal that all Tibetan areas—composed of the three provinces of Ü-Tsang, Kham, and Amdo—be governed under a single administration to ensure a uniform policy across the Tibetan plateau. This is, in fact, not a new idea. Before his death in 1989, the Panchen Lama, acting in his capacity as the vice chairman of the National People's Congress within the People's Republic of China, stated that the desire for the establishment of an autonomous region for a unified Tibetan nationality was appropriate and in accordance with the legal rules. By "legal rules," the Panchen Lama was referring to the Chinese Communist Party's own nationalities doctrine. This states that autonomous territorial units should correspond to places where nationalities live in compact and contiguous areas. According to this doctrine, the entire Tibetan plateau—composed of the three provinces of Ü-Tsang, Kham, and Amdo—should be within a single autonomous region. Also, earlier in 1956, a special committee was set up by the Chinese Central Government that included the senior Communist Party member Sangye Yeshe (known also as Tien Bao)—a rare early Tibetan Communist who had the confidence of Chairman Mao—to draft a detailed plan for the integration of the Tibetan areas into a single autonomous region. This initiative was thwarted by ultra-leftist elements within the Chinese Communist Party. There is also a precedent in the People's Republic of China's dealings with other nationalities where districts once split into separate areas were later brought under a single administration. In 1979, for example, the breakaway areas of Inner Mongolia were brought back within the autonomous region of Inner Mongolia. The heart of the matter is really about what might be the best way to protect the Tibetan people with their distinct language, culture, and spiritual heritage.

In our dealings with Beijing, on our side, there was indeed a clarity of purpose and a recognizable line of command by which my envoys were reporting directly to me and I, in turn, was speaking on behalf of the Tibetan people, both within Tibet and in exile. Especially when the second series of dialogues began, the leaders of the team were explicitly designated as my envoys. This meant that the Chinese side would always know who they were talking to. But for us as outsiders, it was difficult to know whom exactly one was dealing with on the Chinese side. First of all, when leadership change takes place in the Chinese Communist Party, what that means can be opaque: in retrospect, there was a radical shift between the era of Mao and that of Deng; yet the nuances of change between Deng and Jiang Zemin, between Jiang and Hu Jintao, and between Hu and Xi Jinping were extremely difficult to gauge and navigate in real time. Moreover, in dealing with any Chinese leader, it is not clear if one is speaking to an empowered individual or someone who is caught in the complex web of power relations with other members of the Politburo. For example, the overtures of Jiang Zemin in 1998 may have been sincere, but they seemed to have been thwarted within the leadership. In view of this point, since Xi Jinping has emerged as the most powerful Chinese leader since Deng Xiaoping, I had hoped that he would seize the opportunity for a bold vision to solve the issue of Tibet. I was aware that President Xi had made positive remarks about the importance of Buddhism, such as in China's struggle against a moral void that has manifested in widespread corruption. This view would later be confirmed when he visited the headquarters of the United Nations Educational, Scientific and Cultural Organization (UNESCO) in Paris, where he made a remark about how Buddhism had made a deep impact on the religious belief, philosophy, literature, and customs of the Chinese people. Some people also told me that Xi's mother was a practicing Buddhist. And, of course, as mentioned earlier, I had personally known Xi Jinping's father, having met him during my visit to Beijing in 1954–1955. Xi's father, who had suffered during the Cultural Revolution, even though he was an ally of Deng Xiaoping, had opposed the brutal crackdown against the students' protest of Tiananmen. So I had hopes that President Xi would have more personal empathy for the Tibetan people. In fact, when it was announced that Xi Jinping would visit Delhi in 2014, I even communicated my wish to meet him in person. Unfortunately, nothing came of this gesture.

Two important questions come to mind: Were the Chinese ever serious about substantive negotiations on Tibet? What lessons should we learn from our history of dealing with the People's Republic of China thus far for the future of our struggle for freedom?

Some of our international supporters have made the point that the Chinese side was never sincere in their intention to resolve the situation. They say that what mattered to China was to be seen talking, rather than to actually talk. Its motives for this in the 1980s would have been to facilitate the negotiations about Hong Kong and Macau (which were, of course, a huge international triumph for Deng Xiaoping), later to enable China to open its economy internationally, and then to attract international acceptance of its coming of age on the world stage, such as the hosting of the Summer Olympic Games in 2008.

I knew Deng Xiaoping personally in the 1950s, and when I received his overture, I genuinely believed that he was serious. This belief was strengthened further when Hu Yaobang visited Tibet and publicly acknowledged some of the mistakes the Chinese Communist Party had made in relation to the Tibetan people, followed by Hu Yaobang's meeting with my brother Gyalo Thondup. Yet the discussions that ensued led nowhere, their proposals never going beyond the issue of my personal status and return.

Let me turn to the second question: What lessons should we learn from our experience in these dialogues? First and foremost, once both sides have made the commitment to the path of negotiation, there needs to be genuine trust in each other's good intention. This is crucial so that events in the world—there will always be events during a long period of dialogue—do not derail the ongoing dialogue. Second, as part of the protection of mutual trust, there needs to be an open line of communication so there is a mechanism to immediately allay any possible suspicions or doubt that could arise for whatever reasons, including especially public statements from either party. Third, in any negotiation where there is enormous power disparity, as was the case with our dialogue, the stronger side needs to demonstrate greater magnanimity and respect to its dialogue partner.

I am told that in a negotiation there will be a give and take on both sides, and my approach has always been to state honestly what I think the solution we are striving to obtain should look like. As my two envoys as well as their colleagues who joined them in the various rounds of talk know, my approach in our dialogues has been sincere and simple. As a monk, honesty matters to me deeply. So I told my envoys that I wanted to present in clear and candid terms what my actual objectives were, rather than starting with some initial "negotiating position" that could then be pared down to what I was actually seeking. Hence, the proposals I have made represent, as I have already stated, major departures from a demand for a restoration of Tibetan independence. They entail significant accommodation on our part. As a people of an occupied country, we Tibetans have the right to the restoration of our independence; but for reasons I have explained above, I believe that it is possible for us Tibetans to find a way to live within the family of the People's Republic of China provided there is a genuine respect for our rights, dignity, and needs as a people with unique linguistic, cultural, religious, and historical heritage.

To date, I do not believe Beijing has succeeded in creating a multi-nation state within which the Tibetan people could truly feel that they have a home. In other words, it has failed to realize what was envisioned in the important part of its name, "People's Republic of China," whose Chinese equivalence contains the word "*gunghe*" (Tibetan, *chithun*), which connotes a "harmonious union." I often cite the example of the Soviet Union (formally known as the Union of Soviet Socialist Republics), before its collapse, as an example at least of a serious attempt at creating a modern multi-nation state. Unlike the name "People's Republic of China," the words "Russia" or "Russian" do not figure anywhere in the name of the modern composite state. This simple fact made it easier for non-Russians to identify with the new state, and made it possible also for even non-Russians like Stalin and Brezhnev to become leaders of the Soviet Union. Communist China, on the other hand, has not yet succeeded in creating an inclusive modern multi-nation state within which the Tibetans could feel at home. The simple truth is no Tibetan will ever say, "I am a Chinese."

My stance on how best to resolve the issue of Tibet has been consistent since direct discussions with Beijing began in 1979. I have called this the Middle Way Approach. At the core of this approach was the search for a robust framework that would offer the ability for the Tibetans to continue to survive as a distinct people with dignity, with their unique language, culture, ecology, and Buddhist faith. Furthermore, in my approach I have always striven to respect the principle that it is important to take seriously the perspectives and interests of both sides. What matters most to China seems to be territorial integrity and stability, while what matters most to us is a genuine autonomy that guarantees self-governance in the arena of language, culture, ecology, and religion. Even if and when a mutually acceptable agreement is found through negotiation, a robust compliance mechanism is essential to ensure that both sides abide by the terms agreed upon. I say this from my own personal experience and from observing the situation of Hong Kong in the last decade.

While our formal dialogue with Beijing came to an end in 2010, up until 2019, I did maintain informal and at the time confidential contacts with Beijing leadership through individual Chinese. Among those who came to see me and speak with me were a few who did seem to have access to important leaders in Beijing. Some of those who came to speak with me had a singular aim: to persuade me to return "home." At these meetings, I made it clear that at present such discussion was quite premature. I said that we should instead work toward paving the way for me to visit China and Tibet, especially on a pilgrimage. Perhaps Beijing felt that, given my age, I might be more amenable now to going back home. Behind this informal invitation might also have been the belief that once the Dalai Lama "returned," the issue of Tibet would be "resolved," with the question answered in the form of my permanent return. If this is the case, this would mean that after several leadership changes over four decades, and despite two series of dialogues (1979–1989 and 2002–2010), Beijing has not moved beyond the five points Hu Yaobang presented, all pertaining exclusively to my own status, with no attempt at addressing the real issue—the well-being of the Tibetan people.

It is most unfortunate that Beijing did not seize on the opportunity I had offered to resolve the issue of Tibet in a manner that is mutually beneficial. I do not believe that Beijing failed to understand what I was offering. The only rational conclusion I can draw is simply this: *Although there might have been at one point a genuine wish and desire to resolve the issue of Tibet through negotiation, there was neither the courage nor the necessary political will to do so on the part of Chinese leadership.* It is my sincere hope that Beijing will find the necessary courage to resolve the long-standing issue of Tibet through peaceful means before it is too late.

CHAPTER 14

＊

What Gives Me Hope

Although to date there has been no meaningful breakthrough with the Beijing government, what gives me hope is that the relationship between the two peoples—Tibetans and Chinese—has not been irreparably damaged. As more and more ordinary Chinese come to understand the issue of Tibet, they are coming to understand and sympathize with our just struggle. On my part too, I have cherished whatever opportunities I have had to engage with Chinese people, especially those who are from mainland China. For example, through the auspices of the Brookings Institution, I have had a series of dialogues with prominent Chinese scholars who deeply care about the future of China. These conversations, which were quite open and candid, took place in Washington, DC, at the Aspen Institute and, memorably, in Ladakh, India. At one such meeting in Washington, DC, an important focus of the conversation turned to the issue of moral crisis in light of the aggressive "get rich" culture sweeping across China. Personally, I have found these conversations deeply helpful in understanding current China and its challenges and opportunities. I have also had similar dialogues with Chinese scholars in other places like Berlin, Geneva, and Hamburg.

Thanks to the noted Chinese intellectual Wang Lixiong, who is married to the amazingly brave Tibetan poet and activist Tsering Woeser, in 2010 I also had the rare opportunity to engage in a live Q and A with Chinese from inside China. Announcing this live internet dialogue a few days earlier, Wang had asked for internet users in China to pose questions to me. Web users were then asked to rank these questions according to their preference, and through this democratic process, eight questions were selected. The questions I was asked I took to be representative of what many people in China truly wanted to know about and from me. So let me briefly share here this exchange of questions and answers.

One question was in relation to my view on the future role of religious leaders in Tibet, and in particular the status of the Dalai Lama and the Panchen Lama. Here, I replied that as early as 1969 I had issued a formal statement that the question of whether the Dalai Lama institution should continue or not is for the Tibetan people to decide. I also told them that as soon as Tibet attains genuine autonomy I would hold no official position in any future Tibetan government.

There was a question about how Chinese and Tibetans can nurture and sustain good relations as two peoples. I stressed that if Chinese and Tibetans were to approach one another on the basis of equality and recognition of each other's shared humanity, there would be no barriers for communication. On this basis, many problems could be solved easily. I said that, in my own personal approach, no matter what country I visit, I always emphasize the importance of our common humanity. I said that even when we meet to discuss some difficult problem, it is crucial for the two sides to first connect with each other at the human level. This is the level where we are all exactly the same. Only when this fact is recognized and mutually honored can the parties address the more challenging issues that might have arisen through differences of race, religion, culture, language, or politics.

I was then asked why the various meetings between the Tibetans and the Chinese government have always proved to be fruitless. What were the exact questions that had been so intractable over the decades? I said that the main problem was that the Chinese government kept on insisting that there is no such thing as a Tibetan issue; there is only the Dalai Lama problem. But the simple truth is that I have no demands of my own. The issue pertains to the fate of the Tibetan people, their culture, language, religion, and fragile ecology. I said that if and when the day comes that the Chinese leadership is ready to face the Tibet question and work for its solution, I will lend my full support, because our objective is to seek a meaningful place for Tibet and its people within the family of the People's Republic of China. I also said that the Beijing government keeps stressing stability in Tibet, but true stability can come only from trust, which cannot be achieved through force and repression.

Personally, I found this live internet dialogue truly memorable. The fact that I could have a live conversation with Chinese brothers and sisters from inside China was almost unbelievable. What I took home from this dialogue was that many thoughtful Chinese, who care about the future of their country, understand the situation of Tibet and recognize that a lasting solution has to be found that can ensure the survival of the Tibetans as a people. This live exchange with Chinese brothers and sisters gave me hope and reinforced my belief, regardless of the status of our relationship at the governmental and "official" level, that so long as Tibetans and Chinese avoid the path of mutual hatred, there will always be a basis for finding a genuine understanding between our two peoples.

In 2013, during a visit to New York, I had the delightful opportunity to engage with the Chinese artist and activist Ai Weiwei. One question he asked me was if I hoped to return to my native land. "Yes, I am hopeful," I said. It is indeed human to miss one's home, even though we Tibetans often say, "Where you are happy, that is your home." I had hoped that I would be able to go back at least once before I die.

Now, with my age approaching ninety, this is looking increasingly unlikely.

During my trips to North America, Europe, Japan, and Australia, Chinese from various backgrounds came to see me—ordinary Chinese, intellectuals, writers, artists, business leaders, individuals with access to senior Beijing leadership, former government and military officials. I also met with some high-level Tibetan lamas and Tibetan officials within the Chinese system who had managed to come to see me. So I have had good opportunities to explain to them the need to resolve the issue of Tibet through a path of strict nonviolence and an approach that is mutually beneficial. One of the most moving and emotional meetings with a Chinese I had was that with the wife of the Chinese Nobel Laureate Liu Xiaobo. I met Liu Xia during a trip to Sweden in 2018. The instant she saw me, Liu Xia burst into tears. I consoled her and expressed my deep admiration of Lui Xiaobo's courageous efforts for human rights in China and also her own courage and support of her husband's mission. She said that she wanted to tell me how her husband had a deep respect for me and truly believed that my Middle Way Approach offered a real basis for resolving the long-standing issue of Tibet. She then gave me a copy of a poetry book by her late husband, and, on my part, I gave her Chinese translations of two of my books.

Anyway, this kind of human-to-human contact between Chinese and Tibetans, at the personal level, should really be nurtured and enhanced. And on the part of the Tibetans, it is crucially important to remember that the Chinese people too have suffered under the oppressive rule of the Communist Party. We must also never forget that nations and countries belong to their peoples, not to their governments. No matter how enduring or powerful they might seem at any given time, governments will come and go, but the peoples will always remain. This is a simple truth.

Also, given the large number of Buddhists in China, at the request of relevant organizations, I had the joy of conducting formal teachings in India specifically for Chinese Buddhists, especially since

2009, when the annual tradition was established to offer teachings for them. Among the attendees were also many monastic members, including some from the monasteries at Mount Wutai Shan. On a few occasions, when individual Chinese from the mainland came to see me privately, some of them would weep in my presence and apologize for the sufferings the Tibetan people had experienced under the Communist Chinese rule. And they expressed their deep gratitude that what Beijing had done to the Tibetans had failed in planting seeds of hatred in Tibetans' hearts for the Chinese people. They said that they felt totally at ease when walking around in Dharamsala (where I live) or Bodh Gaya, where thousands of Tibetan Buddhists converge during winter for pilgrimages and Buddhist teachings.

During one of my visits to Paris, I had a meeting with a group of Chinese that I shall never forget. One young man—a student from Inner Mongolia—stood up and said that he had an important message for me from his grandfather. He explained that his grandfather had been part of the cavalry in the People's Liberation Army that attacked Tibet in 1950. All these years later, he asked his grandson to apologize to me on his behalf. I was touched by the depth of sincerity with which the grandson conveyed this apology on behalf of his grandfather.

CHAPTER 15

Situation Today and the Path Forward

Sadly, at present the situation inside Tibet looks grim. The policies of Xi Jinping, who visited Tibet in 2021 (the first visit of a Chinese leader in more than thirty years), seem to be focused on the tightening of control and intensification of measures aimed at assimilation. For example, on the language front, Chinese is being enforced as the primary medium in education, aimed at creating a generation of Tibetans whose first language will be Chinese, not Tibetan. There are worrying reports of children—according to some sources, up to a million—being taken away from their families and placed in Mandarin-only boarding schools, suggesting that the Chinese government is adopting a totally discredited colonial practice. Alarmed by this new development, in December 2023 the European Parliament passed a resolution condemning this kind of forced assimilation of Tibetan children in Chinese state-run boarding schools and called for immediate cessation of the practice. Similar concerns were raised by the United Nations Human Rights Council as well as the United States Congress. This practice, in fact, contradicts China's own constitution, which guarantees that "all nationalities have the freedom to use and develop their own language."

It is also in direct violation of the Law on Regional National Autonomy, which stipulates that schools and other educational institutions with "ethnic minority students may use their own language for teaching." I am deeply concerned by this situation.

On the religious front, there is a new policy of direct control by the Party over monasteries and nunneries, imposing intensified surveillance and control over the monastic communities. I am told that today there are police stations within the compounds of many monasteries. The Tibetan monasteries are also being forced to have Communist Chinese officials within the administration of the monasteries' management. This tightening around the Tibetan people's religious life, including especially the monasteries, began in 2017 with a specific policy adopted by China's State Council's Regulation on Religious Affairs. In brief, various new regulations are being introduced, all aimed at what the Chinese authorities call promoting "Tibetan Buddhism with Chinese characteristics." One of these new regulations states that the monastic curriculum must include courses on politics, laws, regulations, policies, Chinese language, and the history of the relationship between Tibet and the "motherland."

With respect to the general Tibetan populace, I am informed that in Lhasa and elsewhere, there has been a significant increase in pervasive surveillance of both everyday life and internet use. Community leaders, environmental campaigners, philanthropists, and social activists are especially targeted. There is still no news on the fate of the Panchen Lama, while any display of the Tibetan national flag or my portrait remains banned. In effect, a new social experiment is being conducted through intimidation and forced assimilation, amplified by the apparatus of new technology and digital media. Increasingly, the Tibetans inside Tibet are being made to feel that what is wrong with them from the Chinese authorities' perspective is simply that they are Tibetans.

If Beijing were to look at past history, it would see that policies of repression and forced assimilation do not actually work. It is, in fact, counterproductive, with the main result being the creation of generations deeply resentful of Communist China's presence on the Tibetan plateau. If the Chinese leadership truly cares about a stable and harmonious country wherein the Tibetan people could feel at home, its policies need to be grounded in respect for the dignity of Tibetans and to take serious note of their fundamental aspiration to thrive as a people with a distinct language, culture, and religion.

If, in the end, Beijing deems our foundational objective to be incompatible within the framework of the People's Republic of China, then the issue of Tibet will remain intractable for generations. I have always stated that, in the end, it is the Tibetan people who should decide their own fate. Not the Dalai Lama or, for that matter, the Beijing leadership. The simple fact is no one likes their home being taken over by uninvited guests with guns. This is nothing but human nature.

I, for one, do not believe it would be so difficult for the Chinese government to make the Tibetans feel welcome and happy within the family of the People's Republic of China. Like all people, Tibetans would like to be respected, have agency within their own home, and have the freedom to be who they are. The aspirations and the needs of the Tibetan people cannot be met simply through economic development. At its core, the issue is not about bread and butter. It is about the very survival of Tibetans as a people. Finding a resolution of the Tibetan issue would undoubtedly have great benefits for the People's Republic of China. First and foremost, it would confer legitimacy to China's presence on the Tibetan plateau, essential for the status and stability of the People's Republic of China as a modern country composed of multiple nationalities willingly joined in a single family.

In the case of Tibet, for instance, it has now been more than seventy years since Communist China's invasion in 1950. Despite the physical control of the country, through brutal force as well as economic inducements, the Tibetan people's resentment, persistent resistance in various forms, and moments of significant uprising have never gone away. Even though generations and economic conditions have changed, very little has changed when it comes to the Tibetan people's perception and attitude toward those they still view as occupiers. The simple fact is that insofar as the Tibetans on the ground are concerned, the Communist Chinese rule in Tibet remains that of a foreign, unwanted, and oppressive occupying power.

The Tibetan people have lost so much. Their homeland has been forcibly invaded and remains under a suffocating rule. The Tibetan language, culture, and religion are under systematic attack through coercive policies of assimilation. Even the very expression of Tibetaness is increasingly being perceived as a threat "to the unity of the motherland." The only leverage the Tibetan people have left is the moral rightness of their cause and the power of truth. The simple fact is Tibet today remains an occupied territory, and it is only the Tibetan people who can confer or deny legitimacy to the presence of China on the Tibetan plateau.

All my life I have advocated for nonviolence. I have done my utmost to restrain the understandable impulses of frustrated Tibetans, both within and outside Tibet. Especially, ever since our direct conversations after my exile began with Beijing in 1979, I have used all my moral authority and leverage with the Tibetan people, persuading them to seek a realistic solution in the form of a genuine autonomy within the framework of the People's Republic of China. I must admit I remain deeply disappointed that Beijing has chosen not to acknowledge this huge accommodation on the part of the Tibetans, and has failed to capitalize on the genuine potential it offered to come to a lasting solution. At the time of publishing this book, I will be approaching my ninetieth year. If no resolution is found while I am alive, the Tibetan people, especially those inside Tibet, will blame the Chinese leadership and the Communist Party for its failure to reach a settlement with me; many Chinese too, especially Buddhists—some people told me that there are more than two hundred million in mainland China who self-identify as Buddhists—will be disappointed with their government for its failure to solve a problem whose solution has been staring at them for so long.

Given my age, understandably many Tibetans are concerned about what will happen when I am no more. On the political front of our campaign for the freedom of the Tibetan people, we now have a substantial population of Tibetans outside in the free world, so our struggle will go on, no matter what. Furthermore, as far as the day-to-day leadership of our movement is concerned, we now have both an elected executive in the office of the Sikyong (president of the Central Tibetan Administration) and a well-established Tibetan Parliament-in-Exile.

People have often asked me if there will be a next Dalai Lama. As early as the 1960s, I have expressed that whether the Dalai Lama institution should continue or not is a matter for the Tibetan people. So if the Tibetan people feel that the institution has served its purpose and there is now no longer any need for a Dalai Lama, then the institution will cease. In which case, I would be the last Dalai Lama, I have stated. I have also said that if there is continued need, then there will be the Fifteenth Dalai Lama. In particular, in 2011, I convened a gathering of the leaders of all major Tibetan religious traditions, and at the conclusion of this meeting, I issued a formal statement in which I stated that when I turn ninety, I will consult the high lamas of the Tibetan religious traditions as well as the Tibetan public, and if there is a consensus that the Dalai Lama institution should continue, then formal responsibility for the recognition of the Fifteenth Dalai Lama should rest with the Gaden Phodrang Trust (the Office of the Dalai Lama). The Gaden Phodrang Trust should follow the procedures of search and recognition in accordance with past Tibetan Buddhist tradition, including, especially, consulting the oath-bound Dharma protectors* historically connected with the lineage of the Dalai Lamas, as was followed carefully in my own case. On my part, I stated that I will also

---

* *Damden chos skyong* in Tibetan, "oath-bound Dharma protectors," connected with the Dalai Lamas include especially Palden Lhamo and Dorje Drakden (known also as Nechung).

leave clear written instructions on this. For more than a decade now, I have received numerous petitions and letters from a wide spectrum of Tibetan people—senior lamas from the various Tibetan traditions, abbots of monasteries, diaspora Tibetan communities across the world, and many prominent and ordinary Tibetans inside Tibet—as well as Tibetan Buddhist communities from the Himalayan region and Mongolia, uniformly asking me to ensure that the Dalai Lama lineage be continued.

In the official statement I issued in 2011, I also pointed out that it is totally inappropriate for Chinese Communists, who explicitly reject religion, including the idea of past and future lives, to meddle in the system of reincarnation of lamas, let alone that of the Dalai Lama. Such meddling, I pointed out, contradicts their own political ideology and only reveals their double standards. Elsewhere, half joking, I have remarked that before Communist China gets involved in the business of recognizing the reincarnation of lamas, including the Dalai Lama, it should first recognize the reincarnations of its past leaders Mao Zedong and Deng Xiaoping! In summing up my thoughts on the question of the reincarnation of the Dalai Lama in that 2011 official statement, I urged that unless the recognition of the next Dalai Lama is done through traditional Tibetan Buddhist methods, no acceptance should be given by the Tibetan people and Tibetan Buddhists across the world to a candidate chosen for political ends by anyone, including those in the People's Republic of China. Now, since the purpose of a reincarnation is to carry on the work of the predecessor, the new Dalai Lama will be born in the free world so that the traditional mission of the Dalai Lama—that is, to be the voice for universal compassion, the spiritual leader of Tibetan Buddhism, and the symbol of Tibet embodying the aspirations of the Tibetan people—will continue.

CHAPTER 16

Appeal

As I end this book, let me take the opportunity to make some appeals as well as share personal expressions of gratitude.

To my fellow Tibetans: Never lose hope, however dark the sky may become. As our saying goes, "If you fall nine times, you get up nine times." Always remember that a bright sun awaits behind the clouds. We are an ancient people with a long history of resilience. For millennia we *tsampa*-eaters have been the custodians of the expansive Tibetan plateau known as the "roof of the world." Throughout our history of more than two millennia, we have navigated through all sorts of ups and downs, always sure of our identity as a people with our distinct language, culture, and religion, and the core values that define us. Today's dark period of Communist Chinese occupation may seem endless, but in our long history, it is but a brief nightmare. As our Buddhist faith teaches us, nothing is immune to the law of impermanence.

Some might think, given my age and Communist China's position as a global power today, that time is not on our side. I disagree. Yes, the Dalai Lama institution plays today an important role in unifying Tibetans everywhere, but let us not forget that while the Dalai Lama institution is only five hundred years old, Tibet's history is older by more than a millennium and a half. So, I have no doubt that our struggle for freedom will go on, for it pertains to the fate of an ancient nation and its people. As an inherently unstable system, totalitarianism definitely does not have time on its side. Time is on the side of the people, Tibetans as well as Chinese, who aspire for freedom.

What we need is patience, unflagging determination, unity, and courage rooted in the clarity of our goal. Today, after more than six decades of being in exile, the issue of Tibet remains strong in the world's consciousness: this is thanks to our unflagging determination and steadfast commitment to our just cause for the freedom of a people. Saving Tibet is a noble work; it is the work of the dharma, which, as Buddhists, we believe to be the true source of happiness for all beings. Therefore, regardless of the provocation and the understandable human urge to respond to violence with violence, I appeal to you never to give in to this impulse. See the humanity even in our oppressors, because, ultimately, it will be with their humanity that we come to some kind of settlement. But this does not mean that we should allow abuse and the violation of our human dignity to go unchallenged. In whatever ways we can, we must stand up against injustice. Nonviolence does not preclude taking a firm stand and expressing our opposition in a forceful way. Mahatma Gandhi has taught the world the enduring power of what a robust and effective nonviolent struggle means. Especially to my fellow Tibetans who are living in free countries, I say, never forget our brothers and sisters who are oppressed in our own homeland. They look to us as their hope in dark times, and expect us to keep bright the flame of our aspiration for a free way of life.

To the great nation of India and our Indian dharma brothers and sisters: You have been my host and my home since 1959. I have spent more of my life in India than in my own homeland of Tibet. I will never forget the amazing and long generosity you have offered to me and my people in exile. The fact that India gave us a new home, a base, is what enabled us, more than anything else, to reestablish our civilization in exile and to keep the torch of justice for Tibet alight for so many decades. We Tibetans have always looked to India as the source and teacher of wisdom, knowledge, and spirituality in our Buddhist tradition that was received from you many centuries ago. Throughout our long religious and cultural history, India (*arya-bhumi*, "the land of the noble ones") has been our guru, and we Tibetans the *chela* (student). I thank you for your unflagging support of me and my people, and I request of you to continue to extend the same as long as we need it.

To Chinese brothers and sisters: I appeal to you to open your hearts to the ongoing plight of the people of Tibet. The Chinese and Tibetan peoples share a common spiritual heritage in Mahayana Buddhism, and cherish compassion for all suffering beings. I assure you that through the long history of my struggle on behalf of the Tibetan people, I have never harbored enmity against the people of China. I have always urged Tibetans not to give in to hatred due to the injustices inflicted by a cruel government in the name of the Chinese people. I ask you to be vigilant against any attempts to promote racial hatred against the Tibetans, through state propaganda aimed at splitting the long history of good feeling, neighborliness, and friendship between our peoples. I appeal to you to make efforts to understand that the Tibetan struggle for freedom is not only just; it is also not anti-Chinese. Help us find a peaceful, lasting solution to the issue of Tibet through dialogue in the spirit of understanding and accommodation. Over the years, many Chinese scholars and intellectuals have spoken out. I believe many Chinese who know the truth about Tibet, its culture, and its people will come out when they are able to express their true feelings without fear of reprisals. Protecting Tibet is a matter important also to the very heart of China itself. I want to share with you that for me, like for so many across the world, one sad thing is that the amazing economic liberalization of China was not matched with progress in respect for human rights and democratic freedom for your people.

To the nations and peoples of the world, especially those who have stood in solidarity with the Tibetan people: Your expressions of concern and support, as well as the attention of the international media on Tibet, continue to encourage us and give us comfort. I thank you and ask you not to forget Tibet at this critical and challenging time in our people's long history.

OVER THE LONG COURSE OF my efforts to save Tibet and its people, quite early on I came to recognize that the survival of Tibet—as a civilization with its distinctive language and Buddhist tradition—is a matter of great importance not only to us Tibetans. Of course, with our cultural heritage that emphasizes harmony with nature, if we Tibetans are empowered, the fragile ecology of the Tibetan plateau can also be safeguarded, especially against unrestrained exploitation. Beyond this, the protection of Tibet is also about the survival and flourishing of a culture that is rooted in compassion and has the potential to be of benefit to humanity. The Tibetan tradition represents today the only surviving custodian of the full spectrum of the rich heritage of the great Nalanda school of Indian Buddhism, from philosophy to logic and linguistics, and from psychology to diverse spiritual practices. At the heart of our tradition is the emphasis on the principle of the interdependence of all things, and also the understanding that compassion grounded in the recognition of shared humanity forms the basis of an ethical way of life leading to happiness for all. As our world becomes more interconnected, all human beings need to learn to rise above narrow self-interest for the sake of each other and for the sake of our fragile planet.

In more than five decades of traveling around the world, a key message I have shared from my culture is the importance of embracing the more compassionate parts of human nature, and how doing so will enable us to promote peace and happiness both at the individual as well as societal levels. One of my deeply held convictions is that if each one of us could embrace what I call "the oneness of humanity"—a visceral sense of our shared human condition that acknowledges the simple fact that just like me everyone else wishes to be happy and does not want suffering—our world would be a better and kinder place for all. As social creatures, each one of us came from a mother's womb and survived thanks to someone else's care, especially our parents', in our most vulnerable period of infancy. This total dependence on another's care and the inborn appreciation of others' care that comes with it are what have imprinted in us the natural capacity to care for others, even for strangers. I sometimes describe this as the human quality of "warmheartedness." This is our basic nature. I truly believe that even as the world becomes ever more complex, any solutions we bring to address our challenges—both at the individual as well as at the societal levels—must take into account this basic nature of who we are. I deeply believe that Tibetan knowledge and our culture of compassion have the potential to offer a rich resource to promote inner peace and happiness for all. So the survival of Tibet and the Tibetan people is in the larger interest of humanity itself.

Let me end this book by sharing the following verses from the eighth-century Buddhist teacher Shantideva, whose writings have remained an enduring source of deep inspiration for me:

> *The sages who have contemplated for many eons*
> *See this [altruism] alone to be of greatest benefit.*
> *Through it, immeasurable beings can obtain,*
> *With ease, the highest state of happiness.*
> *Those who wish to undo hundreds of miseries of existence,*
> *And those who seek to relieve creatures of their sorrows,*
> *Also those who long to enjoy many hundreds of joys,*
> *They must never abandon the altruistic awakening mind.*
> *My I be the protector to those without protector;*
> *May I be the guide to those traveling on the road;*
> *May I become a boat, a causeway, and a bridge*

For those who long to reach the further shore.
Just like the great elements such as earth,
As well as like space, at all times,
May I be a sustenance of many kinds
For an immeasurable number of beings.
Likewise, for beings whose expanse
Reaches to the furthermost edges of space,
At all times and until they all attain nirvana,
May I remain a source of sustenance for all.
For as long as space endures,
For as long as sentient beings remain,
Until then, may I too remain,
And dispel the miseries of the world.

Acknowledgments

✳

I would like to thank first and foremost India, its people and its leaders, for their kind hospitality, boundless generosity in support of me and the Tibetan refugees, and unwavering concern for the fate of the Tibetan people. Let me also express my thanks to all the individuals, organizations, and governments who have stood in solidarity with our just cause and whenever necessary have spoken out. In particular, I thank so many across the world who have lent their voice and sympathy through joining the network of various Tibet support groups. I convey my deep admiration for my fellow Tibetans, inside as well as outside Tibet, for their unflagging steadfastness in standing up for their rights and freedom. This has always been a major source of encouragement and vitality for me in my work on behalf of the Tibetan people. In relation to this book, I thank my longtime English translator, Thupten Jinpa, for assisting me in the process of writing; Jaś Elsner for working closely with Jinpa; those who have helped read the manuscript and offered critical comments; my staff for making all necessary arrangements; my agent for this book, Stephanie Tade, for organizing the publication; and William Morrow for publishing the book.

❋

Tibet: A Historical Overview

L et me address a point that kept being brought up in the various rounds of discussions by the Chinese counterparts: that there must be a consensus on the historical status of Tibet along the lines Beijing claims. For example, at times a demand had been made that I issue a formal statement affirming their claim that Tibet has been an "inalienable part of China since ancient times." It is unclear to what extent they view this to be a precondition for serious negotiation, or if the Chinese delegates have been constantly instructed by their superiors to reiterate this as a face-saving device to avoid delving into any substantive negotiation.

My position on this point of past history has been simple and consistent. I have stated that as a Buddhist monk, it is against my vows to tell a lie, and that includes saying that Tibet has been an "inalienable part of China since ancient times," when I do not believe this to be true. Through my envoys, we have made it clear to Beijing that just as it may have its own version of history, we Tibetans also have our own view of history. Similarly, contemporary historians who are studying the long history of the relationship between Tibet and China will have their own understanding of the long and complex history of the two nations. If Beijing insists on our acceptance of its version of history to be a pre-condition for any substantive negotiation, then what is being asked for is total submission, including even of our own narrative of our history!

Here is a brief overview of our history as I understand it. From the seventh to the end of the ninth century, Tibet was a powerful nation under its Purgyal empire, whose army at one point even raided the Tang capital Chang'an (present day Xi'an), forcing the Tang emperor to flee. The most notable testament of the equal and independent status of the two empires at this time is the treaty of 821–822, inscribed on a pillar in Lhasa in both Tibetan and Chinese, with identical copies set up in the Tang capital Chang'an and at the agreed border of the two countries. This treaty was established between the Tibetan Emperor Tri Ralpachen and the Tang Emperor Muzong. Its text contains the following:

> Both Tibet and China shall keep the country and frontiers of which they are now in possession. The whole region to the east of that being the country of Great China, and the whole region to the west being assuredly the country of Great Tibet. From either side of that frontier there shall be no warfare, no hostile invasions, no seizure of territory. . . .
>
> . . . Between the two countries no smoke or dust shall appear. Not even a word of sudden alarm or of enmity shall be spoken, and from those who guard the frontier upwards, all shall live at ease without suspicion or fear, their land being their land, and their bed, their bed. Dwelling in peace they shall win the blessing of happiness for ten thousand generations. The sound of praise shall extend to every place reached by the sun and moon. And in order that this agreement, establishing a great era when Tibetans shall be happy in Tibet and Chinese shall be happy in China shall never be changed, the Three Jewels, the body of saints, the sun and moon, planets and stars have been invoked as witnesses.

In the second half of the ninth century the Tibetan empire splintered into multiple smaller kingdoms. Soon after, China's Tang dynasty too came to an end, and China also split into multiple kingdoms and dynasties. Finally, in the latter half of the tenth century, the Chinese Song dynasty emerged, reigning over a territory much reduced from that of the Tang empire. During this period after the end of Tibet's imperial age and the Tang dynasty, there was very little contact between Tibet and China. Then, in the early thirteenth century, vast parts of central, inner, and eastern Asia fell to the Mongol armies of Genghis Khan. In 1260, one of Genghis's grandsons, Kublai Khan, emerged as the great khan of the Mongols. Thereupon Kublai named Drogon Chogyal Phagpa (known also as Phagpa Lama, a nephew of the great Tibetan master Sakya Pandita) the national preceptor (*koushih*), effectively the head of Buddhism within Kublai's domain. Thus began what we Tibetans call the "priest-patron" (*chöyon*) relationship, whereby the Mongol khan offered patronage to senior Tibetan lamas. In 1271, when Kublai proclaimed the Yuan dynasty as Mongol rulers of China, he appointed Phagpa Lama to be the imperial preceptor (*tishih*), with his religious leadership extending across the territories of China. The founding of the Yuan dynasty in 1271 and the final defeat of the Song dynasty in southern China later marked the Mongols' full control over China itself as part of Kublai's imperial realm.* The Mongol overlordship of Tibet through Phagpa Lama's Sakya school came to an end in 1354, when the Phagmo Drupa dynasty established its rule in Tibet. In China, the Mongol Yuan rule came to an end in 1368,

---

* After careful study, the noted specialist on the Yuan dynasty Herbert Franke concludes (in "Tibetans in Yuan China," 301) that "most of Tibet proper remained outside the direct control of the Sino-Mongol bureaucracy and that even the border regions were throughout the Yuan dynasty an unruly and troubled region." Unlike China, according to historians such as Franke, Tibet was actually never under the direct rule or full control of the Mongols.

with the emergence of the native Chinese Ming dynasty. During the Ming dynasty (1368–1644), the relations between Tibet and China were largely spiritual and ceremonial.* As a native Chinese dynasty, the Ming saw itself as having regained independence for China from Mongol control—that is, from foreign rule, just as Tibet achieved independence from the Mongols more than a decade earlier.

In the first half of the seventeenth century, the militarily ascendant Manchuria proclaimed the new Qing dynasty and, following the seizure of Beijing from the Ming, began its rule over China as well. During the reign of the Manchu Qing Emperor Shunzhi, the Fifth Dalai Lama established diplomatic relations with the Qing court and in 1653 visited Beijing, where he was greeted as a fellow sovereign by the Qing emperor. This visit by the Dalai Lama strengthened the relationship between the Manchu emperor and Tibet, ushering in a very rich period of interaction between the Qing rulers and important Tibetan lamas, especially the Dalai Lama, on the priest-patron model. Manchu Qing emperors, being devout followers of Tibetan Buddhism, took their role as patrons seriously. In accordance with the Manchu emperor's status as a protecting patron, at the request of the Tibetans, the Qing sent an army to repel the several thousand Dzungar soldiers who had entered central Tibet in 1717, helped restore the Seventh Dalai Lama to his throne in 1720, and established the tradition of *amban*s, resident imperial representatives of the Manchu court. Later, toward the end of the

---

* Interestingly, the new Ming dynasty chose to continue the practice of conferring formal titles or honors on important Tibetan figures, including high lamas. That the Ming emperor had no influence in Tibet is demonstrated by the fact that the fourteenth-century Tibetan master Tsongkhapa declined the Yongle emperor's invitation to visit Beijing on at least two known occasions (Thupten Jinpa, *Tsongkhapa: A Buddha in the Land of Snows*, Boulder: Shambhala Publications, 2019, 226–30), and later both the Third and the Fourth Dalai Lamas declined similar invitations from China's Ming emperor.

eighteenth century, again at the request of the Tibetans, the Manchu emperor sent troops to help defeat Nepalese invaders.* In essence, the Qing was a Manchu empire whose imperial family were devout Tibetan Buddhists and whose domain contained both the nations of Tibet and China alongside other nations.† The primary Manchu identity of the Qing is illustrated by the fact that the Qing emperor's senior representative in Lhasa was normally an ethnic Manchu or a Mongol. The end

---

* Judging by historical records, the Qing emperors never seemed to have physically controlled Tibet, and the Tibetans, at least in central Tibet, never paid taxes to the Qing's representative, the *amban*. Even in the case of around fifteen hundred troops stationed at one point in central Tibet, their primary role seems to have been that of protection rather than as a colonial ruling force. This primarily protective role of the Manchu emperor, his *amban*s, and the Qing troops in Tibet can be discerned in a letter to the Eighth Dalai Lama. There, the Manchu general in charge of the Qing garrison in Tibet writes: "This demonstrates the emperor's concern that Tibet comes to no harm and that welfare be ensured in perpetuity. . . . The emperor will withdraw the Ambans and the garrison. . . . Moreover, if similar situations occur in future the emperor will have nothing to do with them. The Tibetans may therefore, decide for themselves as to what is in their favor and what is not or what is heavy and what is light, and make a choice of their own." English translation of this citation is from Smith, *Tibetan Nation*, 136.

† On the exact nature of the relationship between the Qing and Tibet, the modern Tibetan studies scholar Gray Tuttle writes in *Tibetan Buddhists in the Making of Modern China* (New York: Columbia University Press, 2007), 63, "Qing relations with Tibet had always been directly handled by the Manchu dynasty (mediated by the Imperial Household Department and the Court of Managing the Frontiers) with the assistance of a handful of Mongolian, Mongour, and Tibetan Buddhist religious leaders and the Tibetan nobility." In a similar vein, the international relations scholar Warren Smith concludes (*Tibetan Nation*, 137): "The nature of the Ch'ing relationship with Tibet remained one between states, or an empire and a semi-autonomous peripheral state, not a relationship between a central government and an outlying part of the same state."

of Manchu Qing dynasty, just after the first decade of the twentieth century, marked also the end of Tibet's priest-patron relationship with the Qing.

In brief, when Communist China's forcible invasion took place, Tibet had its own national government, currency, passports, postal service, military, foreign relations—for instance, Tibet refused the Allies permission to transport weapons across its territory to supply China against Japan during the Second World War. In other words, Tibet had the key attributes of an independent country. This position of independence remained the status quo until the Communist Chinese invasion of 1950.

The above, in brief, is what I believe to be the history of my country. In fact, an eminent Chinese scholar, Professor Hon-Shiang Lau, whom I first met in 2016 in Brussels, told me that his own careful research into Chinese sources reveals no evidence at all that Tibet had ever been part of China. He said that he was at the time writing a book presenting the results of his multi-year research.

The resolution of the issue of Tibet *is not* and *should not be* contingent on the two sides having a consensus on past history. I have always stated that as to the exact historical status of Tibet at any particular time, this is a matter for historians looking dispassionately at the past, on the basis of available evidence. No one can change past history, certainly not me. History is not a political decision to be made in the present. As to the course of the future, this is indeed within the remit of political decision-making now. I truly believe that if both sides are genuinely committed to establishing a future together based on a mutually beneficial relationship, there is no need to insist that the two parties agree on exactly the same version of the past.

APPENDIX B

Treaty Between Tibet and China AD 821–822

TRANSLATION FROM THE TIBETAN TEXT*

The Great King of Tibet, the Miraculous Divine Lord, and the Great King of China, the Chinese Ruler Huangdi, being in the relationship of nephew and uncle, have conferred together for the alliance of their kingdoms. They have made and ratified a great agreement. Gods and men all know it and bear witness so that it may never be changed; and an account of the agreement has been engraved on this stone pillar to inform future ages and generations. The Miraculous

---

* The English translation of the treaty presented here is the version available at https://www.claudearpi.net/wp-content/uploads/2016/11/821822Treatybetween TibetanChina-1.pdf; reproduced here with permission from Claude Arpi. For an earlier translation of the treaty by H. E. Richardson, see "The Sino-Tibetan Treaty Inscription of AD 821–823 at Lhasa," *Journal of Royal Asiatic Society* 2 (1978), 153–54.

Divine Lord Trisong Detsen and the Chinese King Wen Wu Hsiao-te Wang-ti, nephew and uncle, seeking in their far-reaching wisdom to prevent all causes of harm to the welfare of their countries now or in the future, have extended their benevolence impartially over all. With the single desire of acting for the peace and benefit of all their subjects, they have agreed on the high purpose of ensuring lasting good; and they have made this great treaty in order to fulfill their decision to restore the former ancient friendship and mutual regard and the old relationship of friendly neighbourliness.

Tibet and China shall abide by the frontiers of which they are now in occupation. All to the east is the country of Great China; and all to the west is, without question, the country of Great Tibet. Henceforth on neither side shall there be waging of war nor seizing of territory. If any person incurs suspicion he shall be arrested; his business shall be inquired into and he shall be escorted back.

Now that the two kingdoms have been allied by this great treaty, it is necessary that messengers should once again be sent by the old route to maintain communications and carry the exchange of friendly messages regarding the harmonious relations between the Nephew and Uncle.

According to the old custom, horses shall be changed at the foot of the Chiang Chun pass, the frontier between Tibet and China. At the Suiyung barrier the Chinese shall meet Tibetan envoys and provide them with all facilities from there onwards. At Ch'ing-shui the Tibetans shall meet Chinese envoys and provide all facilities. On both sides they shall be treated with customary honour and respect in conformity with the friendly relations between Nephew and Uncle.

Between the two countries no smoke nor dust shall be seen. There shall be no sudden alarms and the very word 'enemy' shall not be spoken. Even the frontier guards shall have no anxiety, nor fear and shall enjoy land and bed at their ease. All shall live in peace and share the blessing of happiness for ten thousand years. The fame of this shall extend to all places reached by the sun and the moon. This solemn agreement has established a great epoch when Tibetans shall be happy in the land of Tibet, and Chinese in the land of China. So that it may never be changed, the Three Precious Jewels of Religion, the Assembly of Saints, the Sun and Moon, Planets and Stars have been invoked as witnesses. An oath has been taken with solemn words and with the sacrifice of animals; and title agreement has been ratified.

If the parties do not act in accordance with this agreement or if they Violate it, whichever it be, Tibet or China, nothing that the other party may do by way of retaliation shall be considered a breach of the treaty on their part. The Kings and Ministers of Tibet and China have taken the prescribed oaths to this effect and the agreement has been written in detail. The two Kings have affixed their seals. The Ministers specially empowered to execute the agreement have inscribed their signatures and copies have been deposited in the royal records of each party.

The treaty is carved in Tibetan and Chinese on one side of a stone pillar near the Jo-Khang, Cathedral of Lhasa. On another side is a historical introduction in Tibetan only; and on the other two sides are bilingual lists of the names of the ministers who witnessed it. The texts have been edited in H. E. Richardson, Ancient Historical Edicts at Lhasa, *vol. 19 of the* Prize Publication Edicts of the Royal Asiatic Society.

Letters to Chinese Leaders
Deng Xiaoping and Jiang Zemin

LETTER TO DENG XIAOPING, MARCH 23, 1981

Your Excellency:

I agree with and believe in the Communist ideology which seeks the well-being of human beings in general and the proletariat in particular, and in Lenin's policy of the equality of nationalities. Similarly, I was pleased with the discussions I had with Chairman Mao on ideology and the policy towards nationalities.

If that same ideology and policy were implemented it would have brought much admiration and happiness. However, if one is to make a general comment on the developments during the past two decades, there has been a lapse in economic and educational progress, the basis of human happiness. Moreover, on account of the hardships caused by the unbearable disruptions, there has been a loss of trust between the

Party and the masses, between the officials and the masses, among the officials themselves, and also among the masses themselves.

By deceiving one another through false assumptions and misrepresentations there has been, in reality, a great lapse and delay in achieving the real goals. Now, signs of dissatisfaction are naturally emerging from all directions and are clear indications that the objectives have not been fulfilled.

To take the case of the situation in Tibet, it is regrettable that some Tibetan officials, who lack the wisdom and competence required for promoting basic human happiness and the short- and long-term welfare of their own people, indulge in flattering Chinese officials and collaborate with these Chinese officials who know nothing about Tibetans and work simply for their temporary fame, indulging in fabricating impressive reports. In reality, the Tibetan people have not only undergone immeasurable sufferings, but large numbers have also unnecessarily lost their lives. Besides, during the Cultural Revolution, there has been immense destruction of Tibet's ancient cultural heritage. All these regrettable events present a brief impression of the past.

Now, taking into account the experiences of the past mistakes, there is a new policy of Seeking Truth from Facts and a policy of modernisation. With regard to the Tibetan issue, I am pleased and applaud Comrade Hu Yaobang's efforts to make every possible attempt to right the wrongs by frankly admitting the past mistakes after his visit to Lhasa.

As you are aware, during the past 20 years, we Tibetans abroad, apart from trying to preserve our national identity and traditional values, have been educating our youth to enable them to decide their future through a knowledge of right conduct, justice, and democratic principles towards a better Tibetan community.

In brief, considering the fact that we are living in alien countries other than our own, we can be proud of our achievements in the history of the refugees in the world. On the political front, we have always pursued the path of truth and justice in our struggle for the legitimate rights of the Tibetan people. We have never indulged in distortions, exaggerations and criticism of the Chinese people. Neither have we harboured any ill will towards them. Above all, we have always held to our position of truth and justice without siding with any of the international political power blocks.

In early 1979, at your invitation, Gyalo Thondup visited China. Through him you had sent a message saying that we should keep in contact with each other. You had also invited us to send fact-finding delegations to Tibet. Thereafter, three fact-finding delegations were able to find out both the positive and negative aspects of the situation in Tibet. If the Tibetan people's identity is preserved and if they are genuinely happy, there is no reason to complain. However, in reality, over 90 percent of the Tibetans are suffering both mentally and physically, and are living in deep sorrow. These sad conditions have not been brought about by natural disasters, but by human actions. Therefore, genuine efforts must be made to resolve the problems in accordance with the existing realities in a reasonable way.

In order to do this, we must improve the relationship between China and Tibet as well as between Tibetans in and outside Tibet. With truth and equality as our foundation, we must try to develop friendship between Tibetans and Chinese through better understanding in the future. The time has come to apply our common wisdom in a spirit of tolerance and broadmindedness to achieve genuine happiness for the Tibetan people with a sense of urgency.

On my part, I remain committed to contribute my efforts for the welfare of all human beings, and in particular the poor and the weak, to the best of my ability without any distinction based on national boundaries. As the Tibetan people have great trust and hope in me, I would like to convey to you their wishes and aspirations for their immediate and future well-being.

I hope you will let me know your views on the foregoing points.

With the assurance of my highest
regard and esteem,
The Dalai Lama

Note Accompanying the March 23, 1981, Letter to Deng Xiaoping

In recent times, in accordance with the contacts made by Beijing through Gyalo Thondup, three fact-finding delegations have already visited Tibet. The fourth one is scheduled to leave in April this year. Although Beijing had already agreed to the deputation of 50 teachers from India to different schools in Tibet for a period of two years and the opening of a liaison office in Lhasa to facilitate mutual contacts, recently Gyalo Thondup received the following message from Beijing through the Xinhua News Agency in Hong Kong:

- As regard the fourth fact-finding delegation, nothing has been confirmed so far. A response will be given later either through Hong Kong or the Chinese embassy in New Delhi.

- Although we have agreed in principle to the opening of a liaison office in Lhasa and the deputation of teachers, it would be better to defer the opening of the liaison office and instead more contact should be made through Hong Kong and the Chinese embassy in Delhi.

- The teachers having been brought up in India with all good facilities would find it difficult to live in Tibet where facilities are lacking at the moment. This could harm their morale. It is therefore suggested that the sending of teachers to Tibet be deferred. For the time being some teachers may be deputed to the nationalities schools inside China from where they could gradually be sent to Tibet. (Subsequently, a message received through the Chinese embassy in Delhi conveyed that the fourth delegation should be postponed for this year.)

The following is our response to the above matters:

- We agree to the postponement of the fourth delegation for this year, as well as the opening of the liaison office in Lhasa for the time being.

- On the matter of sending teachers to Tibet, since the teachers are already aware of the difficult conditions in the schools in Tibet, this will neither lower their morale nor come in the way of carrying out their tasks. Above all, the main reason for sending the teachers is to uplift the standard of education of the students living in difficult conditions. We hope you will reconsider this matter. The teachers will be concerned solely with educational matters and will not indulge in any political activities. There is, therefore, no need to worry on this point.

LETTER TO DENG XIAOPING, SEPTEMBER 11, 1992

Dear Mr. Deng Xiaoping,

I am pleased that direct contact has once again been established between us. I hope that this will lead to an improvement of relations and the development of mutual understanding and trust.

I have been informed of the discussions Mr. Ding Guangen had with Gyalo Thondup on June 22, 1992, and the position of the Government of China concerning negotiations for a solution to the Tibetan question. I am disappointed with the hard and inflexible position conveyed by Mr. Ding Guangen, particularly the emphasis on pre-conditions for negotiations. However, I remain committed to the belief that our problems can be solved only through negotiations, held in an atmosphere of sincerity and openness, for the benefit of both the Tibetan and Chinese people. To make this possible, neither side should put up obstacles, and neither side should, therefore, state pre-conditions.

For meaningful negotiations to take place it is essential to have mutual trust. Therefore, in order to create trust I believe it is important for the leaders and people of China to know of the endeavours I have made so far. My three representatives carry with them a letter from me, accompanied by a detailed note of my views and my efforts through the years to promote negotiations in the best interests of the Tibetan and Chinese people. They will answer and discuss any questions and points you wish to raise. It is my hope that through these renewed discussions we will find a way that will lead us to negotiations.

On my part, I have put forward many ideas to solve our problem. I believe that it is now time for the Chinese government to make a genuinely meaningful proposal if you wish to see Tibet and China live together in peace. I, therefore, sincerely hope that you will respond in a spirit of openness and friendship.

Yours sincerely,
The Dalai Lama

LETTER TO JIANG ZEMIN, SEPTEMBER 11, 1992

Dear Mr. Zemin,

I am pleased that direct contact has once again been established between us. I hope that this will lead to an improvement of relations and the development of mutual understanding and trust.

I have been informed of the discussions Mr. Ding Guangen had with Gyalo Thondup on June 22, 1992, and the position of the Government of China concerning negotiations for a solution to the Tibetan question. I am disappointed with the hard and inflexible position conveyed by Mr. Ding Guangen, particularly the emphasis on preconditions for negotiations.

However, I remain committed to the belief that our problems can be solved only through negotiations, held in an atmosphere of sincerity and openness, for the benefit of both the Tibetan and Chinese people. To make this possible, neither side should put up obstacles, and neither side should, therefore, state pre-conditions.

For meaningful negotiations to take place it is essential to have mutual trust. Therefore, in order to create trust, I believe it is important for the leaders and people of China to know of the endeavours I have made so far. My three representatives carry with them a letter from me, accompanied by a detailed note of my views and my efforts through the years to promote negotiations in the best interests of the Tibetan and Chinese people. They will answer and discuss any questions and points you wish to raise. It is my hope that through these renewed discussions we will find a way that will lead us to negotiations.

On my part, I have put forward many ideas to solve our problem. I believe that it is now time for the Chinese government to make a genuinely meaningful proposal if you wish to see Tibet and China live together in peace. I, therefore, sincerely hope that you will respond in a spirit of openness and friendship.

Yours sincerely,
The Dalai Lama

Note Accompanying the September 11, 1992, Letters to Deng Xiaoping and Jiang Zemin

On June 22, 1992, Mr. Ding Guangen, head of the United Front Works Department of CCP Central Committee, met with Mr. Gyalo Thondup in Beijing and restated the assurance given by Mr. Deng Xiaoping to Mr. Gyalo Thondup in 1979 that the Chinese government was willing to discuss and resolve any issue with us except total independence. Mr. Ding Guangen also said that, in the Chinese government's view, "the Dalai Lama is continuing with independence activities," but the Chinese government was willing to immediately start negotiations as soon as I give up the independence of Tibet. This position, repeatedly stated in the past by the Chinese government, shows that the Chinese leadership still does not understand my ideas regarding the Tibetan-

Chinese relationship. Therefore, I take this opportunity to clarify my position through this note.

1. It is an established fact that Tibet and China existed as separate countries in the past. However, as a result of misrepresentations of Tibet's unique relations with the Mongol and the Manchu Emperors, disputes arose between Tibet and the Kuomintang and the present Chinese government. The fact that the Chinese government found it necessary to conclude a "17-Point Agreement" with the Tibetan government in 1951 clearly shows the Chinese government's acknowledgement of Tibet's unique position.

2. When I visited Beijing in 1954, I had the impression that most of the Communist party leaders I met there were honest, straightforward and open-minded. Chairman Mao Zedong, in particular, told me on several occasions that the Chinese were in Tibet only to help Tibet harness its natural resources and use them for the development of the country; General Zhang Jingwu and General Fan Ming were in Tibet to help me and the people of Tibet, and not to rule the Tibetan government and people, and that all Chinese officials in Tibet were there to help us and to be withdrawn when Tibet had progressed. Any Chinese official who did not act accordingly would be sent back to China. Chairman Mao went on to say that it had now been decided to establish a "Preparatory Committee for the Establishment of the Tibet Autonomous Region" instead of the earlier plan to put Tibet under the direct control of the Chinese government through a "Military-Political Commission."

   At my last meeting with Chairman Mao, before I left China, he gave me a long explanation about democracy. He said that I must provide leadership and advised me on how to keep in touch with the views of the people. He spoke in a gentle and compassionate manner which was moving and inspiring.

While in Beijing, I told Premier Zhou Enlai that we Tibetans were fully aware of our need to develop politically, socially and economically and that in fact I had already taken steps towards this.

On my way back to Tibet, I told General Zhang Guohua that I had gone to China with doubts and anxiety about the future of my people and country, but had now returned with great hope and optimism and a very positive impression of the Chinese leaders. My innate desire to serve my people, especially the poor and the weak, and the prospect of mutual cooperation and friendship between Tibet and China made me feel hopeful and optimistic about Tibet's future development. This was how I felt at that time about the Tibetan-Chinese relationship.

3. When the "Tibet Autonomous Region Preparatory Committee" was set up in Lhasa in 1956, there was no alternative but to work sincerely with it for the interest and benefit of both parties. However, by then the Chinese authorities had already started to use unthinkable brutal force to impose Communism on the Tibetan people of the Kham and Amdo areas, particularly in Lithang. This increased the resentment of the Tibetans against Chinese policies, leading to open resistance.

I could not believe that Chairman Mao would have approved of such repressive policy because of the promises he had made to me when I was in China. I, therefore, wrote three letters to him explaining the situation and seeking an end to the repression. Regrettably, there was no reply to my letters.

In late 1956, I visited India to attend Buddha Jayanti, the anniversary of the birth of Buddha. At that time, many Tibetans advised me not to return to Tibet, and to continue talks with China from India. I also felt that I should stay in India for the time being. While in India, I met Premier Zhou Enlai and told him how deeply saddened I was by the military repression inflicted upon Tibetans in Kham and Amdo in the name of "reforms." Premier Zhou Enlai said that he regarded these matters as mistakes committed by Chinese officials and that "reforms" in Tibet would be carried out only in accordance with the wishes of the Tibetan people, and that in fact the Chinese government had already decided to postpone the "reforms" in Tibet by six years. He then urged me to return to Tibet as soon as possible in order to prevent further outbreaks of unrest.

According to the Indian Prime Minister, Jawaharlal Nehru, Premier Zhou Enlai told him that the Chinese government "did not consider Tibet as a province of China. The people were different from the people of China proper. Therefore, they (the Chinese) considered Tibet as an autonomous region which could enjoy autonomy." Prime Minister Nehru told me that he had assurances from Premier Zhou Enlai that Tibet's autonomy would be respected and, therefore, advised me to make efforts to safeguard it and cooperate with China in bringing about reforms.

By then, the situation in Tibet had become extremely dangerous and desperate. Nevertheless, I decided to return to Tibet to give the Chinese government another opportunity to be able to implement their promises. On my return to Lhasa through Dromo, Gyangtse and Shigatse, I had many meetings with Tibetan and Chinese officials; I told them that the Chinese were not in Tibet to rule the Tibetans, that the Tibetans were not subjects of China, and that since the Chinese leaders had promised to establish Tibet as an autonomous region with full internal freedoms, we all had to work to make it succeed. I emphasised the point that the leaders of China had assured me that all Chinese personnel in Tibet were there to help us, and that if they behaved otherwise, they would be going against the order of their own government. I believe, I was once again doing my best to promote cooperation between Tibet and China.

4. However, because of the harsh military repression in the Kham and Amdo parts of eastern Tibet, thousands of young and old Tibetans,

unable to live under such circumstances, began to arrive in Lhasa as refugees. As a result of these Chinese actions the Tibetan people felt great anxiety and began to lose faith in the promises made by China. This led to greater resentment and a worsening of the situation. Nevertheless, I continued to counsel my people to seek a peaceful solution and to show restraint. At the risk of losing the trust of the Tibetan people I did my best to prevent a breakdown of the communications with the Chinese officials in Lhasa. But the situation continued to deteriorate and finally exploded in the tragic events of 1959 which forced me to leave Tibet.

Faced with such a desperate situation, I had no alternative but to appeal to the United Nations. The United Nations, in turn, passed three resolutions on Tibet in 1959, 1961 and 1965, wherein it called for the "cessation of practices which deprived Tibetan people of their fundamental human rights and freedoms including their right to self-determination" and asked member States to make all possible efforts towards achieving that purpose.

The Chinese government did not respect the United Nations resolutions. In the meantime, the Cultural Revolution started and there was absolutely no opportunity for solving the Tibetan-Chinese problems. It was, in fact, not even possible to identify a leader with whom we could talk.

5. In spite of my unfulfilled hopes and disappointments in dealing with the Chinese government, and since Tibet and China will always remain as neighbours, I am convinced that we must strive to find a way to coexist in peace and help each other. This, I believe, is possible and worthy of our efforts. With this conviction I said in my statement to the Tibetan people on March 10, 1971: "In spite of the fact that we Tibetans have to oppose Communist China, I can never bring myself to hate her people. Hatred is not a sign of strength, but of weakness. When Lord Buddha said that hatred cannot be overcome by hatred, he was not only being spiritual. But

his words reflect the practical reality of life. Whatever one achieves through hatred will not last long. On the other hand, hatred will only generate more problems. And for the Tibetan people who are faced with such a tragic situation, hatred will only bring additional depression. Moreover, how can we hate a people who do not know what they are doing? How can we hate millions of Chinese, who have no power and are helplessly led by their leaders? We cannot even hate the Chinese leaders for they have suffered tremendously for their nation and the cause which they believe to be right. I do not believe in hatred, but I do believe, as I have always done, that one day truth and justice will triumph."

In my March 10 statement of 1973, referring to the Chinese claim of Tibetans being made the "masters of the country" after being "liberated from the three big feudal lords" and enjoying "unprecedented progress and happiness," I stated: "The aim of the struggle of the Tibetans outside Tibet is the attainment of the happiness of the Tibetan people. If the Tibetans in Tibet are truly happy under Chinese rule then there is no reason for us here in exile to argue otherwise."

Again in my 1979 March 10 statement, I welcomed Mr. Deng Xiaoping's statement "to seek truth from facts," to give the Chinese people their long-cherished rights, and of the need to acknowledge one's own mistakes and shortcomings. While commending these signs of honesty, progress and openness, I said: "The present Chinese leaders should give up the past dogmatic narrow-mindedness and fear of losing face and recognise the present world situation. They should accept their mistakes, the realities, and the right of all peoples of the human race to equality and happiness. Acceptance of this should not be merely on paper; it should be put into practice. If these are accepted and strictly followed, all problems can be solved with honesty and justice." With this conviction I renewed my efforts to promote reconciliation and friendship between China and Tibet.

6. In 1979, Mr. Deng Xiaoping invited Mr. Gyalo Thondup to Beijing and told him that apart from the question of total independence all other issues could be discussed and all problems can be resolved. Mr. Deng further told Mr. Thondup that we must keep in contact with each other and that we could send fact-finding delegations to Tibet. This naturally gave us great hopes of resolving our problem peacefully and we started sending delegations to Tibet.

On March 23, 1981, I sent a letter to Mr. Deng Xiaoping, in which I said, "The three fact-finding delegations have been able to find out both the positive and negative aspects of the situation in Tibet. If the Tibetan people's identity is preserved and if they are genuinely happy, there is no reason to complain. However, in reality over 90 percent of the Tibetans are suffering both mentally and physically, and are living in deep sorrow. These sad conditions had not been brought about by natural disasters, but by human actions. Therefore, genuine efforts must be made to solve the problem in accordance with the existing realities in a reasonable way.

"In order to do this, we must improve the relationship between China and Tibet as well as between Tibetans in and outside Tibet. With truth and equality as our foundation, we must try to develop friendship between Tibetans and Chinese through better understanding in the future. The time has come to apply our common wisdom in a spirit of tolerance and broadmindedness to achieve genuine happiness for the Tibetan people with a sense of urgency.

"On my part, I remain committed to contribute my efforts to the welfare of all human beings, and in particular the poor and the weak, to the best of my ability without making any distinction based on national boundaries. . . .

"I hope you will let me know your views on the foregoing points."

There was no reply to my letter. Instead, on July 28, 1981, General Secretary Hu Yaobang gave Mr. Gyalo Thondup a document, entitled "Five Point Policy Towards the Dalai Lama."

This was a surprise and a great disappointment. The reason for our consistent efforts to deal with the Chinese government is to achieve lasting and genuine happiness for six million Tibetans who must live as neighbours of China from generation to generation. However, the Chinese leadership chose to ignore this and, instead, attempted to reduce the whole issue to that of my personal status and the conditions for my return without any willingness to address the real underlying issues.

Nevertheless, I continued to place hope in Mr. Deng Xiaoping's statement "seeking truth from facts" and his policy of liberalisation. Therefore, I sent several delegations to Tibet and China and wherever there was an opportunity we explained our views to promote understanding through discussion and dialogue. As initially suggested by Mr. Deng Xiaoping I agreed to send Tibetan teachers from India to improve the education of Tibetans in Tibet. But for one reason or the other the Chinese government did not accept this.

These contacts resulted in four fact-finding delegations to Tibet, two delegations to Beijing, and the start of family visitations between the Tibetans in Tibet and in exile. However, these steps did not lead to any substantial progress in resolving the problems between us owing to the rigidity of the Chinese leaders' positions which, I believe, failed to reflect Mr. Deng Xiaoping's policies.

7. Once again, I did not give up hope. This was reflected in my annual March 10 statements to the Tibetan people in 1981, 1983, 1984 and 1985, wherein I said the following:

". . . past history has disappeared in the past. What is more relevant is that in the future there actually must be real peace and happiness through developing friendly and meaningful relations between China and Tibet. For this to be realised, it is important for both sides to work hard to have tolerant understanding and be open-minded" (1981).

"The right to express one's ideas and to make every effort to implement them enables people everywhere to become creative and progressive. This engenders human society to make rapid progress and experience genuine harmony. . . . The deprivation of freedom to express one's views, either by force or by other means, is absolutely anachronistic and a brutal form of oppression. . . . The people of the world will not only oppose it, but will condemn it. Hence, the six million Tibetan people must have the right to preserve and enhance their cultural identity and religious freedom, the right to determine their own destiny and manage their own affairs, and find fulfillment of their free self-expression, without interference from any quarters. This is reasonable and just" (1983).

"Irrespective of varying degrees of development and economic disparities, continents, nations, communities, families, in fact, all individuals are dependent on one another for their existence and well-beings. Every human being wishes for happiness and does not want suffering. By clearly realising this, we must develop mutual compassion, love, and a fundamental sense of justice. In such an atmosphere there is hope that problems between nations and problems within families can be gradually overcome and that people can live in peace and harmony. Instead, if people adopt an attitude of selfishness, domination and jealousy, the world at large, as well as individuals, will never enjoy peace and harmony. Therefore, I believe that human relations based on mutual compassion and love is fundamentally important to human happiness" (1984).

". . . in order to achieve genuine happiness in any human society, freedom of thought is extremely important. This freedom of thought can only be achieved from mutual trust, mutual understanding and the absence of fear. . . . In the case of Tibet and China too, unless we can remove the state of mutual fear and mistrust, unless we can develop a genuine sense of friendship and goodwill the problems that we face today will continue to exist.

"It is important for both of us to learn about one another. . . .

It is now for the Chinese to act according to the enlightened ideals and principles of the modern times; to come forward with an open mind and make a serious attempt to know and understand the Tibetan people's viewpoint and their true feelings and aspirations. . . . It is wrong to react with suspicion or offence to the opinions that are contrary to one's own way of thinking. It is essential that differences of opinion be examined and discussed openly. When differing viewpoints are frankly stated and sensibly discussed on an equal footing, the decisions or agreements reached as a result will be genuine and beneficial to all concerned. But so long as there is a contradiction between thought and action, there can never be genuine and meaningful agreements.

"So, at this time, I feel the most important thing for us is to keep in close contact, to express our views frankly and to make sincere efforts to understand each other. And, through eventual improvement in human relationship, I am confident that our problems can be solved to our mutual satisfaction" (1985).

In these and other ways I expressed my views clearly. But, there was no reciprocity to my conciliatory approaches.

8. Since all the exchanges between Tibetans and Chinese yielded no results, I felt compelled to make public my views on the steps necessary for an agreeable solution to the fundamental issues. On September 21, 1987, I announced a Five Point Peace Plan in the United States of America. In its introduction, I said that in the hope of real reconciliation and a lasting solution to the problem, it was my desire to take the first step with this initiative. This plan, I hoped, would in the future contribute to the friendship and cooperation among all the neighbouring countries including the Chinese people for their good and benefit. The basic elements were:

i. Transformation of the whole of Tibet into a zone of ahimsa (peace and nonviolence);

ii. Abandonment of China's population transfer policy which threatens the very existence of the Tibetans as a people;

iii. Respect for the Tibetan people's fundamental human rights and democratic freedoms;

iv. Restoration and protection of Tibet's natural environment and the abandonment of China's use of Tibet for the production of nuclear weapons and dumping of nuclear waste;

v. Commencement of earnest negotiations on the future status of Tibet and relations between the Tibetan and the Chinese peoples.

As a response to this initiative, Mr. Yan Mingfu met Mr. Gyalo Thondup on October 17, 1987, and delivered a message containing five points criticising me for my above peace initiative and accusing me of having instigated the demonstrations in Lhasa of September 27, 1987, and of having worked against the interests of Tibetan people.

This response, far from giving a serious thought to my sincere proposal for reconciliation, was disappointing and demeaning.

Despite this, I tried once again to clarify our views in a detailed 14-point response on December 17, 1987.

9. On June 15, 1988, at the European Parliament in Strasbourg, I once again elaborated on the Five Point Peace Plan. I proposed as a framework for negotiations to secure the basic rights of the Tibetan people, China could remain responsible for Tibet's foreign policy and maintain a restricted number of military installations in Tibet for defence until a regional peace conference is convened and Tibet is transformed into a neutral peace sanctuary. I was criticised by many Tibetans for this proposal. My idea was to make it possible for China and Tibet to stay together in lasting friendship and to secure the right for Tibetans to govern their own country. I sincerely believe that in the future a demilitarised Tibet as a zone

of ahimsa will contribute to harmony and peace not only between Tibetans and Chinese, but to all the neighbouring countries and the entire region.

10. On September 23, 1988, the Chinese government issued a statement that China was willing to begin negotiations with us. The announcement stated that the date and venue for the negotiations would be left to the Dalai Lama. We welcomed this announcement from Beijing and responded on October 25, 1988, proposing January 1989 as the time and Geneva, an internationally recognized neutral venue, as our choices. We announced that we had a negotiating team ready and named the members of the team.

The Chinese government responded on November 18, 1988, rejecting Geneva and expressing preference for Beijing or else Hong Kong as the venue. They further stated that my negotiating team could not include "a foreigner" and consist only of "younger people," and that it should have older people, including Mr. Gyalo Thondup. We explained that the foreigner was only a legal advisor and not an actual member of the negotiating team and that Mr. Gyalo Thondup would also be included as an advisor to the team.

With a flexible and open attitude we accommodated the Chinese government's requests and agreed to send representatives to Hong Kong to hold preliminary meetings with representatives of the Chinese government. Unfortunately, when both sides had finally agreed on Hong Kong as the site for preliminary discussions the Chinese government refused to communicate any further and failed to live up to their own suggestion.

11. Although I championed this proposal for over two years there was no evidence of consideration or even an acknowledgement from the Chinese government.

Therefore, in my March 10 statement in 1991, I was compelled to state that unless the Chinese government responded in the near future I would consider myself free from any obligation to abide by the proposal I made in France.

Since there appears to be no benefit from the many solutions I had advocated concerning Tibet and China, I had to find a new way. Therefore, in a speech at Yale University on October 9, 1991, I said:

". . . I am considering the possibility of a visit to Tibet as early as possible. I have in mind two purposes for such a visit.

"First, I want to ascertain the situation in Tibet myself on the spot and communicate directly with my people. By doing so, I also hope to help the Chinese leadership to understand the true feelings of Tibetans. It would be important, therefore, for senior Chinese leaders to accompany me on such a visit, and that outside observers, including the press, be present to see and report their findings.

"Second, I wish to advise and persuade my people not to abandon nonviolence as the appropriate form of struggle. My ability to talk to my people can be a key factor in bringing about a peaceful solution. My visit could be a new opportunity to promote understanding and create a basis for a negotiated solution."

Unfortunately this overture was immediately opposed by the Chinese government. At that time, I was asked on many occasions by the press whether I was renewing the call for Tibetan independence since I had declared that the Strasbourg proposal was no longer valid. To these questions, I stated that I did not want to comment.

12. The Chinese government has, with great doubt and suspicion, described our struggle as a movement to restore the "old society" and that it was not in the interest of the Tibetan people but for the personal status and interest of the Dalai Lama. Since my youth, I was aware of the many faults of the existing system in Tibet and wanted to improve it. At that time I started the process of reform in Tibet. Soon after our flight to India we introduced democracy in our exile community, step by step. I repeatedly urged my people to follow this path. As a result, our exiled community now implements a sys-

tem in full accordance with universal democratic principles. It is impossible for Tibet to ever revert to the old system of government. Whether my efforts for the Tibetan cause are as charged by the Chinese for my personal position and benefit or not is clear from my repeated statements that in a future Tibet, I will not assume any governmental responsibility or hold any political position. Furthermore, this is reflected clearly in the Charter which governs the Tibetan Administration in Exile and in the "Guidelines for Future Tibet's Polity and the Basic Features of Its Constitution," which I announced on February 26, 1992.

In the conclusion of these guidelines, I suggested that "Tibet shall not be influenced or swayed by the policies and ideologies of other countries but remain a neutral state in the true sense of the term. It shall maintain a harmonious relationship with its neighbours on equal terms and for mutual benefits. It shall maintain a cordial and fraternal relationship with all nations, without any sense of hostility and enmity."

Similarly, in my statement of March 10, 1992, I stated, "When a genuinely cordial relationship is established between the Tibetans and the Chinese, it will enable us not only to resolve the disputes between our two nations in this century, but will also enable the Tibetans to make a significant contribution through our rich cultural tradition for mental peace among the millions of young Chinese."

My endeavours to establish a personal relationship with Chinese leaders include my offer, presented through your Embassy in New Delhi in the latter part of 1980, for a meeting with General Secretary Hu Yaobang during one of his visits abroad at any convenient place. Again in December 1991, when Premier Li Peng visited New Delhi, I proposed to meet him there. These overtures were to no avail.

13. An impartial review of the above points will clearly show that my ideas and successive efforts have consistently sought solutions that will allow Tibet and China to live together in peace. In the light of these facts it

is difficult to understand the purpose of the Chinese government's position that Mr. Deng Xiaoping's statement on Tibet of 1979 still stands and that as soon as "the Dalai Lama gives up his splittist activities," negotiations could start. This position has been repeated over and over again with no specific responses to my many initiatives.

If China wants Tibet to stay with China, then China must create the necessary conditions for this. The time has come now for the Chinese to show the way for Tibet and China to live together in friendship. A detailed step-by-step outline regarding Tibet's basic status should be spelt out. If such a clear outline is given, regardless of the possibility of an agreement or not, we Tibetans can then make a decision whether to live with China or not. If we Tibetans obtain our basic rights to our satisfaction, then we are not incapable of seeing the possible advantages of living with the Chinese.

I trust in the farsightedness and wisdom of China's leaders and hope that they will take into consideration the current global political changes and the need to resolve the Tibetan problem peacefully, promoting genuine lasting friendship between our two neighbouring peoples.

LETTER OF CONDOLENCE TO JIANG ZEMIN, 1997

Your Excellency,

On the passing away of Mr. Deng Xiaoping, I wish to express my condolence to members of his family and to the people and government of the People's Republic of China. The demise of Mr. Deng Xiaoping is a great loss for China.

I met Mr. Deng Xiaoping when I visited China in 1954. He was a revolutionary and a great leader of China, with an exceptional courage, perseverance, capability and leadership ability.

In the case of Tibet in 1979, Mr. Deng Xiaoping invited my elder brother Mr. Gyalo Thondup to Beijing and stated to him that apart from the question of total independence of Tibet, all other issues could be discussed and resolved. Encouraged by the overall changes in China and the new pragmatic attitude towards the issue of Tibet, I have, since then, consistently and sincerely made attempts to engage the Chinese government in earnest negotiations over the future of Tibet. Sadly, the Chinese government has not responded positively to my proposals and initiatives over the past 18 years for a negotiated resolution of our problem within the framework stated by Mr. Deng Xiaoping.

It is very regrettable that serious negotiations on the issue of Tibet could not take place during Mr. Deng's lifetime. However, I firmly believe that the absence of Mr. Deng provides new opportunities and challenges for both Tibetans and the Chinese. I very much hope that under your leadership the Government of China will realise the wisdom of resolving the issue of Tibet through negotiations in a spirit of reconciliation and compromise. For my part, I remain committed to the belief that our problem can be solved only through negotiations, held in an atmosphere of sincerity and openness.

With prayers and good wishes,
Yours sincerely,
The Dalai Lama

LETTER TO JIANG ZEMIN, 1997*

Your Excellency,

As you and other members of the Chinese leadership prepare for the crucial forthcoming Party Congress, I would like to make yet another effort to press the need for an early solution to the issue of Tibet.

---

* This letter was hand delivered by US Senator Dianne Feinstein and her husband, Richard Blum, when they met with President Jiang Zemin in Beijing on September 8, 1997.

Since nearly five decades, the Tibetan problem has resulted in much suffering to the Tibetan people, physically and emotionally. Moreover, the inability to resolve the Tibetan problem has been tarnishing increasingly the international image and reputation of the great nation of China.

I have great personal respect and admiration for China and sincerely wish it to be a leading member of the comity of nations. The earlier we can find a mutually acceptable solution to the Tibetan issue, the better it will be for Tibetans and the Chinese peoples. I continue to believe that, given earnest efforts from both sides, we can find such a solution. On my part, I have taken every opportunity to clarify some of the misgivings that the Chinese leaders seem to have concerning my position.

It is my belief that it is more important to look forward to the future than dwell in the past. The important thing is the maximum benefit for the concerned people. With this conviction, I have been proposing a solution to the Tibet issue that does not require the separation of Tibet from China. If you examine my proposal, as I had outlined it in 1988, you will find that it is consistent with the policy China is adopting on issues like Hong Kong and Taiwan. My proposal is no different from this "one country, two systems" political concept and is clearly within the framework formulated by Mr. Deng Xiaoping on the issue of Tibet.

In past recent years, lack of direct contact between our two sides has increased misunderstanding and distrust, resulting in a deepened sense of alienation from each other. This is very unfortunate and does neither serve the interest of the Tibetans nor that of your Government. For centuries Tibetans and Chinese have lived side by side. In future, too, we will continue to do so. Despite the growing international support for Tibet, ultimately it is for Tibetans and Chinese to find a mutually acceptable solution.

It is, therefore, the time for all of us to act with courage, vision and wisdom. I remain willing to dedicate my remaining life to the service of reconciliation, mutual respect and friendship between the Tibetan and

Chinese peoples. I would like to assure you that you will find in me a committed partner in searching for a mutually acceptable and beneficial resolution of the Tibetan problem.

I would, therefore, like to propose meetings at the earliest possible time, between my representatives and officials of the Chinese leadership, which will provide the opportunity for us to understand each other's thinking. There is a need to initiate new openings, conducive to building confidence and trust. It is my hope that the Government under your leadership will act wisely and pragmatically and give us a favourable response at an early date.

With my prayers and best wishes,

Yours sincerely,

The Dalai Lama

＊

Memorandum on Genuine Autonomy for the Tibetan People

I. INTRODUCTION

Since the renewal of direct contact with the Central Government of the People's Republic of China (PRC) in 2002, extensive discussions have been held between the envoys of His Holiness the 14th Dalai Lama and representatives of the Central Government. In these discussions we have put forth clearly the aspirations of Tibetans. The essence of the Middle Way Approach is to secure genuine autonomy for the Tibetan people within the scope of the Constitution of the PRC. This is of mutual benefit and based on the long-term interest of both the Tibetan and Chinese peoples. We remain firmly committed not to seek separation or independence. We are seeking a solution to the Tibetan problem through genuine autonomy, which is compatible with the principles on autonomy in the Constitution of the People's Republic of China (PRC). The protection and development of the unique Tibetan identity in all its aspects serves the larger interest of humanity in general and those of the Tibetan and Chinese people in particular.

During the seventh round of talks in Beijing on 1 and 2 July 2008, the Vice Chairman of the Chinese People's Political Consultative Conference and the Minister of the Central United Front Work Department, Mr. Du Qinglin, explicitly invited suggestions from His Holiness the Dalai Lama for the stability and development of Tibet. The Executive Vice Minister of the Central United Front Work Department, Mr. Zhu Weiqun, further said they would like to hear our views on the degree or form of autonomy we are seeking as well as on all aspects of regional autonomy within the scope of the Constitution of the PRC. Accordingly, this memorandum puts forth our position on genuine autonomy and how the specific needs of the Tibetan nationality for autonomy and self-government can be met through application of the principles on autonomy of the Constitution of the People's Republic of China, as we understand them. On this basis, His Holiness the Dalai Lama is confident that the basic needs of the Tibetan nationality can be met through genuine autonomy within the PRC. The PRC is a multi-national state, and as in many other parts of the world, it seeks to resolve the nationality question through autonomy and the self-government of the minority nationalities. The Constitution of the PRC contains fundamental principles on autonomy and self-government whose objectives are compatible with the needs and aspirations of the Tibetans. Regional national autonomy is aimed at opposing both the oppression and the separation of nationalities by rejecting both Han Chauvinism and local nationalism. It is intended to ensure the protection of the culture and the identity of minority nationalities by empowering them to become masters of their own affairs. To a very considerable extent Tibetan needs can be met within the constitutional principles on autonomy, as we understand them. On several points, the Constitution gives significant discretionary powers to state organs in the decision-making and on the operation of the system of autonomy. These discretionary powers can be exercised to facilitate genuine autonomy for Tibetans in ways that would respond to the uniqueness of the Tibetan situation. In implementing these principles, legislation relevant to autonomy may consequently need to be reviewed or amended to respond to the specific characteristics and needs of the Tibetan nationality. Given goodwill on both sides, outstanding problems can be resolved within the constitutional principles on autonomy. In this way national unity and stability and harmonious relations between the Tibetan and other nationalities will be established.

II. RESPECT FOR THE INTEGRITY OF THE TIBETAN NATIONALITY

Tibetans belong to one minority nationality regardless of the current administrative division. The integrity of the Tibetan nationality must be respected. That is the spirit, the intent and the principle underlying the constitutional concept of national regional autonomy as well as the principle of equality of nationalities. There is no dispute about the fact that Tibetans share the same language, culture, spiritual tradition, core values and customs, that they belong to the same ethnic group and that they have a strong sense of common identity. Tibetans share a common history and despite periods of political or administrative divisions, Tibetans continuously remained united by their religion, culture, education, language, way of life and by their unique high-plateau environment. The Tibetan nationality lives in one contiguous area on the Tibetan plateau, which they have inhabited for millennia and to which they are therefore indigenous. For purposes of the constitutional principles of national regional autonomy Tibetans in the PRC in fact live as a single nationality all over the Tibetan plateau. On account of the above reasons, the PRC has recognised the Tibetan nationality as one of the 55 minority nationalities.

III. TIBETAN ASPIRATIONS

Tibetans have a rich and distinct history, culture and spiritual tradition, all of which form valuable parts of the heritage of humanity. Not only do Tibetans wish to preserve their own heritage, which they cherish, but equally they wish to further develop their culture and spiritual life and knowledge in ways that are particularly suited to the needs and conditions of humanity in the 21st century.

As a part of the multi-national state of the PRC, Tibetans can benefit greatly from the rapid economic and scientific development the country is experiencing. While wanting to actively participate and contribute to this development, we want to ensure that this happens without the people losing their Tibetan identity, culture and core values and without putting the distinct and fragile environment of the Tibetan plateau, to which Tibetans are indigenous, at risk.

The uniqueness of the Tibetan situation has consistently been recognised within the PRC and has been reflected in the terms of the "17-Point Agreement" and in statements and policies of successive leaders of the PRC since then, and should remain the basis for defining the scope and structure of the specific autonomy to be exercised by the Tibetan nationality within the PRC. The Constitution reflects a fundamental principle of flexibility to accommodate special situations, including the special characteristics and needs of minority nationalities.

His Holiness the Dalai Lama's commitment to seek a solution for the Tibetan people within the PRC is clear and unambiguous. This position is in full compliance and agreement with paramount leader Deng Xiaoping's statement in which he emphasised that except for independence all other issues could be resolved through dialogue. Whereas, we are committed, therefore, to fully respect the territorial integrity of the PRC, we expect the Central Government to recognise and fully respect the integrity of the Tibetan nationality and its right to exercise genuine autonomy within the PRC. We believe that this is the basis for resolving the differences between us and promoting unity, stability and harmony among nationalities.

For Tibetans to advance as a distinct nationality within the PRC, they need to continue to progress and develop economically, socially and politically in ways that correspond to the development of the PRC and the world as a whole while respecting and nurturing the Tibetan characteristics of such development. For this to happen, it is imperative that the right of Tibetans to govern themselves be recognised and implemented throughout the region where they live in compact communities in the PRC, in accordance with the Tibetan nationality's own needs, priorities and characteristics.

The Tibetan people's culture and identity can only be preserved and promoted by the Tibetans themselves and not by any others. Therefore, Tibetans should be capable of self-help, self-development and self-government, and an optimal balance needs to be found between this and the necessary and welcome guidance and assistance for Tibet from the Central Government and other provinces and regions of the PRC.

IV. BASIC NEEDS OF TIBETANS: SUBJECT MATTERS OF SELF-GOVERNMENT

1) Language

Language is the most important attribute of the Tibetan people's identity. Tibetan is the primary means of communication, the language in which their literature, their spiritual texts and historical as well as scientific works are written. The Tibetan language is not only at the same high level as that of Sanskrit in terms of grammar, but is also the only one that has the capability of translating from Sanskrit without an iota of error. Therefore, Tibetan language has not only the richest and best-translated literatures, many scholars even contend that it has also the richest and largest number of literary compositions.

The Constitution of the PRC, in Article 4, guarantees the freedom of all nationalities "to use and develop their own spoken and written languages . . ."

In order for Tibetans to use and develop their own language, Tibetan must be respected as the main spoken and written language. Similarly, the principal language of the Tibetan autonomous areas needs to be Tibetan.

This principle is broadly recognised in the Constitution in Article 121, which states, "the organs of self-government of the national autonomous areas employ the spoken and written language or language in common use in the locality." Article 10 of the Law on Regional National Autonomy (LRNA) provides that these organs "shall guarantee the freedom of the nationalities in these areas to use and develop their own spoken and written languages. . . ."

Consistent with the principle of recognition of Tibetan as the main language in Tibetan areas, the LRNA (Article 36) also allows the autonomous government authorities to decide on "the language used in instruction and enrollment procedures" with regard to education. This implies recognition of the principle that the principal medium of education be Tibetan.

2) Culture

The concept of national regional autonomy is primarily for the purpose of preservation of the culture of minority nationalities. Consequently, the Constitution of PRC contains references to cultural preservation in Articles 22, 47 and 119 and also in Article 38 of the LRNA. To Tibetans, Tibetan culture is closely connected to our religion, tradition, language and identity, which are facing threats at various levels. Since Tibetans live within the multi-national state of the PRC, this distinct Tibetan cultural heritage needs protection through appropriate constitutional provisions.

3) Religion

Religion is fundamental to Tibetans and Buddhism is closely linked to their identity. We recognise the importance of separation of church and state, but this should not affect the freedom and practice of believers. It is impossible for Tibetans to imagine personal or community freedom without the freedom of belief, conscience and religion. The Constitution recognises the importance of religion and protects the right to profess it. Article 36 guarantees all citizens the right to the freedom of religious belief. No one can compel another to believe in or not to believe in any religion. Discrimination on the basis of religion is forbidden.

An interpretation of the constitutional principle in light of international standard would also cover the freedom of the manner of belief or worship. The freedom covers the right of monasteries to be organised and run according to Buddhist monastic tradition, to engage in teachings and studies, and to enroll any number of monks and nuns or age group in accordance with these rules. The normal practice to hold public teachings and the empowerment of large gatherings is covered by this freedom and the state should not interfere in religious practices and traditions, such as the relationship between a teacher and his disciple, management of monastic institutions, and the recognition of reincarnations.

4) Education

The desire of Tibetans to develop and administer their own education system in cooperation and in coordination with the central government's ministry of education is supported by the principles contained in the Constitution with regard to education. So is the aspiration to engage in and contribute to the development of science and technology. We note the increasing recognition in international scientific development of the contribution which Buddhist psychology, metaphysics, cosmology and the understanding of the mind is making to modern science.

Whereas, under Article 19 of the Constitution the state takes on the overall responsibility to provide education for its citizens, Article 119 recognises the principle that "[T]he organs of self-government of the national autonomous areas independently administer educational . . . affairs in their respective areas . . ." This principle is also reflected in Article 36 of the LRNA.

Since the degree of autonomy in decision-making is unclear, the point to be emphasised is that the Tibetan need to exercise genuine autonomy with regard to its own nationality's education and this is supported by the principles of the Constitution on autonomy.

As for the aspiration to engage in and contribute to the development of scientific knowledge and technology, the Constitution (Article 119) and the LRNA (Article 39) clearly recognise the right of autonomous areas to develop scientific knowledge and technology.

5) Environment Protection

Tibet is the prime source of Asia's great rivers. It also has the earth's loftiest mountains as well as the world's most extensive and highest plateau, rich in mineral resources, ancient forests, and many deep valleys untouched by human disturbances.

This environmental protection practice was enhanced by the Tibetan people's traditional respect for all forms of life, which prohibits the harming of all sentient beings, whether human or animal. Tibet used to be an unspoiled wilderness sanctuary in a unique natural environment.

Today, Tibet's traditional environment is suffering irreparable damage. The effects of this are especially notable on the grasslands, the croplands, the forests, the water resources and the wildlife.

In view of this, according to Articles 45 and 66 of the LNRA, the Tibetan people should be given the right over the environment and allow them to follow their traditional conservation practices.

6) Utilisation of Natural Resources

With respect to the protection and management of the natural environment and the utilisation of natural resources the Constitution and the LRNA only acknowledge a limited role for the organs of self-government of the autonomous areas (see LRNA Articles 27, 28, 45, 66, and Article 118 of the Constitution, which pledges that the state "shall give due consideration to the interests of [the national autonomous areas]"). The LRNA recognises the importance for the autonomous areas to protect and develop forests and grasslands (Article 27) and to "give priority to the rational exploitation and utilization of the natural resources that the local authorities are entitled to develop," but only within the limits of state plans and legal stipulations. In fact, the central role of the State in these matters is reflected in the Constitution (Article 9).

The principles of autonomy enunciated in the Constitution cannot, in our view, truly lead to Tibetans becoming masters of their own destiny if they are not sufficiently involved in decision-making on utilisation of natural resources such as mineral resources, waters, forests, mountains, grasslands, etc.

The ownership of land is the foundation on which the development of natural resources, taxes and revenues of an economy are based. Therefore, it is essential that only the nationality of the autonomous region shall have the legal authority to transfer or lease land, except land owned by the state. In the same manner, the autonomous region must have the independent authority to formulate and implement developmental plans concurrent to the state plans.

7) Economic Development and Trade

Economic development in Tibet is welcome and much needed. The Tibetan people remain one of the most economically backward regions within the PRC.

The Constitution recognises the principle that the autonomous authorities have an important role to play in the economic development of their areas in view of local characteristics and needs (Article 118 of the Constitution, also reflected in LRNA Article 25). The Constitution also recognises the principle of autonomy in the administration and management of finances (Article 117, and LRNA Article 32). At the same time, the Constitution also recognises the importance of providing State funding and assistance to the autonomous areas to accelerate development (Article 122, LRNA Article 22).

Similarly, Article 31 of the LRNA recognises the competence of autonomous areas, especially those such as Tibet, adjoining foreign countries, to conduct border trade as well as trade with foreign countries. The recognition of these principles is important to the Tibetan nationality given the region's proximity to foreign countries with which the people have cultural, religious, ethnic and economic affinities.

The assistance rendered by the Central Government and the provinces has temporary benefits, but in the long run if the Tibetan people are not self-reliant and become dependent on others it has greater harm. Therefore, an important objective of autonomy is to make the Tibetan people economically self-reliant.

8) Public Health

The Constitution enunciates the responsibility of the State to provide health and medical services (Article 21). Article 119 recognises that this is an area of responsibility of the autonomous areas. The LRNA (Article 40) also recognises the right of organs of self-government of the autonomous areas to "make independent decisions on plans for developing local medical and health services and for advancing both modern and the traditional medicine of the nationalities."

The existing health system fails to adequately cover the needs of the rural Tibetan population. According to the principles of the above-mentioned laws, the regional autonomous organs need to have the competencies and resources to cover the health need of the entire Tibetan population. They also need the competencies to promote the traditional Tibetan medical and astro system strictly according to traditional practice.

9) Public Security

In matters of public security it is important that the majority of security personnel consists of members of the local nationality who understand and respect local customs and traditions.

What is lacking in Tibetan areas is absence of decision-making authority in the hands of local Tibetan officials.

An important aspect of autonomy and self-government is the responsibility for the internal public order and security of the autonomous areas. The Constitution (Article 120) and LRNA (Article 24) recognise the importance of local involvement and authorise autonomous areas to organise their security within "the military system of the State and practical needs and with the approval of the State Council."

10) Regulation on Population Migration

The fundamental objective of national regional autonomy and self-government is the preservation of the identity, culture, language and so forth of the minority nationality and to ensure that it is the master of its own affairs. When applied to a particular territory in which the minority nationality lives in a concentrated community or communities, the very principle and purpose of national regional autonomy is disregarded if large-scale migration and settlement of the majority Han nationality and other nationalities is encouraged and allowed. Major demographic changes that result from such migration will have the effect of assimilating rather than integrating the Tibetan nationality into the Han nationality and gradually extinguishing the distinct culture and identity of the Tibetan nationality. Also, the influx of large numbers of Han and other nationalities into Tibetan areas will fundamentally change the conditions necessary for the exercise of regional autonomy since the constitutional criteria for the exercise of autonomy, namely that the minority nationality "live in compact communities" in a particular territory is changed and undermined by the population movements and transfers. If such migrations and settlements continue uncontrolled, Tibetans will no longer live in a compact community or communities and will consequently no longer be entitled, under the Constitution, to national regional autonomy. This would effectively violate the very principles of the Constitution in its approach to the nationalities issue.

There is precedent in the PRC for restriction on the movement or residence of citizens. There is only a very limited recognition of the right of autonomous areas to work out measures to control "the transient population" in those areas. To us it would be vital that the autonomous organs of self-government have the authority to regulate the residence, settlement and employment or economic activities of persons who wish to move to Tibetan areas from other parts of the PRC in order to ensure respect for and the realisation of the objectives of the principle of autonomy.

It is not our intention to expel the non-Tibetans who have permanently settled in Tibet and have lived there and grown up there for a considerable time. Our concern is the induced massive movement of primarily Han but also some other nationalities into many areas of Tibet, upsetting existing communities, marginalising the Tibetan population there and threatening the fragile natural environment.

11) Cultural, Educational and Religious Exchanges with Other Countries

Besides the importance of exchanges and cooperation between the Tibetan nationality and other nationalities, provinces, and regions of the PRC in the subject matters of autonomy, such as culture, art, education, science, public health, sports, religion, environment, economy and so forth, the power of autonomous areas to conduct such exchanges with foreign countries in these areas is also recognised in the LRNA (Article 42).

V. APPLICATION OF A SINGLE ADMINISTRATION FOR THE TIBETAN NATIONALITY IN THE PRC

In order for the Tibetan nationality to develop and flourish with its distinct identity, culture and spiritual tradition through the exercise of self-government on the above-mentioned basic Tibetan needs, the entire community, comprising all the areas currently designated by the PRC as Tibetan autonomous areas, should be under one single administrative entity. The current administrative divisions, by which Tibetan communities are ruled and administered under different provinces and regions of the PRC, foments fragmentation, promotes unequal development, and weakens the ability of the Tibetan nationality to protect and promote its common cultural, spiritual and ethnic identity. Rather than respecting the integrity of the nationality, this policy promotes its fragmentation and disregards the spirit of autonomy. Whereas the other major minority nationalities such as the Uyghurs and Mongols govern themselves almost entirely within their respective single autonomous regions, Tibetans remain as if they were several minority nationalities instead of one.

Bringing all the Tibetans currently living in designated Tibetan autonomous areas within a single autonomous administrative unit is entirely in accordance with the constitutional principle contained in Article 4, also reflected in the LRNA (Article 2), that "regional autonomy is practiced in areas where people of minority nationalities live in concentrated communities." The LRNA describes regional national autonomy as the "basic policy adopted by the Communist Party of China for the solution of the national question in China" and explains its meaning and intent in its Preface:

the minority nationalities, under unified state leadership, practice regional autonomy in areas where they live in concentrated communities and set up organs of self-government for the exercise of the power of autonomy. Regional national autonomy embodies the state's full respect for and guarantee of the right of the minority nationalities to administer their internal affairs and its adherence to the principle of equality, unity and common prosperity of all nationalities.

It is clear that the Tibetan nationality within the PRC will be able to exercise its right to govern itself and administer its internal affairs effectively only once it can do so through an organ of self-government that has jurisdiction over the Tibetan nationality as a whole.

The LRNA recognises the principle that boundaries of national autonomous areas may need to be modified. The need for the application of the fundamental principles of the Constitution on regional autonomy through respect of the integrity of the Tibetan nationality is not only totally legitimate, but the administrative changes that may be required to achieve this in no way violate constitutional principles. There are several precedents where this has been actually done.

VI. THE NATURE AND STRUCTURE OF THE AUTONOMY

The extent to which the right to self-government and self-administration can be exercised on the preceding subject matters largely determines the genuine character of Tibetan autonomy. The task at hand is therefore to look into the manner in which autonomy can be regulated and exercised for it to effectively respond to the unique situation and basic needs of the Tibetan nationality.

The exercise of genuine autonomy would include the right of Tibetans to create their own regional government and government institutions and processes that are best suited to their needs and characteristics.

It would require that the People's Congress of the autonomous region have the power to legislate on all matters within the competencies of the region (that is, the subject matters referred to above) and that other organs of the autonomous government have the power to execute and administer decisions autonomously. Autonomy also entails representation and meaningful participation in national decision-making in the Central Government. Processes for effective consultation and close cooperation or joint decision-making between the Central Government and the regional government on areas of common interest also need to be in place for the autonomy to be effective.

A crucial element of genuine autonomy is the guarantee the Constitution or other laws provide that powers and responsibilities allocated to the autonomous region cannot be unilaterally abrogated or changed. This means that neither the Central Government nor the autonomous region's government should be able, without the consent of the other, to change the basic features of the autonomy.

The parameters and specifics of such genuine autonomy for Tibet that respond to the unique needs and conditions of the Tibetan people and region should be set out in some detail in regulations on the exercise of autonomy, as provided for in Article 116 of the Constitution (enacted in LRNA Article 19) or, if it is found to be more appropriate, in a separate set of laws or regulations adopted for that purpose. The Constitution, including Article 31, provides the flexibility to adopt special laws to respond to unique situations such as the Tibetan one, while respecting the established social, economic and political system of the country.

The Constitution in Section VI provides for organs of self-government of national autonomous regions and acknowledges their power to legislate. Thus Article 116 (enacted in Article 19 of the LRNA) refers to their power to enact "separate regulations in light of the political, economic and cultural characteristics of the nationality or nationalities in the areas concerned." Similarly, the Constitution recognises the power of autonomous administration in a number of areas

(Article 117–120) as well as the power of autonomous governments to apply flexibility in implementing the laws and policies of the Central Government and higher state organs to suit the conditions of the autonomous area concerned (Article 115).

The above-mentioned legal provisions do contain significant limitations to the decision-making authority of the autonomous organs of government. But the Constitution nevertheless recognises the principle that organs of self-government make laws and policy decisions that address local needs and that these may be different from those adopted elsewhere, including by the Central Government.

Although the needs of the Tibetans are broadly consistent with the principles on autonomy contained in the Constitution, as we have shown, their realisation is impeded because of the existence of a number of problems, which makes the implementation of those principles today difficult or ineffective.

Implementation of genuine autonomy, for example, requires clear divisions of powers and responsibilities between the Central Government and the government of the autonomous region with respect to subject matter competency. Currently there is no such clarity and the scope of legislative powers of autonomous regions is both uncertain and severely restricted. Thus, whereas the Constitution intends to recognise the special need for autonomous regions to legislate on many matters that affect them, the requirements of Article 116 for prior approval at the highest level of the Central Government—by the Standing Committee of National People's Congress (NPC)—inhibit the implementation of this principle of autonomy. In reality, it is only autonomous regional congresses that expressly require such approval, while the congresses of ordinary (not autonomous) provinces of the PRC do not need prior permission and merely report the passage of regulations to the Standing Committee of the NPC "for the record" (Article 100).

The exercise of autonomy is further subject to a considerable number of laws and regulations, according to Article 115 of the Constitution. Certain laws effectively restrict the autonomy of the autonomous region, while others are not always consistent with one another. The result is that the exact scope of the autonomy is unclear and is not fixed, since it is unilaterally changed with the enactment of laws and regulations at higher levels of the state, and even by changes in policy. There is also no adequate process for consultation or for settling differences that arise between the organs of the Central Government and of the regional government with respect to the scope and exercise of autonomy. In practice, the resulting uncertainty limits the initiative of regional authorities and impedes the exercise of genuine autonomy by Tibetans today.

We do not at this stage wish to enter into details regarding these and other impediments to the exercise of genuine autonomy today by Tibetans, but mention them by way of example so that these may be addressed in the appropriate manner in our dialogue in the future. We will continue to study the Constitution and other relevant legal provisions and, when appropriate, will be pleased to provide further analysis of these issues, as we understand them.

VII. THE WAY FORWARD

As stated at the beginning of this memorandum, our intention is to explore how the needs of the Tibetan nationality can be met within the framework of PRC since we believe these needs are consistent with the principles of the Constitution on autonomy. As His Holiness the Dalai Lama stated on a number of occasions, we have no hidden agenda. We have no intention at all of using any agreement on genuine autonomy as stepping stone for separation from the PRC.

The objective of the Tibetan Government in Exile is to represent the interests of the Tibetan people and to speak on their behalf. Therefore, it will no longer be needed and will be dissolved once an agreement is reached between us. In fact, His Holiness has reiterated his decision not to accept any political office in Tibet at any time in the future. His Holiness the Dalai Lama, nevertheless, plans to use all his personal influence to ensure such an agreement would have the legitimacy necessary to obtain the support of the Tibetan people.

Given these strong commitments, we propose that the next step in this process be the agreement to start serious discussions on the points raised in this memorandum. For this purpose we propose that we discuss and agree on a mutually agreeable mechanism or mechanisms and a timetable to do so effectively.

✳

A Note on the "Memorandum on Genuine Autonomy for the Tibetan People"

INTRODUCTION

This Note addresses the principal concerns and objections raised by the Chinese Central Government regarding the substance of the "Memorandum on Genuine Autonomy for the Tibetan People" (hereinafter "the Memorandum") which was presented to the Government of the People's Republic of China (PRC) on October 31, 2008, at the eighth round of talks in Beijing.

Having carefully studied the responses and reactions of Minister Du Qinglin and Executive Vice Minister Zhu Weiqun conveyed during the talks, including the written Note, and in statements made by the Chinese Central Government following the talks, it seems that some issues raised in the Memorandum may have been misunderstood, while others appear to have not been understood by the Chinese Central Government.

The Chinese Central Government maintains that the Memorandum contravenes the Constitution of the PRC as well as the "three adherences."* The Tibetan side believes that the Tibetan people's needs, as set out in the Memorandum, can be met within the framework and spirit of the Constitution and its principles on autonomy and that these proposals do not contravene or conflict with the "three adherences." We believe that the present Note will help to clarify this.

His Holiness the Dalai Lama started internal discussions, as early as in 1974, to find ways to resolve the future status of Tibet through an autonomy arrangement instead of seeking independence. In 1979 Chinese leader Deng Xiaoping expressed willingness to discuss and resolve all issues except the independence of Tibet. Since then His Holiness the Dalai Lama has taken numerous initiatives to bring about a mutually acceptable negotiated solution to the question of Tibet. In doing so His Holiness the Dalai Lama has steadfastly followed the Middle Way Approach, which means the pursuit of a mutually acceptable and mutually beneficial solution through negotiations, in the spirit of reconciliation and compromise. The Five Point Peace Plan and the Strasbourg Proposal were presented in this spirit. With the failure to elicit any positive response from the Chinese Central Government to these initiatives, along with the imposition of martial law in March 1989 and the deterioration of the situation in Tibet, His Holiness the Dalai Lama felt compelled to state in 1991 that his Strasbourg Proposal had become ineffectual. His Holiness the Dalai Lama nevertheless maintained his commitment to the Middle Way Approach.

The re-establishment of a dialogue process between the Chinese Central Government and representatives of His Holiness the Dalai Lama in 2002 provided the opportunity for each side to explain their positions and to gain a better understanding of the concerns, needs

---

* The "three adherences" as stipulated by the Central Government are: (1) the leadership of the Chinese Communist Party; (2) socialism with Chinese characteristics; and (3) the Regional National Autonomy system.

and interests of the other side. Moreover, taking into consideration the Chinese Central Government's real concerns, needs and interests, His Holiness the Dalai Lama has given much thought with due consideration to the reality of the situation. This reflects His Holiness the Dalai Lama's flexibility, openness and pragmatism and, above all, sincerity and determination to seek a mutually beneficial solution.

The "Memorandum on Genuine Autonomy for the Tibetan People" was prepared in response to the suggestion from the Chinese Central Government made at the seventh round of talks in July 2008. However, the Chinese Central Government's reactions and main criticisms of the Memorandum appear to be based not on the merits of that proposal which was officially presented to it, but on earlier proposals that were made public as well as other statements made at different times and contexts.

The Memorandum and the present Note strongly reemphasise that His Holiness the Dalai Lama is not seeking independence or separation but a solution within the framework of the Constitution and its principles on autonomy as reiterated many times in the past.

The Special General Meeting of the Tibetans in Diaspora held in November 2008 in Dharamsala reconfirmed for the time being the mandate for the continuation of the dialogue process with the PRC on the basis of the Middle Way Approach. On their part, members of the international community urged both sides to return to the talks. A number of them expressed the opinion that the Memorandum can form a good basis for discussion.

1. RESPECTING THE SOVEREIGNTY AND TERRITORIAL INTEGRITY OF THE PRC

His Holiness the Dalai Lama has repeatedly stated that he is not seeking separation of Tibet from the People's Republic of China, and that he is not seeking independence for Tibet. He seeks a sustainable solution within the PRC. This position is stated unambiguously in the Memorandum.

The Memorandum calls for the exercise of genuine autonomy, not for independence, "semi-independence," or "independence in disguised form." The substance of the Memorandum, which explains what is meant by genuine autonomy, makes this unambiguously clear. The form and degree of autonomy proposed in the Memorandum is consistent with the principles on autonomy in the Constitution of the PRC. Autonomous regions in different parts of the world exercise the kind of self-governance that is proposed in the Memorandum, without thereby challenging or threatening the sovereignty and unity of the state of which they are a part. This is true of autonomous regions within unitary states as well as those with federal characteristics. Observers of the situation, including unbiased political leaders and scholars in the international community, have also acknowledged that the Memorandum is a call for autonomy *within* the PRC and not for independence or separation *from* the PRC.

The Chinese government's viewpoint on the history of Tibet is different from that held by Tibetans and His Holiness the Dalai Lama is fully aware that Tibetans cannot agree to it. History is a past event and it cannot be altered. However, His Holiness the Dalai Lama's position is forward-looking, not backward grasping. He does not wish to make this difference on history to be an obstacle in seeking a mutually beneficial common future within the PRC.

The Chinese Central Government's responses to the Memorandum reveal a persistent suspicion on its part that His Holiness's proposals are tactical initiatives to advance the hidden agenda of independence. His Holiness the Dalai Lama is aware of the PRC's concerns and sensitivities with regard to the legitimacy of the present situation in Tibet. For this reason His Holiness the Dalai Lama has conveyed through his Envoys and publicly stated that he stands ready to lend his moral authority to endow an autonomy agreement, once reached, with the legitimacy it will need to gain the support of the people and to be properly implemented.

2. RESPECTING THE CONSTITUTION OF THE PRC

The Memorandum explicitly states that the genuine autonomy sought by His Holiness the Dalai Lama for the Tibetan people is to be accommodated within the framework of the Constitution and its principles on autonomy, not outside of it.

The fundamental principle underlying the concept of national regional autonomy is to preserve and protect a minority nationality's identity, language, custom, tradition and culture in a multi-national state based on equality and cooperation. The Constitution provides for the establishment of organs of self-government where the national minorities live in concentrated communities in order for them to exercise the power of autonomy. In conformity with this principle, the White Paper on *Regional Ethnic Autonomy in Tibet* (May 2004) states that minority nationalities are "arbiters of their own destiny and masters of their own affairs."

Within the parameters of its underlying principles, a Constitution needs to be responsive to the needs of the times and adapt to new or changed circumstances. The leaders of the PRC have demonstrated the flexibility of the Constitution of the PRC in their interpretation and implementation of it, and have also enacted modifications and amendments in response to changing circumstances. If applied to the Tibetan situation, such flexibility would, as is stated in the Memorandum, indeed permit the accommodation of the Tibetan needs within the framework of the Constitution and its principles on autonomy.

3. RESPECTING THE "THREE ADHERENCES"

The position of His Holiness the Dalai Lama, as presented in the Memorandum, in no way challenges or brings into question the leadership of the Chinese Communist Party in the PRC. At the same time, it is reasonable to expect that, in order to promote unity, stability and a harmonious society, the Party would change its attitude of treating Tibetan culture, religion and identity as a threat.

The Memorandum also does not challenge the socialist system of the PRC. Nothing in it suggests a demand for a change to this system or for its exclusion from Tibetan areas. As for His Holiness the Dalai Lama's views on socialism, it is well known that he has always favoured a socialist economy and ideology that promotes equality and benefits to uplift the poorer sections of society.

His Holiness the Dalai Lama's call for genuine autonomy within the PRC recognises the principles on autonomy for minority nation-alities contained in the Constitution of the PRC and is in line with the declared intent of those principles. As pointed out in the Memo-randum, the current implementation of the provisions on autonomy, however, effectively results in the denial of genuine autonomy to the Tibetans and fails to provide for the exercise of the right of Tibetans to govern themselves and to be "masters of their own affairs." Today, important decisions pertaining to the welfare of Tibetans are not be-ing made by Tibetans. Implementing the proposed genuine autonomy explained in the Memorandum would ensure for the Tibetans the ability to exercise the right to true autonomy and therefore to become masters of their own affairs, in line with the Constitutional principles on autonomy.

Thus, the Memorandum for genuine autonomy does not oppose the "three adherences."

4. RESPECTING THE HIERARCHY AND AUTHORITY OF THE CHINESE CENTRAL GOVERNMENT

The proposals contained in the Memorandum in no way imply a de-nial of the authority of the National People's Congress (NPC) and other organs of the Chinese Central Government. As stated in the Memorandum, the proposal fully respects the hierarchical differences between the Central Government and its organs, including the NPC, and the autonomous government of Tibet.

Any form of genuine autonomy entails a division and allocation of powers and responsibilities, including that of making laws and regulations, between the central and the autonomous local government. Of course, the power to adopt laws and regulations is limited to the areas of competency of the autonomous region. This is true in unitary states as well as in federal systems.

This principle is also recognised in the Constitution. The spirit of the Constitutional provisions on autonomy is to give autonomous regions *broader* decision-making authority over and above that enjoyed by ordinary provinces. But today, the requirement for prior approval by the Standing Committee of the NPC for all laws and regulations of the autonomous regions (Article 116 of the Constitution) is exercised in a way that in fact leaves the autonomous regions with much less authority to make decisions that suit local conditions than that of the ordinary (not autonomous) provinces of China.

Whenever there is a division and allocation of decision-making power between different levels of government (between the Central Government and the autonomous government), it is important to have processes in place for consultation and cooperation. This helps to improve mutual understanding and to ensure that contradictions and possible inconsistencies in policies, laws and regulations are minimised. It also reduces the chances of disputes arising regarding the exercise of the powers allocated to these different organs of government. Such processes and mechanisms do not put the Central and autonomous governments on equal footing, nor do they imply the rejection of the leadership of the Central Government.

The important feature of entrenchment of autonomy arrangements in the Constitution or in other appropriate ways also does not imply equality of status between the Central and local government nor does it restrict or weaken the authority of the former. The measure is intended to provide (legal) security to both the autonomous and the central authorities that neither can unilaterally change the basic features of the autonomy they have set up, and that a process of consultation must take place at least for fundamental changes to be enacted.

5. CONCERNS RAISED BY THE CHINESE CENTRAL GOVERNMENT ON SPECIFIC COMPETENCIES REFERRED TO IN THE MEMORANDUM

a) Public Security

Concern was raised over the inclusion of public security aspects in the package of competencies allocated to the autonomous region in the Memorandum because the government apparently interpreted this to mean defence matters. National defence and public security are two different matters. His Holiness the Dalai Lama is clear on the point that the responsibility for national defence of the PRC is and should remain with the Central Government. This is not a competency to be exercised by the autonomous region. This is indeed the case in most autonomy arrangements. The Memorandum in fact refers specifically to "internal public order and security," and makes the important point that the majority of the security personnel should be Tibetans, because they understand the local customs and traditions. It also helps to curb local incidents leading to disharmony among the nationalities. The Memorandum in this respect is consistent with the principle enunciated in Article 120 of the Constitution (reflected also in Article 24 of the LRNA), which states:

> The organs of self-government of the national autonomous areas may, in accordance with the military system of the state and practical local needs and with approval of the State Council, organise local public security forces for the maintenance of public order.

It should also be emphasised in this context that the Memorandum at no point proposes the withdrawal of People's Liberation Army (PLA) from Tibetan areas.

b) Language

The protection, use, and development of the Tibetan language are one of the crucial issues for the exercise of genuine autonomy by Tibetans. The emphasis on the need to respect Tibetan as the main or principal language in the Tibetan areas is not controversial, since a similar position is expressed in the Chinese Central Government's White Paper on *Regional Ethnic Autonomy in Tibet*, where it is stated that regulations adopted by the Tibet regional government prescribe that "equal attention be given to Tibetan and Han-Chinese languages in the Tibetan Autonomous region, *with the Tibetan language as the major one . . .*" (emphasis added). Moreover, the very usage of "main language" in the Memorandum clearly implies the use of other languages, too.

The absence of a demand in the Memorandum that Chinese should also be used and taught should not be interpreted as an "exclusion" of this language, which is the principal and common language in the PRC as a whole. It should also be noted in this context that the leadership in exile has taken steps to encourage Tibetans in exile to learn Chinese.

Tibetan proposal which emphasises the study of the Tibetan people's own language should therefore not be interpreted as being a "separatist view."

c) Regulation of Population Migration

The Memorandum proposes that the local government of the autonomous region should have the competency to regulate the residence, settlement and employment or economic activities of persons who wish to move to Tibetan areas from elsewhere. This is a common feature of autonomy and is certainly not without precedent in the PRC.

A number of countries have instituted systems or adopted laws to protect vulnerable regions or indigenous and minority peoples from excessive immigration from other parts of the country. The Memorandum explicitly states that it is *not* suggesting the expulsion of non-

Tibetans who have lived in Tibetan areas for years. His Holiness the Dalai Lama and the Kashag also made this clear in earlier statements, as did the Envoys in their discussions with their Chinese counterparts. In an address to the European Parliament on December 4, 2008, His Holiness the Dalai Lama reiterated that "our intention is not to expel non-Tibetans. Our concern is the induced mass movement of primarily Han, but also some other nationalities, into many Tibetan areas, which in turn marginalises the native Tibetan population and threatens Tibet's fragile environment." From this it is clear that His Holiness is not at all suggesting that Tibet be inhabited by only Tibetans, with other nationalities not being able to do so. The issue concerns the appropriate division of powers regarding the regulation of transient, seasonal workers and new settlers so as to protect the vulnerable population indigenous to Tibetan areas.

In responding to the Memorandum the Chinese Central Government rejected the proposition that the autonomous authorities would regulate the entrance and economic activities of persons from other parts of the PRC in part because "in the Constitution and the Law on Regional National Autonomy there are no provisions to restrict transient population." In fact, the Law on Regional National Autonomy, in its Article 43, explicitly mandates such a regulation:

> In accordance with legal stipulations, the organs of self-government of national autonomous areas shall work out measures for control of the transient population.

Thus, the Tibetan proposal contained in the Memorandum in this regard is not incompatible with the Constitution.

d) Religion

The point made in the Memorandum, that Tibetans be free to practice their religion according to their own beliefs, is entirely consistent with the principles of religious freedom contained in the Constitution of the PRC. It is also consistent with the principle of separation of religion and polity adopted in many countries of the world.

Article 36 of the Constitution guarantees that no one can "compel citizens to believe in or not to believe in any religion." We endorse this principle but observe that today the government authorities do interfere in important ways in the ability of Tibetans to practice their religion.

The spiritual relationship between master and student and the giving of religious teachings, etc., are essential components of the Dharma practice. Restricting these is a violation of religious freedom. Similarly, the interference and direct involvement by the state and its institutions in matters of recognition of reincarnated lamas, as provided in the regulation on the management of reincarnated lamas adopted by the State on July 18, 2007, is a grave violation of the freedom of religious belief enshrined in the Constitution.

The practice of religion is widespread and fundamental to the Tibetan people. Rather than seeing Buddhist practice as a threat, concerned authorities should respect it. Traditionally or historically Buddhism has always been a major unifying and positive factor between the Tibetan and Chinese peoples.

e) Single Administration

The desire of Tibetans to be governed within one autonomous region is fully in keeping with the principles on autonomy of the Constitution. The rationale for the need to respect the integrity of the Tibetan nationality is clearly stated in the Memorandum and does not mean "Greater or Smaller Tibet." In fact, as pointed out in the Memorandum, the Law on Regional National Autonomy itself allows for this kind of modification of administrative boundaries if proper procedures are followed. Thus the proposal in no way violates the Constitution.

As the Envoys pointed out in earlier rounds of talks, many Chinese leaders, including Premier Zhou Enlai, Vice Premier Chen Yi and

Party Secretary Hu Yaobang, supported the consideration of bringing all Tibetan areas under a single administration. Some of the most senior Tibetan leaders in the PRC, including the 10th Panchen Lama, Ngabö Ngawang Jigme and Bapa Phuntsok Wangyal have also called for this and affirming that doing so would be in accordance with the PRC's Constitution and its laws. In 1956 a special committee, which included senior Communist Party member Sangye Yeshi (Tian Bao), was appointed by the Chinese Central Government to make a detailed plan for the integration of the Tibetan areas into a single autonomous region, but the work was later stopped on account of ultra-leftist elements.

The fundamental reason for the need to integrate the Tibetan areas under one administrative region is to address the deeply felt desire of Tibetans to exercise their autonomy as a people and to protect and develop their culture and spiritual values in this context. This is also the fundamental premise and purpose of the Constitutional principles on regional national autonomy as reflected in Article 4 of the Constitution. Tibetans are concerned about the integrity of the Tibetan nationality, which the proposal respects and which the continuation of the present system does not. Their common historical heritage, spiritual and cultural identity, language and even their particular affinity to the unique Tibetan plateau environment is what binds Tibetans as one nationality. Within the PRC, Tibetans are recognized as one nationality and not several nationalities. Those Tibetans presently living in Tibet autonomous prefectures and counties incorporated into other provinces also belong to the same Tibetan nationality. Tibetans, including His Holiness the Dalai Lama, are primarily concerned about the protection and development of Tibetan culture, spiritual values, national identity and the environment. Tibetans are not asking for the expansion of Tibetan autonomous areas. They are only demanding that those areas already recognised as Tibetan autonomous areas come under a single administration, as is the case in the other autonomous regions of the PRC. So long as Tibetans do not have the opportunity to govern themselves under a single administration, preservation of Tibetan culture and way of life cannot be done effectively. Today more than half of the Tibetan population is subjected to the priorities and interests first and foremost of different provincial governments in which they have no significant role.

As explained in the Memorandum, the Tibetan people can only genuinely exercise regional national autonomy if they can have their own autonomous government, people's congress and other organs of self-government with jurisdiction over the Tibetan nationality as a whole. This principle is reflected in the Constitution, which recognises the right of minority nationalities to practice regional autonomy "in areas where they live in concentrated communities" and to "set up organs of self-government for the exercise of the power of autonomy" (Article 4). If the "state's full respect for and guarantee of the right of the minority nationalities to administer their internal affairs" solemnly declared in the preamble of the Law on Regional National Autonomy is interpreted not to include the right to choose to form an autonomous region that encompasses the whole people in the contiguous areas where its members live in concentrated communities, the Constitutional principles on autonomy are themselves undermined.

Keeping Tibetans divided and subject to different laws and regulations denies the people the exercise of genuine autonomy and makes it difficult for them to maintain their distinct cultural identity. It is not impossible for the Central Government to make the necessary administrative adjustment when elsewhere in the PRC, notably in the case of Inner Mongolia, Ningxia and Guangxi Autonomous Regions, it has done just that.

f) Political, Social and Economic System

His Holiness the Dalai Lama has repeatedly and consistently stated that no one, least of all he, has any intention to restore the old political, social and economic system that existed in Tibet prior to 1959. It would be the intention of a future autonomous Tibet to further improve the social, economic and political situation of Tibetans, not to return to the past. It is disturbing and puzzling that the Chinese government persists, despite all evidence to the contrary, to accuse His Holiness the Dalai Lama and his Administration of the intention to restore the old system.

All countries and societies in the world, including China, have had political systems in the past that would be entirely unacceptable today. The old Tibetan system is no exception. The world has evolved socially and politically and has made enormous strides in terms of the recognition of human rights and standards of living. Tibetans in exile have developed their own modern democratic system as well as education and health systems and institutions. In this way, Tibetans have become citizens of the world at par with those of other countries. It is obvious that Tibetans in the PRC have also advanced under Chinese rule and improved their social, education, health and economic situation. However, the standard of living of the Tibetan people remains the most backward in the PRC and Tibetan human rights are not being respected.

6. RECOGNISING THE CORE ISSUE

His Holiness the Dalai Lama and other members of the exiled leadership have no personal demands to make. His Holiness the Dalai Lama's concern is with the rights and welfare of the Tibetan people. Therefore, the fundamental issue that needs to be resolved is the faithful implementation of genuine autonomy that will enable the Tibetan people to govern themselves in accordance with their own genius and needs.

His Holiness the Dalai Lama speaks on behalf of the Tibetan people, with whom he has a deep and historical relationship and one based on full trust. In fact, on no issue are Tibetans as completely in agreement as on their demand for the return of His Holiness the Dalai Lama to Tibet. It cannot be disputed that His Holiness the Dalai Lama legitimately represents the Tibetan people, and he is certainly viewed as their true representative and spokesperson by them. It is indeed only by means of dialogue with His Holiness the Dalai Lama that the Tibetan issue can be resolved. The recognition of this reality is important.

This emphasises the point, often made by His Holiness the Dalai Lama, that his engagement for the cause of Tibet is not for the purpose of claiming certain personal rights or political position for him, nor attempting to stake claims for the Tibetan administration in exile. Once an agreement is reached, the Tibetan Government-in-Exile will be dissolved and the Tibetans working in Tibet should carry on the main responsibility of administering Tibet. His Holiness the Dalai Lama made it clear on numerous occasions that he will not hold any political position in Tibet.

7. HIS HOLINESS THE DALAI LAMA'S COOPERATION

His Holiness the Dalai Lama has offered, and remains prepared, to formally issue a statement that would serve to allay the Chinese Central Government's doubts and concerns as to his position and intentions on matters that have been identified above.

The formulation of the statement should be done after ample consultations between representatives of His Holiness the Dalai Lama and the Chinese Central Government, respectively, to ensure that such a statement would satisfy the fundamental needs of the Chinese Central Government as well as those of the Tibetan people.

It is important that both parties address any concern directly with their counterparts, and not use those issues as ways to block the dialogue process as has occurred in the past.

His Holiness the Dalai Lama is taking this initiative in the belief that it is possible to find common ground with the People's Republic of China consistent with the principles on autonomy contained in PRC's Constitution and with the interests of the Tibetan people. In that spirit, it is the expectation and hope of His Holiness the Dalai Lama that the representatives of the PRC will use the opportunity presented by the Memorandum and this Note to deepen discussion and make substantive progress in order to develop mutual understanding.

Notes

Introduction

xii   *The document began with the statement: Tibet Since 1951: Liberation, Development and Prosperity* (The State Council Information Office of the People's Republic of China, May 2021), 3–4. http://english.www.gov.cn/archive /whitepaper/202105/21/content_WS60a724e7c6d0df57f98d9da2.html.

xiii   *A series of resolutions has been passed:* On the important international resolutions passed on Tibet, see https://tibet.net/international-resolutions-and -recognitions-on-tibet-1959-to-2021/.

Chapter 1: The Invasion and Our New Master

2   *To the Secretary General:* Full text in Dalai Lama, *My Land and My People* (New York: Grand Central Publishing, 1997), appendix II. Reacting to the Chinese invasion of Tibet, on December 7, 1950, Prime Minister Jawaharlal Nehru made a statement to the Indian Parliament in which he declared, "Since Tibet is not the same as China, it should ultimately be the wishes of the people of Tibet that should prevail."

8   *Referring to the foraging for food:* This statement is reported in Edgar Snow, *Red Star Over China* (New York: Random House, 1938), 193.

Chapter 3: A Visit to India

19   *bombing the monastery:* For a detailed account of the bombing of Lithang Monastery in March 1956 and the massacre of Tibetans in other parts of eastern Tibet around this time, see Jianglin Li, *When the Iron Bird Flies: China's Secret War in Tibet* (California: Stanford University Press, 2022), especially chapters 3–6.

20 *Every devout Buddhist:* Dalai Lama, *My Land and My People* (New York: Grand Central Publishing, 1997), 121.

20 *I expressed my deep admiration:* The full text of an English translation of the Dalai Lama's address is available in W. D. Shakabpa, *Tibet: A Political History* (New Haven: Yale University Press, 1967), 329–31.

22 *The trip to India was also:* Jianglin Li's *Agony in Tibet: Lhasa 1959*, trans. Susan Wilf (Cambridge: Harvard University Press, 2016), chap. 2, contains a detailed account of the Dalai Lama's meetings with Zhou and the latter's meetings with Nehru during the Dalai Lama's visit to India in 1956.

24 *Zhou had even dangled:* This is attested to in Jawaharlal Nehru, *Selected Works of Jawaharlal Nehru*, series 2, vol. 36 (New Delhi: Jawaharlal Memorial Fund, 2005), 600.

Chapter 4: Fleeing Home

27 *Of course, as a student of the Buddha:* The Dalai Lama's refusal is reported in John Kenneth Knaus, *Orphans of the Cold War: America and the Tibetan Struggle for Survival* (New York: Public Affairs, 1999), 141.

32 *In the past, for several thousand years:* An English translation of this pronouncement as well as a Wylie (transliteration) version of the Tibetan text can be found in Melvyn C. Goldstein, *A History of Modern Tibet*, vol. 4, *In the Eye of the Storm* (Berkeley: University of California, 2019), 473, appendix B.

33 *As part of the US government's overall strategy:* This Tibetan resistance movement later regrouped and came to be based in Mustang, Nepal. Eventually, it was a taped message from the Dalai Lama himself, brought by a delegation from Dharamsala, headed by Phuntsok Tashi Takla, the Dalai Lama's brother-in-law and chief security officer, which persuaded the Tibetan resistance force to disarm. For a detailed account of the history of US support for Tibet, especially its support of the Tibetan resistance fighters, see Knaus, *Orphans of the Cold War* (New York: Public Affairs, 1999).

Chapter 5: A Geopolitical Reflection

36 *An early chronicle says that this king:* The Old Tibetan Chronicle, Pelliot Tibétain MS 1286; English translation of the excerpts from Matthew T. Kapstein, *The Tibetans* (Oxford: Blackwell, 2006), 35.

40 *I am now almost fifty-eight years old:* English translation of the excerpts from Glenn H. Mullin, *The Fourteen Dalai Lamas: A Sacred Legacy of Reincarnation* (Santa Fe: Clear Light Publishers, 2001), 437–39.

43 *expansion of China almost up to our gates:* The full text of Sardar Patel's letter

to Prime Minister Jawaharlal Nehru can be found in *Indian Leaders on Tibet*, 5–11. https://tibet.net/indian-leaders-on-Tibet/.

45 *In the end, a careless, instrumental:* On why Tibet matters, especially from an ecological perspective, and for an account of Communist China's destruction of Tibet's ecosystems, see Michael Buckley, *Meltdown in Tibet: China's Reckless Destruction of Ecosystems from the Highlands of Tibet to the Delta of Asia* (New York: Palgrave Macmillan, 2014).

45 *a noted Chinese environmental scientist:* This is cited in He Huaihong, *Social Ethics in a Changing China: Moral Decay or Ethical Awakening?* (Washington, DC: Brooking Institution Press, 2015).

Chapter 6: Devastation at Home and Rebuilding in Exile

48 *I concluded by saying that I hoped:* The full text of this first press statement from the Dalai Lama can be found in *Facts About the 17-Point "Agreement" Between Tibet and China* (Dharamsala: Department of Information and International Relations, 2022), 110–13. https://tibet.net/facts-about-17-point-agreement -between-tibet-and-china-2001/.

49 *No one expects India to go to war:* The full text of this statement can be found in *Indian Leaders on Tibet*, 18–19. https://tibet.net/indian-leaders-on-Tibet/.

50 *If a treaty is violated by one:* The full text of this press statement is available in *Facts About the 17-Point "Agreement,"* 114–17. https://tibet.net/facts-about -17-point-agreement-between-tibet-and-china-2001/.

50 *All that we had heard:* International Commission of Jurists, *The Question of Tibet and the Rule of Law* (Geneva: International Commission of Jurists, 1959), iv, 17, 18, 68.

50 *In the second report:* International Commission of Jurists, *Tibet and the Chinese People's Republic: A Report to the International Commission of Jurists by Its Legal Inquiry Committee on Tibet* (Geneva: International Commission of Jurists, 1960), 13.

51 *So while in Delhi that September:* The full text of this letter to the UN secretary-general can be found in Dalai Lama, *My Land and My People* (New York: Grand Central Publishing, 1997), 218–20.

51 *On October 21, 1959, the General Assembly:* The full text of this and other subsequent UN resolutions on Tibet can be found in Central Tibetan Administration, *International Resolutions and Recognitions on Tibet (1959 to 2021)*, 6th ed. (Dharamsala: Department of Information and International Relations, 2021).

51 *two letters from the Secretary of State Christian A. Herter:* The full text of the October 1960 letter from the secretary of state to the Dalai Lama is available at https://history.state.gov/historicaldocuments/frus1958-60v19/d402.

53 *At this ceremony, representing the Tibetan people:* The original Tibetan text and

an English translation of this great oath are found in Lodi Gyaltsen Gyari, *The Dalai Lama's Special Envoy: Memoirs of a Lifetime in Pursuit of a Reunited Tibet* (New York: Columbia University Press, 2022), appendix A.

54 *The document also includes, as Article 36:* An English translation of the entire text of this Constitution of Tibet promulgated on March 10, 1963, can be found at https://www.tibetjustice.org/materials/tibet/tibet2.html.

54 *Over the course of years, this document:* This constitution, in the wake of the Dalai Lama's semiretirement in 1991 and full devolution of political authority to an elected leadership in 2011, has been revised and the full text of this revised document can be found at https://tibet.net/about-cta/constitution.

57 *Because of many errors of mistakes:* The Tibet Information Network (TIN) in the United Kingdom was able to obtain a copy of this lengthy petition, whose English translation was published under the title *A Poisoned Arrow: The Secret Report of the 10th Panchen Lama* (London: Tibetan Information Network, 1997), 113–14.

58 *Once a nationality's language, costumes, customs: Poisoned Arrow,* 69.

58 *Before democratic reform, there were more than 2500: Poisoned Arrow,* 52.

59 *in March 1987, he spoke candidly:* The full text of the English translation of the Panchen Lama's speech to the Tibet Autonomous Region's Standing Committee in Beijing during the People's Congress of 1987 can be found in Central Tibetan Administration, *The Panchen Lama Speaks* (Dharamsala: Department of Information and International Relations, 1991).

60 *Since liberation, there has certainly been:* As reported in the *China Daily,* January 25, 1989, and cited in Isabel Hilton, *The Search for the Panchen Lama* (London: Viking, 1999).

61 *I was told that he described the Communist Chinese:* Secretary Schlesinger's actual statements are cited in Warren Smith, *Tibetan Nation* (Boulder: Westview Press, 1996), 560n58.

Chapter 7: Overtures Toward a Dialogue

63 *If the six million Tibetans in Tibet are really happy:* The full text of the statement is available at https://www.dalailama.com/messages/tibet/10th-march-archive/1978.

64 *"But except for independence":* The Dalai Lama's brother provides a detailed account of this first meeting with Deng Xiaoping in his memoir, Gyalo Thondup and Anne F. Thurston, *The Noodle Maker of Kalimpong* (New York: Public Affairs, 2015), 258–62.

69 *If the Tibetan people's identity is preserved:* The full text of the Dalai Lama's letter to Deng Xiaoping can be found at https://tibet.net/important-issues/sino-tibetan-dialogue/important-statements-of-his-holiness-the-dalai-lama/his-holiness-letter-to-deng-xiaoping/.

71   *For this to be realized, I said, it was important:* The full text of this March 10 Statement of 1981 can be found at https://www.dalailama.com/messages /tibet/10th-march-archive/1981.

Chapter 8: Reaching Out to Our Fourth Refuge

74   *The letter expressed support for direct talks:* Point 14 of Sec. 1243 of Foreign Relations Authorization Act, Fiscal Years 1988 and 1989, H.R. 1777, 100th Cong. (1987) (enacted).

74   *The world is increasingly interdependent:* The full text of the Dalai Lama's Five Point Peace Plan presented at the United States Congressional Human Rights Caucus can be found at https://www.dalailama.com/messages/tibet /five-point-peace-plan.

76   *The whole of Tibet known as Cholka-Sum:* The full text of the Strasbourg Proposal is found at https://www.dalailama.com/messages/tibet/strasbourg -proposal-1988.

80   *Despite my explicit public announcement:* The text of the New Delhi Chinese Embassy's press statement, as it appeared in *News from China,* no. 40 (September 28, 1990), is cited in Dawa Norbu, "China's Dialogue with the Dalai Lama 1978–90: Prenegotiation Stage or Dead End?," *Public Affairs* 64, no. 3 (Autumn 1991): 351–72.

84   *I accept the prize with profound gratitude:* The full text of the Dalai Lama's formal acceptance speech at the Nobel Peace Prize ceremony can be found at https:// www.nobelprize.org/prizes/peace/1989/lama/acceptance-speech/#:~:text=I%20 accept%20the%20prize%20with,life%20taught%20and%20inspired%20me.

Chapter 9: In the Aftermath of Tiananmen

89   *[It] is the sense of the Congress that Tibet:* The full text of the resolution is available at https://www.congress.gov/bill/102nd-congress/house-concurrent -resolution/145/text.

90   *I have had the pleasure to meet with every holder:* On July 12, 2024, President Joe Biden signed into law the Promotion of a Resolution to the Tibet-China Dispute Act, which states "that U.S. government statements and documents counter, as appropriate, disinformation about Tibet by China's government and the Chinese Communist Party, including disinformation about Tibet's history and institutions." https://www.congress.gov/bill/118th-congress/senate-bill/138.

90   *I particularly noted how this amazing transition:* The full text of this speech can be found at https://tibet.net/important-issues/sino-tibetan-dialogue/important -statements-of-his-holiness-the-dalai-lama/embracing-the-enemy/.

92   *If China wants Tibet to stay with China:* The full text of this detailed note

accompanying the Dalai Lama's letter to Jiang Zemin is presented in appendix C and can also be found at https://tibet.net/important-issues/sino-tibetan-dialogue/important-statements-of-his-holiness-the-dalai-lama/note-accompanying-his-holiness-letters-to-deng-xiaoping-and-jiang-zemin-dated-september-11-1992/.

93 *The document presents a series of arguments:* https://en.humanrights.cn/1992/09/30/9ed6ff95f0ce4c2099928bafef562f98.html.

94 *For example, one of their official statements:* English translation as cited in Robert Barnett, ed., *Cutting Off the Serpent's Head: Tightening Control in Tibet, 1994–1995* (London: Human Rights Watch, Tibet Information Network, 1996), 32.

94 *This same document then urged the monastic community:* Barnett, *Cutting Off the Serpent's Head,* 33.

94 *Ethnic education cannot be regarded successful:* Barnett, *Cutting Off the Serpent's Head,* 42.

Chapter 10: Practices I Find Helpful in the Face of Suffering

96 *I truly believe that a movement rooted in hatred:* The full text of this March 10 Statement is found at https://www.dalailama.com/messages/tibet/10th-march-archive/1976.

Chapter 11: As the Millennium Came to an End

107 *Without seeking independence for Tibet:* The full text of this statement can be found at https://tibet.net/important-issues/sino-tibetan-dialogue/the-middle-way-approach-a-framework-for-resolving-the-issue-of-tibet-2/.

108 *The document concluded that "the exiled Dalai Lama":* http://un.china-mission.gov.cn/eng/gyzg/bp/199802/t19980201_8410934.htm.

109 *Actually, as long as the Dalai Lama:* The full text of this press conference is available at https://china.usc.edu/president-clinton-and-president-jiang-zemin-%E6%B1%9F%E6%B3%BD%E6%B0%91-news-conference-beijing-1998.

Chapter 12: The Final Series of Dialogues

113 *On March 18, 2008, the leader of the Communist Party in Tibet:* This was reported in Christopher Bodeen, "Dalai Lama 'a Wolf in Monk's robes': China," *Toronto Star,* March 19, 2008, citing the *Tibet Daily* newspaper.

115 *invited to speak at the US Congressional Gold Medal Ceremony:* The full text of the Dalai Lama's speech at the US Congressional Gold Medal Ceremony is found at https://www.dalailama.com/messages/acceptance-speeches/u-s-congressional-gold-medal/congressional-gold-medal.

115 *I emphasized that the Chinese and Tibetan people share a common spiritual heritage:* The full texts of these appeals from the Dalai Lama can found at https://www.dalailama.com/messages/tibet.

116 *While our position had been clear for years:* The full text of this "Memorandum on Genuine Autonomy for the Tibetan People" is contained in appendix D and can also be found at https://tibet.net/important-issues/sino-tibetan-dialogue/memorandum-on-geniune-autonomy-for-the-tibetan-people/.

117 *This same line of criticism was repeated later in China's white paper:* The full text is available at http://un.china-mission.gov.cn/eng/gyzg/xizang/200903/t20090303_8410897.htm.

118 *Confronted with such unreasonable and excessively negative responses:* The full text of the Dalai Lama's address to the plenary session of the European Parliament can be found at https://tibet.net/address-to-the-plenary-session-of-the-european-parliament/.

118 *Despite their immediate and willful attack on our proposal:* The full text of this note on the memorandum is presented in appendix E and can also be found at https://tibet.net/important-issues/sino-tibetan-dialogue/note-on-the-memorandum-on-genuine-autonomy-for-the-tibetan-people/.

118 *On March 19, 2011, when I was seventy-five years old:* The full text of the Dalai Lama's remarks on retirement can be found at https://www.dalailama.com/messages/retirement-and-reincarnation/retirement-remarks.

Chapter 13: Taking Stock

123 *One explicit response from Beijing:* https://www.chinadaily.com.cn/kindle/2013-10/23/content_17052580.htm.

Chapter 14: What Gives Me Hope

132 *I also said that the Beijing government keeps stressing stability:* The full English translation of this live internet Q and A with the Dalai Lama can be found at https://www.nybooks.com/online/2010/05/24/talking-about-tibet/?printpage=true.

Chapter 15: Situation Today and the Path Forward

135 *according to some sources:* One such source is https://www.ohchr.org/en/press-releases/2023/02/china-un-experts-alarmed-separation-1-million-tibetan-children-families-and.

139 *In particular, in 2011, I convened a gathering:* The full text of this statement (in English translation) can be found at https://www.dalailama.com/news/2011

/statement-of-his-holiness-the-fourteenth-dalai-lama-tenzin-gyatso-on
-the-issue-of-his-reincarnation.

Chapter 16: Appeal

145   *The sages who have contemplated:* These verses are from Śāntideva, *Bodhicāryā-*
      vatāra (*A Guide to the Bodhisattva Way*), 1.7–8, 3.17, 21–22, and 10:55. Trans-
      lated by the editor of this book.

Appendix A: Tibet: A Historical Overview

150   *Both Tibet and China shall keep the country:* The source for this English transla-
      tion: H. E. Richardson, "The Sino-Tibetan Treaty Inscription of AD 821–823
      at Lhasa," *Journal of the Royal Asiatic Society* 2 (1978): 153–54.

154   *He said that he was at the time writing a book:* Hon-Shiang Lau was a chair pro-
      fessor at the City University of Hong Kong and his book in Chinese, *Tibet Was*
      Never Part of China Since Antiquity, was later published in Taiwan in 2019.

Appendix D: Memorandum on Genuine Autonomy for the Tibetan People

182   *Memorandum on Genuine Autonomy for the Tibetan People:* Presented by the
      Dalai Lama's delegation to their Chinese counterparts on October 31, 2008,
      at the eighth round of talks of the second cycle of formal dialogues, 2002–
      2010. English translation: https://tibet.net/important-issues/sino-tibetan
      -dialogue/memorandum-on-geniune-autonomy-for-the-tibetan-people/.

Appendix E: A Note on the "Memorandum on Genuine Autonomy for the Tibetan People"

200   *A Note on the "Memorandum on Genuine Autonomy for the Tibetan People":* This
      note was formally presented by the envoys of His Holiness the Dalai Lama
      to their Chinese counterparts during the ninth round of dialogues in Beijing.
      English translation: https://tibet.net/important-issues/sino-tibetan-dialogue
      /note-on-the-memorandum-on-genuine-autonomy-for-the-tibetan-people/.

Selected Bibliography

*

A Poisoned Arrow: The Secret Report of the 10th Panchen Lama. London: Tibetan Information Network, 1997.

Avedon, John F. *In Exile from the Land of Snows*. New York: Vintage Books, 1986.

Barnett, Robert, ed. *Cutting Off the Serpent's Head*. London: Human Rights Watch, Tibet Information Network, 1996.

Barnett, Robert, and Shirin Akiner, eds. *Resistance and Reform in Tibet*. London: C. Hearst & Co., 1994.

Brook, Timothy, Michael van Walt van Praag, and Miek Boltjes, eds. *Sacred Mandates: Asian International Relations Since Chinggis Khan*. Chicago: University of Chicago Press, 2018.

Buckley, Michael. *Meltdown in Tibet: China's Reckless Destruction of Ecosystems from the Highlands of Tibet to the Delta of Asia*. New York: Palgrave Macmillan, 2014.

Dalai Lama, the. *Freedom in Exile*. London: Hodder & Stoughton, 1990.

Dalai Lama, the. *My Land and My People*. New York: Grand Central, 1997; first published in 1962 by Weidenfeld & Nicolson.

Franke, Herbert. "Tibetans in Yuan China." In *China Under Mongol Rule*, edited by John D. Langlois. Princeton: Princeton University Press, 1981.

Goldstein, Melvyn C. *A History of Modern Tibet*. Vol. 1, *The Demise of Lamaist State, 1913–1951*. Berkeley: University of California Press, 1989.

Goldstein, Melvyn C. *A History of Modern Tibet*. Vol. 4, *In the Eye of the Storm: 1957–1959*. Berkeley: University of California Press, 2019.

Gyari, Lodi Gyaltsen. *The Dalai Lama's Special Envoy: Memoirs of a Lifetime in Pursuit of a Reunited Tibet.* New York: Columbia University Press, 2022.

International Commission of Jurists. *The Question of Tibet and the Rule of Law.* Geneva: International Commission of Jurists, 1959.

International Commission of Jurists. *Tibet and the Chinese People's Republic: A Report to the International Commission of Jurists by Its Legal Inquiry Committee on Tibet.* Geneva: International Commission of Jurists, 1960.

Knaus, John Kenneth. *Orphans of the Cold War: America and the Tibetan Struggle for Survival.* New York: Public Affairs, 1999.

Laird, Thomas, with the Dalai Lama. *The Story of Tibet: Conversations with the Dalai Lama.* New York: Atlantic Books, 2006.

Li, Jianglin. *Agony in Tibet: Lhasa 1959.* Translated by Susan Wilf. Cambridge: Harvard University Press, 2016.

Li, Jianglin. *When the Iron Bird Flies: China's Secret War in Tibet.* Translated by Stacy Masher. California: Stanford University Press, 2022.

McCorquodale, Robert, and Nicholas Orosz, eds. *Tibet: The Position in International Law.* Report of the Conference of International Lawyers on Issues Relating to Self-Determination and Independence for Tibet. London: Serindia, 1994.

Schwartz, Ronald D. *Circle of Protest: Political Ritual in the Tibetan Uprising, 1987–1992.* New York: Columbia University Press, 1995.

Shakabpa, W. D. *Tibet: A Political History.* New Haven: Yale University Press, 1967. Reprinted by Potala Publications in 1984.

Shakya, Tsering. *The Dragon in the Land of Snows.* London: Pimlico, 1999.

Smith, Warren. *Tibetan Nation.* Boulder: Westview Press, 1996.

Thondup, Gyalo, and Anne F. Thurston. *The Noodle Maker of Kalimpong.* New York: Public Affairs, 2015.

van Schaik, Sam. *Tibet: A History.* New Haven: Yale University Press, 2011.

van Walt van Praag, Michael C. *The Status of Tibet: History, Rights, and Prospects in International Law.* Boulder: Westview Press, 1987.

van Walt van Praag, Michael C., and Miek Boltjes. *Tibet Brief 20/20.* Outskirts Press, 2020.

Woeser, Tsering. *Tibet on Fire: Self-Immolations Against Chinese Rule.* Translated by Kevin Carrico. New York: Verso, 2016.

Index

Index

Index